THE CALIFORNIA STATE

Environmental Education Guide

A Curriculum Guide for Kindergarten Through Sixth Grade

Carolie Sly, Coordinator
Leslie Comnes, Consultant
Celia Cuomo, Consultant

William Berck, Superintendent, Alameda County Office of Education,
313 West Winton Avenue, Hayward, California 94544-1198.

This book is dedicated to RUDY SCHAFER, whose energetic support of environmental programs and commitment to the people behind them have made him a mentor for those of us working with kids and the environment.

Address for ordering information:
Alameda County Office of Education
313 West Winton Avenue
Hayward, California 94544-1198

Financial support for this project came from the California State Department of Education's environmental license plate fund and the Alameda County Office of Education.

Editing: John Bateson

Classroom Photos: Kathleen Ferguson

Illustrations: Hope Epstein

Quilt: East Bay Heritage Quilters

Quilt Photos: Gary Sinick

Book design and production: Bookman Productions

Library of Congress Cataloging-in-Publication Data

The California State environmental education guide.
Includes index.
1. Environmental education—Study and teaching (Elementary)—California. 2. Nature study—Study and teaching (Elementary)—California. 3. Human ecology—Study and teaching (Elementary)—California. I. Sly, Carolie, 1950– . II. Comnes, Leslie, 1957– . III. Cuomo, Celia, 1956– .
LB1583.3.C35 1988 372.3′57 87–35850

ISBN 0-88067-000-2

Printed in the United States of America

Contents

Acknowledgments

These people participated as creative advisors early on in the curriculum design process. They came to Asilomar to help us improve the "old" *EE Guide* and, instead, encouraged us to move from "what is" to "what could be."

State Advisory Committee

Bob Flasher, East Bay Municipal Utilities District, Orinda, Calif.
Rick Foster, Tahoe City, Calif.
Margaret Gayle-McCreary, Alameda County Office of Education, Hayward, Calif.
Jane Gill, Valley View School, Richmond, Calif.
Doris Harnsberger, San Anselmo, Calif.
Mark Joiner, Contra Costa County Office of Education, Pleasant Hill, Calif.
Carol Lambert, Fullerton School District, Fullerton, Calif.
Chuck Lavaroni, Marin County, Calif.
Linda Martin, Monterey Bay Aquarium, Monterey, Calif.
Marilyn Nishio, East Bay Regional Park District, Alameda, Calif.
Kathleen O'Connell, Santa Catalina Lower School, Monterey, Calif.
Anitra Pawley, Tahoe City, Calif.
Gina Purin, Golden Empire Health Planning Center, Sacramento, Calif.
Dr. Karen Reynolds, California State University, San Jose, Calif.
Rudy Schafer, State Department of Education, Sacramento, Calif.
Augie Scornaienchi, Alameda County Office of Education, Hayward, Calif.
Laura Stockton, West High School, Bakersfield, Calif.
Lillian Watts-Booker, King Estates Junior High School, Oakland, Calif.

National Advisory Committee

Dr. Cheryl Charles, Boulder, Colo.
Dr. John Disinger, ERIC/SMEAC, Columbus, Ohio
Bob Flasher, East Bay Municipal Utility District, Orinda, Calif.
Dr. William Hammond, Fort Myers School District, Fort Myers, Fla.
Mark Joiner, Contra Costa County Office of Education, Pleasant Hill, Calif.
Richard Merrill, Mt. Diablo Unified School District, Pleasant Hill, Calif.
Dr. Doug Miller, National Wildlife Federation, Washington, D.C.
Dr. Esther Railton, California State University, Hayward, Calif.
Dr. Robert Samples, Boulder, Colo.
Alan Sandler, American Institute of Architects, Washington, D.C.
Rudy Schafer, State Department of Education, Sacramento, Calif.
Clay Schoenfeld, University of Wisconsin, Madison Center for Environmental Communication and Education, Madison, Wisc.
Augie Scornaienchi, Alameda County Office of Education, Hayward, Calif.
Dr. Darleen Stoner, California State University Pomona, Calif.
Dr. William Stapp, University of Michigan, Ann Arbor, Mich.
Zack Taylor, State Department of Education, Sacramento, Calif.

These teachers came together to identify the themes that should be addressed in an environmental education guide and the kinds of activities that would teach those themes. Their ideas evolved into the units and action projects in this guide.

Betty Allen, Robert Down School, Pacific Grove, Calif.
Sandy Bredt, Yellow Brick Road School, El Cerrito, Calif.
Sandy Brislain, Benicia, Calif.
Evelyn Cormier, Ardenwood School, Fremont, Calif.
Kathie Donald, Laurel School, Oakland, Calif.

Bob Flasher, East Bay Municipal Utilities District, Orinda, Calif.
Audrey Fong, Franklin School, San Jose, Calif.
Jack Gage, Castro Valley, Calif.
Patty Galvan, Mary Farmer School, Benicia, Calif.
Carolyn Garcelon, Cleo Gordon Elementary School, Fairfield, Calif.
Jane Gill, Valley View School, Richmond, Calif.
Gretchen Gillfillan, Sleepy Hollow School, Orinda, Calif.
Julie Ginocchio, Walnut Heights Elementary School, Walnut Creek, Calif.
Doris Harnsberger, San Anselmo, Calif.
Toris Jaeger, Orinda Union Elementary School District, Orinda, Calif.
Cecilia Lasky, Bidwell School, Antioch, Calif.
Maryellen LaTone, Isadore Cohen Elementary School, Sacramento, Calif.
Barbara Ann Novelli, Robert Down School, Pacific Grove, Calif.
Kathleen O'Connell, Santa Catalina Lower School, Monterey, Calif.
Vic Ramos, H. Glenn Richardson School, Fairfield, Calif.
Diane Renzi, Isadore Cohen Elementary School, Sacramento, Calif.
Michael Stevenson, El Gabilan Elementary School, Salinas, Calif.
Juli Takenaka, Cooper School, Vallejo, Calif.

These teachers field-tested the units in this book with their students during the 1986–87 school year. Their feedback was invaluable for making this a book that works for real teachers and students. They have also been our professional cheerleaders; we sustained a high level of motivation because of their enthusiasm.

Sandi Adams, Cornell School, Albany, Calif.
Sandy Bredt, Yellow Brick Road School, El Cerrito, Calif.
Ellen Blinderman, Yellow Brick Road School, El Cerrito, Calif.
Evelyn Cormier, Ardenwood School, Fremont, Calif.
Bette Kasow, Crocker Highlands School, Oakland, Calif.
Cecilia Lasky, Bidwell School, Antioch, Calif.
Maryellen LaTone, Isadore Cohen Elementary School, Sacramento, Calif.
Kathleen O'Connell, Santa Catalina Lower School, Monterey, Calif.
Juli Takenaka, Cooper School, Vallejo, Calif.

These teachers allowed us to take photographs of their students participating in selected lessons from the guide.

Sandi Adams, Cornell School, Albany, Calif.
Evelyn Cormier, Ardenwood School, Fremont, Calif.
Bette Kasow, Crocker Highlands School, Oakland, Calif.
Richard Hadlock, Berkeley Arts Magnet School, Berkeley, Calif.

These people reviewed the draft document and provided valuable comments and suggestions.

Dr. Diane Conradsen, San Jose State University, San Jose, Calif.
Bob Flasher, East Bay Municipal Utilities District, Orinda, Calif.
Audrey Fong, Franklin School, San Jose, Calif.
Carolyn Garcelon, Cleo Gordon Elementary School, Fairfield, Calif.
Gretchen Gillfillan, Sleepy Hollow Elementary School, Orinda, Calif.
Dr. Michael Kutilek, San Jose State University, San Jose, Calif.
Dr. Kevin Padian, University of California, Berkeley, Calif.
Dr. Esther Railton, California State University, Hayward, Calif.
Karen Reynolds, California State University, San Jose, Calif.
Alan Sandler, American Institute of Architects, Washington, D.C.
Frank R. Schiavo, San Jose State University, San Jose, Calif.

Members of the East Bay Heritage Quilters designed and made the quilt for the cover photograph.

Mabry Benson
Janet Hellerich
Lucille Hilty
Sigrid Ilvesta
Anne Ito
Terry Loy
Kathie Paulist
Randy Joy Poduin
Kay Sakanashi
Setsuko Shimizu
Janet Shore
Louise Sullivan

Tami Tanabe
Peg Tetlow
Martha Vlahos
Margo Weeks
Joyce Williams
Valerie Yeaton

These people served as advisors for the Energy unit.

Alan Comnes, California Public Utilities Commission, San Francisco, Calif.
Bonnie Cornwall, California Energy Extension Service, Sacramento, Calif.
Phil Gay, California Energy Education Forum, San Diego, Calif.
Bette Kasow, Crocker Highlands School, Oakland, Calif.
Christine Riley, Pacific Gas and Electric, San Francisco, Calif.
Dickson Schwarzbach, California Energy Extension Service, Sacramento, Calif.

These people served as advisors on a variety of lessons in the guide.

Sandy Bredt, Yellow Brick Road School, El Cerrito, Calif.
Charlice W. Danielsen, California Native Plant Society, Kensington, Calif.
Susan Goltsman, Project PLAE, Berkeley, Calif.
Tim Gordon, East Bay Regional Park District, Berkeley, Calif.
Ann Jensen, Lawrence Hall of Science, Berkeley, Calif.
Becky Wheat, Berkeley Arts Magnet School, Berkeley, Calif.

Sandy Bredt assisted with the compilation of the Resource Agencies section.

Several people at the Alameda County Office of Education supported our work in a variety of capacities.

Augie Scornaienchi, Assistant Superintendent, is recognized as a leader in environmental education; he was primarily responsible for the first *EE Guide* and was instrumental in securing funding for the production of this document.

Karl Klausner, Administrator, Program Operations, served as a conduit between the design staff and the outside world to make sure we did things in a legal, professional, and relatively punctual manner.

Darlene Hester worked diligently and meticulously to repeatedly revise the draft. In addition, she worked as a member of the design team to keep all the parts organized and updated.

Rita Schoenenberger stepped in at a critical time to finish up the final draft and get it to the publisher.

Mary Fisher worked on early drafts of the guide and offered ongoing computer support.

Rodger Ball applied his computer expertise to the indexes and front matter.

Judi Harris provided critical support during the final stages of production.

Betty Brown coordinated a myriad of secretaries who worked briefly for the design team. Many thanks to all whose names are too numerous to mention.

Introduction

The purpose of this guide is to provide teachers and other educators with classroom lessons and instructional techniques that build a fundamental understanding of the environment. The guide is aimed at grades kindergarten through sixth and consists of eight instructional units and six action projects. Each unit is organized around a theme and the lessons within each unit build upon each other sequentially to provide an increasingly sophisticated understanding of the theme. Lessons are based upon concepts that are taken directly from the California State Department of Education frameworks. All units integrate content areas, consider developmental levels of learning and learning styles, and balance content and learning processes. The *California State Environmental Education Guide* is designed to encourage teachers to view the teaching and learning process as an art as well as a science. The guide is meant to be flexible; teachers can apply their professional knowledge and intuition as they and their students explore the complex interrelationships of what we call "the environment."

How Units Are Organized

The eight units follow a consistent format. Introductions include information about advance planning to help the teacher prepare before unit instruction begins. Some units have ongoing projects or require materials that take time to gather.

Timelines indicate the approximate time needed to teach each activity within a unit (you may wish or need to spend more time on some activities and less on others). Timelines do not include time to do evaluation, extension ideas, or home learning.

Discussion questions can be used to clarify, summarize, or reflect upon an activity. When discussion questions are important during particular steps of an activity, they are included in the procedure.

The evaluation section tells how teachers can assess students' thinking, formally and informally. Evaluation suggestions provide alternative ways of allowing students to express their ideas so that, as the unit progresses, teachers develop a deeper clarity regarding each student's level of understanding.

Home learning activities require parents and children to work together applying what students learn in school to their immediate environment. The purpose of home learning activities varies from lesson to lesson. Sometimes home learning activities are meant to strengthen students' understanding of an idea presented in class. Sometimes information from the home learning activity is essential to the next day's activity (although these activities can be modified easily to eliminate the need for the home learning activity). Other times home learning activities introduce a concept or idea which will be presented the following day (these home learning suggestions have little connection to the lesson they follow but are included so that they precede the lesson the following day). All home learning suggestions tie in directly with classroom instruction; they are not designed as busywork.

The role of parents is critical to the success of the home learning activities. The teacher will have to judge the level of cooperation of students' parents and adjust the number and content of the home learning activities accordingly. Sample letters to parents are included to help the teacher communicate the purposes and procedures of home learning activities to parents.

Action Projects

The six action projects are designed to provide teachers and students with ways to participate in a cycle of investigation, action, and reflection. Action projects address concerns that are closely related to the themes of the instructional units. They may be done in conjunction with a unit or conducted separately. Either way, they should be useful to any teacher who wants his or her students to develop behavior that has a positive effect on the environment.

Other Elements

There are additional ways this guide can be useful to teachers and other educators. The "Help for the Beginning Teacher" chapter has background information and self-study exercises for new teachers with little knowledge of environmental education. The "California State Resource Agencies" section includes information on teaching materials available from various state agencies. The indexes identify units that can be combined to teach topics other than the unit themes.

California Frameworks

The following California state frameworks were used as a basis for the units in this guide:

Science Framework Addendum, 1984
Mathematics Framework, 1985
English-Language Arts Framework, 1987
History-Social Science Framework, 1981
Visual and Performing Arts Framework, 1982

These frameworks can be ordered from the California Department of Education, P.O. Box 271, Sacramento, Calif. 95802-0271.

Historical Background

It has been nearly 20 years since the California State Legislature first wrote into the Education Code a requirement that instruction in the wise use of natural resources and the protection of environmental quality be provided in all appropriate subject matter fields, grades one through twelve. To assist schools in meeting this instructional obligation, the Legislature authorized the Department of Education to use personalized license plate funds to subsidize school community environmental education projects focusing on demonstrated local needs. This the Department of Education has done, with support from the California State Resources Agency.

In California, as in most other states, there has been a close relationship between resource management agency personnel and environmental educators. This relationship exists because professionals in both fields recognize that through their work they are shaping the future. The role of resource managers is to extend the usability of natural resources and to promote the highest possible level of environmental quality far into the future. The goal of educators is to develop human resources so that the highest quality of life will be possible for the maximum number of people. Both agencies are involved in conservation. Resource managers conserve natural resources; educators conserve human resources. The success of one depends on the success of the other.

Educators and resource managers agree that they should work together on programs of value to schools. These programs should aim to provide students with the skills, knowledge, and attitudes necessary to make intelligent personal and social decisions concerning the environment and its resources.

In 1983, as a result of many meetings between educators and resource managers, a set of four environmental education guides keyed to the County Superintendents' Course of Study was developed. These guides spelled out an instructional response to the Education Code. They showed teachers at all levels how appropriate environmental concepts could be integrated throughout an entire curriculum in nearly all subject matter fields.

The guides were produced as the result of a unique working relationship between three public agencies—the California State Resources Agency, the State Department of Education, and the Alameda County Office of Education. The Resources Agency awarded a one-time license plate grant for the production of the guides and provided information. The Department of Education contributed management services and assisted with the writing and production. Alameda County provided personnel and facilities to design and produce the guides and printed the guides on a cost-recovery basis.

Since 1983 the guides have been used in thousands of schools in California and elsewhere (the French government purchased 200 copies for schools in Paris). The result is that the Education Code mandate has been an instructional reality in a majority of schools in the state. The environmental education guides have also served to promote a better understanding of the work of resource management personnel and of the services and materials they offer schools.

Even the best instructional materials reach a point where their usefulness starts to decline, however. So it was with the environmental education guides. Rather than revise and reprint them, a careful assessment was made. It was noted that most secondary schools are organized around subject matter fields and that such an arrangement does not lend itself to the interdisciplinary instructional approach called for in the guides. As a result, the guides were not being used much at this level. It was also noted that the National Wildlife Federation had recently produced a middle school instructional program, "Conservation Learning Activities in Science and Social Science" (CLASS Project), which was undergoing extensive modification to increase its value to California educators (the California version of the CLASS Project will be ready for use in the schools during the 1987–1988 school year).

After evaluating these factors, it was decided that a new environmental education guide would be developed focusing on the needs of students in kindergarten through sixth grade. The middle school program component will be provided by the CLASS Project, California version.

Another factor which was considered when developing both the environmental education guides and the CLASS Project was the mandate for energy education expressed in Assembly Bill 1333 (Hauser), which was approved by the Legislature and signed by the Governor in 1985. Because this legislation called for the development of appropriate energy instructional materials at all levels, the new environmental education guide includes an instructional unit on this important topic. The California CLASS materials also have an entire section addressed to energy education for use in middle school science and social studies classes.

Much hard work by Alameda County staff and consultants has gone into this publication. In addition, many teachers have provided valuable assistance by serving as advisors and field-testing the materials with their students. Many resource managers have also contributed valuable information and comments.

This guide is, in effect, a partnership. The hope is that it will result in a better future for our lands and for tomorrow's citizens.

Diversity of Life

Kindergarten and First Grade

Introduction to the Unit

This unit introduces kindergarten and first-grade students to the notion of diversity among living things. Students also sort, classify, and sequence living things according to various characteristics.

Sorting, classifying, and sequencing are key abilities of human learning. By understanding what things go together, we begin to make sense of our environment. Concepts related to grouping information usually are emphasized in math and science instruction, thus this unit has a strong math and science emphasis.

Children aged four to seven tend to group objects according to perceptual attributes (like color, shape, or size) and to classify objects according to one attribute at a time. As they develop, children are able to classify objects according to two attributes simultaneously and according to abstract characteristics. The activities in this unit lay the groundwork for more complex forms of classification.

The first five activities focus on perceptual likenesses and differences among living things. By focusing on one attribute, students begin to identify variations among fellow classmates, then begin to identify variations among other living things. The next three activities allow students to consider more complex ways of grouping living things as students learn that animals vary in the ways they look, move, obtain and conserve food and water, behave, reproduce, and protect themselves. The final five activities help students understand that plants are living things, that plants vary in the ways they are adapted to meet their needs, and that all living things grow and change over time.

Advance Planning

Live animals are required for the activities "Animals Alike and Different," "Comparing Three Live Animals," and "Comparing Three Living Things." You will need to consider ways to house, feed, and care for the animals.

Plants are required in the activities "Comparing Three Living Things" and "Life Cycle of a Plant." The latter activity requires seeds, seedlings, and mature plants of the same species. Since this is the final activity of the unit, there should be time to grow the seedlings and mature plants if they are planted when the unit begins.

All activities require students to bring pictures or information from home. Keep this in mind as you plan so that you can anticipate times when you will need parent cooperation.

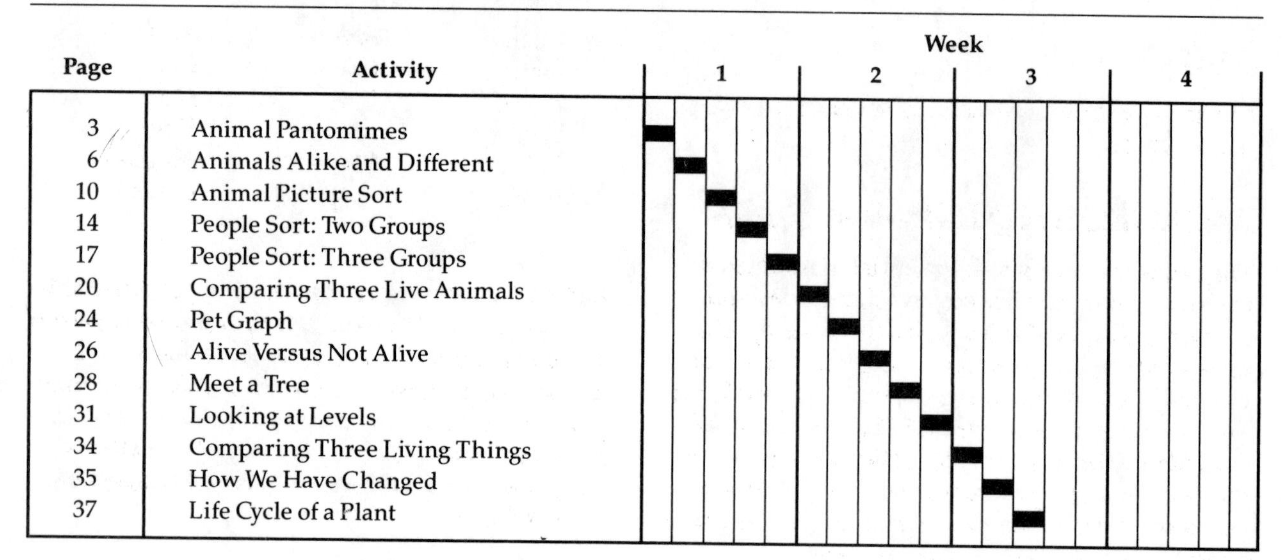

Page	Activity
3	Animal Pantomimes
6	Animals Alike and Different
10	Animal Picture Sort
14	People Sort: Two Groups
17	People Sort: Three Groups
20	Comparing Three Live Animals
24	Pet Graph
26	Alive Versus Not Alive
28	Meet a Tree
31	Looking at Levels
34	Comparing Three Living Things
35	How We Have Changed
37	Life Cycle of a Plant

ANIMAL PANTOMIMES

SUMMARY OF ACTIVITY

Through dramatization, students become aware of ways in which animals differ from each other.

Through language and dramatization, students express ideas about diversity and begin to build a language that describes the characteristics of living things.

Time: 30 minutes

Setting: A large space to move around in, preferably outdoors

Materials:
- Picture book or set of pictures depicting various animals
- Drawing paper
- Crayons

Subjects: Science, language arts, physical education, performing arts

Key Words: Alike, different, describe

RELATED CALIFORNIA FRAMEWORK CONCEPTS

There is great diversity among living things. (*Science Framework Addendum*)

Dramatizations can be used to express ideas, intentions, or feelings. (Adapted from *Visual and Performing Arts Framework*)

OBJECTIVE

Through pantomime, students describe animal characteristics.

BACKGROUND INFORMATION

The notion of diversity is essential to understanding how animal species survive day-to-day and over time. Each animal species has developed a set of adaptive characteristics that allow it to survive within its habitat and reproduce its own kind. Animals vary in appearance, behavior, and anatomy. Most adaptive characteristics fall into one of the following categories: regulation of body temperature, method of obtaining food or water, locomotion, reproduction, and protection.

For children at the kindergarten to first-grade level, the concept of diversity is introduced by building an awareness of and an appreciation for the variety that exists among living things.

PREPARATION AND LEAD-UP

Read to students the book *Quick as a Cricket,* by Audrey Wood (optional). Call on volunteers to pantomime a few of the lines from the book. Ask, "Can someone show us what it would look like to be 'as slow as a snail'? Can someone show us what it might look like to be 'as sad as a basset'?"

PROCEDURE

1. Briefly describe some of the ways animals differ from each other. You may want to use the book *Quick as a Cricket* as a way to introduce students to the idea that animals differ in the way they look, move, eat, behave, and where they live.

2. Lead the class to a space where there is plenty of room to move around. Point out the boundaries, introduce a signal to indicate when students should stop and listen for the next animal name, and tell students they are not to make physical contact as they pantomime each kind of animal. Have students pantomime the following animals:

Duck	Bee	Butterfly
Rabbit	Hawk	Lion
Snake	Seal	Dog
Kangaroo	Gorilla	Deer
Bat	Elephant	Mouse
Monkey	Porpoise	Lizard

3. Have students take turns thinking of other animals to act out. Then discuss differences between the animals (see the discussion questions) and summarize by comparing pairs of animals using students' words. (For example, "You have told us that a bat is small and a lion is big, that both are furry, and that a bat can fly while a lion stays on the ground.")

DISCUSSION QUESTIONS

Which animals did you most enjoy being and why? How did it feel to be a bat? A snake? A lion?

Did you like being a big animal or a small animal? Why?

Did you like being an animal that could fly? That could swim?

EVALUATION

Have each student draw a picture of two of the animals listed. Students can then dictate at least two comparison statements describing how the two animals are alike or different.

EXTENSION IDEAS

- Have students make animals out of clay and sort them according to attributes. For example, animals could be sorted into groups according to whether they spend most of their time on land, in the air, or in the water.
- Have students go outside and observe real animals such as birds, ants, snails, and squirrels. Ask students to describe and compare movements of these animals.
- Have students participate in a guessing game. Tape an animal picture on one student's back. Have the student turn around so that other students can see the picture. Call on the class to give descriptive clues about the animal without giving the animal's name. The student wearing the picture tries to guess the animal's identity.

HOME LEARNING SUGGESTION

(Use as lead-up to the next activity)

Ask parents to help their children find a picture of an animal in a book, magazine, or on a calendar (see the sample letter). Parents and students can

discuss how that particular animal gets its food and eats it, moves, protects itself, has babies, and keeps warm or cool. Ask students to bring in the picture, if possible, and to be prepared to tell something about the animal and something they would like to know about the animal. If students have few books or magazines at home, ask parents and students to look for an animal on television.

RESOURCE

For Students

Wood, Audrey. *Quick as a Cricket*. Singapore: Child Play Ltd., 1982. This picture book uses similes to compare animals to a child.

Sample Letter

Dear Parent:

Please help your child find a picture of an animal in a book, magazine, or on a calendar. Once you have found an appropriate picture, discuss:

- How the animal gets its food and eats it.
- How the animal moves.
- How the animal protects itself.
- How the animal has babies.
- How the animal keeps warm or cool.

You don't have to know all of the answers. The purpose is to get your child to start thinking about the answers (besides, it will probably be more fun and relaxing for you if you don't feel as if you have to provide all of the answers).

If possible, allow your child to bring the picture to class. Help your child be prepared to tell something about the animal and ask something more he or she would like to know about the animal.

Thank you.

ANIMALS ALIKE AND DIFFERENT

SUMMARY OF ACTIVITY

Students explore ways that animals are alike and different.

Time: 60 minutes (may vary depending upon group sizes and the number of adult helpers)

Setting: Classroom

Materials:
- Pictures of animals
- Two live animals and the equipment necessary to house them in the classroom for several days
- Paper towels

Subjects: Science, language arts, math

Key Words: Texture, behavior, alike, different, habitat

RELATED CALIFORNIA FRAMEWORK CONCEPTS

There is great diversity among living things. (*Science Framework Addendum*)

Objects can be classified and sorted using one or more attributes by observing similarities and differences, describing and recording relationships, and making generalizations. (Adapted from *Mathematics Framework*)

Animals have characteristics by which they can be described and identified. (*Science Framework Addendum*)

Talking and listening are important ways by which people communicate with and learn from each other. (Adapted from *English-Language Arts Framework*)

OBJECTIVE

Students observe live animals and look at pictures of animals, then describe ways animals are similar and different.

BACKGROUND INFORMATION

It is important that students have opportunities to examine live animals in order to better understand and be able to make generalizations about living things. Finding appropriate live animals, setting up environments that keep the animals healthy and contained, and caring for the animals over weekends and school vacations is extra work for the teacher. On the more positive side, most children have a strong curiosity and sense of caring for live animals. By capitalizing on these attributes, you will find that students' enthusiasm for learning about live animals outweighs the hassles of locating and caring for the animals.

Animals like snails, mealworms, and earthworms are good for starters because they are easy to care for. Be sure to find out about an animal's needs, habits, and temperament before you purchase more adventuresome animals from a pet store. You may want to ask students to volunteer to bring their *small* pet to school.

As much as possible allow students to take responsibility for ongoing care of the animals. This will teach students about responsibility and caring and will also deepen their understanding of how animals vary in the ways they move, eat, sleep, and behave.

PREPARATION AND LEAD-UP

Bring to class two kinds of live animals for comparison. Snails, mealworms, and earthworms are easily available. Snails often can be found in gardens; mealworms can be purchased from a pet store, and earthworms from a bait shop. Establish an environment so that the animals can remain in the classroom for the remainder of the unit.

Set up the classroom so that two groups of students can participate in two different activities without interfering with each other. Arrange to have a teacher's aide or a parent volunteer lead the two groups. One group will "meet" the two live animals; the other will share the results from the home learning assignment.

PROCEDURE

1. Introduce the entire class to the two live animals. Explain where the animals came from and offer to answer three questions about each animal. Tell students that the rest of their questions and comments will be addressed at the live animals work station. Explain that while one group is at the live animals work station, the other group will discuss the home learning assignment. Tell students that the groups will rotate in 15 minutes so everyone will get the opportunity to participate in both work stations.

2. Arrange the group at the live animals work station so that everyone can see both animals up close (if the group is big, you may want to have more than one of each kind of animal). Show students how to handle the animals carefully and, if possible, allow each student to hold an animal. Have paper towels handy in case a quick cleanup is necessary.

Allow students to ask questions freely. Do not feel you must have all the answers, however. Use this time to arouse students' curiosity about the animals—students will have the opportunity to learn more about the animals later. If students have few questions, stimulate their thinking (see the discussion questions).

For the home learning group, ask each student to share the results of his or her home learning assignment from the previous activity. Ask students to 1) identify the animal in their picture (and show the picture if they were able to bring it); 2) share what they found out about the animal (how it moves, protects itself, has babies, gets food and eats it, and stays warm or cool); and 3) tell what more they would like to know about the animal. Make sure adult helpers know that neither they nor you need be able to answer the latter; it is okay to have questions that do not have immediate answers. The purpose of this aspect of the activity is to arouse students' curiosity. If there is time, let each student describe what it might feel like to be a particular animal.

3. After students have participated in both work stations, summarize the activity by stating that both work stations allowed students to take a closer look at animals and to begin to ask questions about how animals are alike and different. Point out that students noticed many things about the animals—how they looked, how big or small they were, how they were shaped, how they behaved, how they moved, and how they got their food. Tell students that they will spend time tomorrow and over the next few days learning more about animals and other living things.

DISCUSSION QUESTIONS

What words can we use to describe each of these animals?

Are these animals the same size? The same color? Do they feel the same? Do they move the same?

EVALUATION

Ask students to think about one of the animals they observed live or in a picture. Have students tell something that they learned about the animal.

EXTENSION IDEAS

- Have students visit each work station several times to learn more about the animals. At the live animals work station groups might place each animal on different surfaces (like sandpaper or glass) and observe its behavior. Students can also draw pictures of the animals.
- Have the home learning group create a poem about an animal. Each student can contribute a word, and the teacher can help the group combine the words into a poem. For example:

Bear
brown, furry
growling, searching, hiding
big, strong
wild.

HOME LEARNING SUGGESTION

(Use as lead-up to the next activity)

Ask students to take a poll of individuals in their family based on the attribute of being left-handed or right-handed. Send the letter on page 8 home with students along with the copycat page.

SOURCE OF ACTIVITY

Adapted from Baratta-Lorton, Mary. *Mathematics Their Way.* Menlo Park, Calif.: Addison-Wesley Publishing Co., 1976.

Sample Letter

Dear Parent:

We are learning about ways in which living things are alike and different. This home learning assignment will help us look at one way that people can be grouped together, based on a common characteristic. Please have your child color in the appropriate squares on the data sheet to indicate whether each person in your family is left-handed or right-handed. We will be discussing the results tomorrow.

Thank you.

Name ______________________________

LEFT-HANDED, RIGHT-HANDED DATA SHEET

List people in your family and circle the hand in the appropriate column to indicate whether that person is left-handed or right-handed.

Name of Family Member	*Left-Handed*	*Right-Handed*

ANIMAL PICTURE SORT

SUMMARY OF ACTIVITY

Students sort and re-sort animal pictures into two groups, using various criteria.

Time: 30 minutes

Setting: A place for the entire class to sit in a circle or horseshoe so that everybody can see everybody else

Materials:
- Two large arrows made of tape or tagboard
- Pictures of various animals, at least one per student
- A graphing board (see the preparation and lead-up)
- Cut-outs of ice cream cones in brown and white (see the home learning suggestion)

Subjects: Science, math, language arts

Key Words: Alike, different, rule, most, least, more than, less than, column, survey

RELATED CALIFORNIA FRAMEWORK CONCEPTS

There is great diversity among living things. Different kinds of living things have characteristics and behaviors by which they can be described, identified, sequenced, and classified. (*Science Framework Addendum*)

Objects can be classified and sorted using one or more attributes by observing similarities and differences, describing and recording relationships, and making generalizations. (Adapted from *Mathematics Framework*)

OBJECTIVE

Students identify criteria for sorting animal pictures according to physical characteristics.

BACKGROUND INFORMATION

Children need many opportunities to sort and re-sort objects in order to begin seeing relationships between objects. By sorting objects in a variety of ways, students come to understand the notion of attribute as an abstract characteristic or quality of an object. They begin to focus on the properties of a given set of objects and to group and label the set accordingly (the introduction to this unit has more information on sorting and classifying).

This activity can be repeated several times as there are many ways to sort a given set of pictures. Emphasize to students that there may be more than one "right" way. Although students try to guess the rule by which pictures are being sorted, other rules may be correct also.

Do not be discouraged if in step four, students have a difficult time thinking of categories to sort by. Use the opportunity to point out that things in the real world rarely fall into two categories easily.

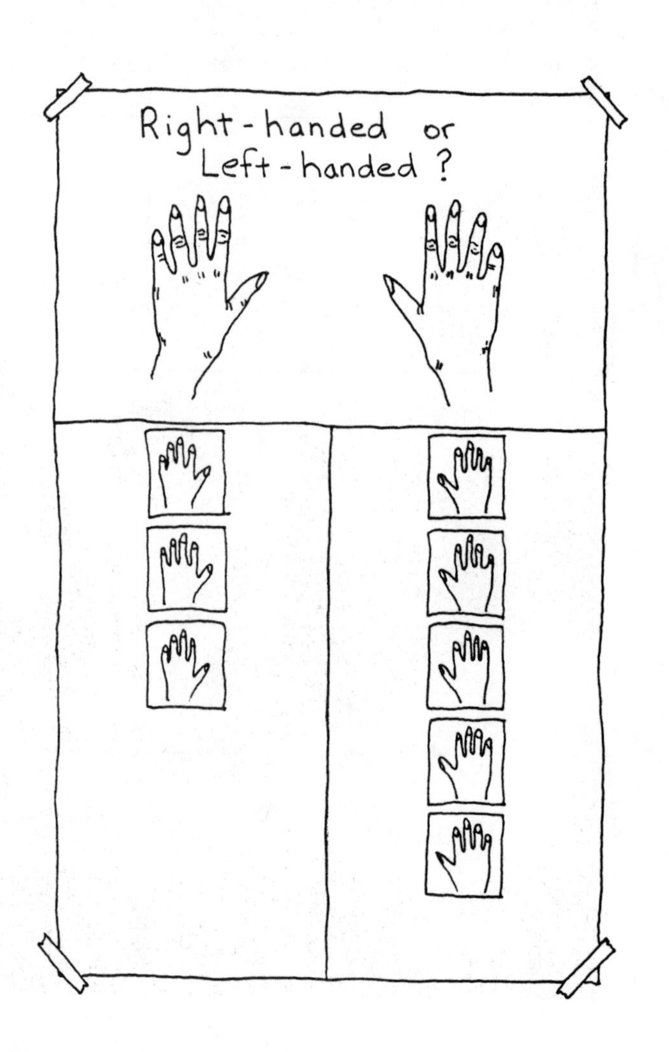

PREPARATION AND LEAD-UP

Collect animal pictures from magazines, calendars, or other sources. The pictures should show examples of a simple attribute; for example, animals with two legs and animals with four legs, animals with tails and animals without tails, animals that can swim and animals that cannot swim, animals that can fly and animals that cannot fly, or animals that live on land and animals that do not live on land.

Using masking tape or tagboard, put two arrows on the floor end to end so that they are pointing in opposite directions. Make sure the arrows are different colors.

Arrange time for students to transfer the results from the previous activity's home learning assignment to a graphing board or construct a class graph of right- and left-handedness (see the illustration). The information will be used in step five of this activity.

PROCEDURE

1. Have students sit in a circle around the arrows. Tell students that you are going to place animal pictures in two groups, putting pictures of the animals that are alike in some way next to the same arrow. Ask students to look at each picture and think about why you are putting certain pictures together. As soon as students think they know the rule by which you are sorting, they are to quietly put their finger on their nose (instead of raising their hand).

2. Begin sorting pictures slowly into two groups, next to the arrows. Give students time to see each picture clearly and consider the new information added by each picture. When most students have their fingers on their noses, call on students to share their theories as to how the pictures are sorted.

3. Give each student a picture. Explain that you will think of a new rule by which to sort the pictures and the class will decide which arrow each picture belongs next to. Place an appropriate picture next to each arrow, then call on students one at a time to hold up their picture. Ask the rest of the class to choose the arrow the picture belongs next to. If there is disagreement, ask one student from each side to defend his or her choice. If the students' arguments do not result in unanimity, tell the class which arrow the picture belongs next to and place it on that side. Continue until all of the pictures have been sorted.

4. Repeat the exercise three times, each time with a new rule for sorting. If appropriate, ask a student to think of a rule and whisper it in your ear. If the rule seems workable (if animals could be sorted into two piles easily), sort pictures using the rule.

5. Remind students of their home learning assignment from the previous activity. Tell them that the assignment was a way of sorting people into two groups, just as students sorted the animal pictures. As a class, look at the completed graphing board. This graph groups people who are alike, based on whether they are right-handed or left-handed. Ask, "What column has the most? What column has the least? Are there more right-handed people or more left-handed people in our survey? How many more right-handed or left-handed people are there altogether?"

6. Explain to students that they have seen there are many ways animals are alike and different, depending on what your rule is. Tell students that their home learning assignment from last night, tonight's home learning assignment, and tomorrow's activity will allow them to look at ways people can be sorted into two groups.

DISCUSSION QUESTIONS

How did we sort the pictures so that animals that are alike were together?

Were the same animals always grouped together? Why not?

Is there any rule we could have used so that *all* of the animals were grouped together?

EVALUATION

Have students sort other objects such as beans, buttons, or seeds into two groups and explain why certain objects were grouped together. This may take place as part of math instruction, particularly if you have math stations set up in your classroom.

EXTENSION IDEAS

- Have each student make a collage of animals. Students can divide a large piece of construction paper into two sections by folding the paper or drawing a line down the middle. Have students cut and paste pictures of animals on each side of the paper, putting animals that are alike together.
- In order to reinforce the usefulness of graphing, post an attendance graph each day. Have students record information about themselves; for example, "Do you have a lunch box or a lunch bag?" The class can decide what question will be graphed the following day.

HOME LEARNING SUGGESTION

(Use as lead-up to the next activity)

Have students take another poll of family members. Students can use the copycat page to record whether family members prefer chocolate or vanilla ice cream.

SOURCE OF ACTIVITY

Adapted from Baratta-Lorton, Mary. *Mathematics Their Way*. Menlo Park, Calif.: Addison-Wesley Publishing Co., 1976.

Name ______________________________

ICE CREAM PREFERENCE DATA SHEET

List people in your family and circle the ice cream cone in the appropriate column to indicate whether each person prefers chocolate or vanilla ice cream.

Name of Family Member	*Chocolate*	*Vanilla*

PEOPLE SORT: TWO GROUPS

SUMMARY OF ACTIVITY

Students sort and re-sort themselves into two groups, based on different attributes.

Time: 30 minutes

Setting: A place big enough for students to move around and form lines

Materials:
- Graphing board (see the preparation and lead-up)
- Masking tape or another way to clearly mark two areas on the floor

Subjects: Science, math, social studies

Key Words: Prefer, more, less, the same, altogether

RELATED CALIFORNIA FRAMEWORK CONCEPTS

Different kinds of living things have characteristics and behaviors by which they can be described, identified, sequenced, and classified. (*Science Framework Addendum*)

Individuals are unique and aware of their similarities and differences. (Adapted from *History-Social Science Framework*)

OBJECTIVE

Students identify similarities and differences among themselves, based on two attributes.

BACKGROUND INFORMATION

Creating graphs of people can be done daily in different ways. For example, one day students can create a line graph by forming two lines based on whether they are shorter or longer than a meter stick, then the next day they can line up in a sequence from shortest to tallest.

This activity provides opportunities for students to sort and re-sort a set of objects—in this case people—according to various attributes. The activity also gives the teacher the chance to assess individual students' abilities to recognize new attributes. Some students will be able to re-sort themselves according to a new attribute; other students will continue to sort according to the first attribute introduced. These differences in abilities indicate students are at different developmental levels.

PREPARATION AND LEAD-UP

Have students transfer the results from the previous activity's home learning assignment to a graphing board, as illustrated.

PROCEDURE

1. Discuss the results of the home learning suggestion about ice cream preferences. Ask, "What column has the most? What column has the least? Do more people prefer chocolate or vanilla? How

many more? How many chocolates and how many vanillas are there altogether?"

2. Tell students, "We are going to sort ourselves into two groups based on some of our old rules and on some new rules." Lead the class to a place where there is plenty of room for students to move around. Place two pieces of masking tape or two markers about 1.5 meters (five feet) apart. Have students line up behind the appropriate marker based on their answer to the question, "Are you right-handed or left-handed?" Some students may not know, so help them decide.

3. When the class has sorted itself, discuss the groupings (see the discussion questions). Then have the class reassemble and ask students, "Which do you prefer, chocolate or vanilla ice cream?" Again have students line up behind the appropriate marker. Repeat the exercise using questions like, "Which do you prefer, apple juice or orange juice? Are you a boy or a girl? Did you bring your lunch or are you going to buy it?" (You may end up with a third group here—students who go home for lunch. Use the opportunity to point out that we rarely fall into two groups; people are so different that it is often difficult to categorize them as being one way or another.) Ask students if they can think of other questions that would sort the class into two groups.

DISCUSSION QUESTIONS

(Ask after each sorting)

Which group has the most people? The least?
What does this tell us about our class?
How many people are in each group?
How many people are there all together?
Does anyone belong in a third group because he or she doesn't fit into either of the two groups?

EVALUATION

Have students draw a picture of two living things like two plants, two animals, or two people. Students can dictate to an adult at least one way that the two living things are alike and at least one way that they are different.

EXTENSION IDEAS

- As a class have students create a picture graph to represent students' responses to one of the sorting rules. Discuss what the graph represents (see the discussion questions).
- Have students create symbolic graphs to represent the same information. For example, students might color in a square with a brown crayon if they prefer chocolate ice cream or use a

yellow crayon if they prefer vanilla ice cream. A symbolic graph consists of symbols (like a slash, dot, or check) that represent individuals.

- Set up a table or box with rocks, pine cones, feathers, fur, nuts, leaves, or other natural objects. Have students sort the objects according to a rule they think of and ask other students to guess the rule.
- Choose a way to sort things seen around the school. Take students on a walk and point out objects that fit into the selected category (for example, objects that move versus objects that do not move). Have students try to guess the rule you are using.

HOME LEARNING SUGGESTION

(Use as lead-up to the next activity)

Send the following letter to parents.

SOURCE OF ACTIVITY

Adapted from Baratta-Lorton, Mary. *Mathematics Their Way*. Menlo Park, Calif.: Addison-Wesley Publishing Co., 1976.

Sample Letter

Dear Parent:

For the past few days our class has been comparing living things by sorting and re-sorting them into two groups. For example, we sorted ourselves into two groups according to whether we had brought a lunch in a lunch box or in a bag, according to whether we prefer chocolate or vanilla ice cream, and according to whether we were wearing white or colored socks.

Now the class will start to think about ways that living things can be sorted into three groups. Please help your child think of at least one way a group of people can be sorted into three groups (for example, into babies, children, and adults). Write down your child's idea and have him or her bring it to school tomorrow. Here are a few more ideas: "Would you like to drive a truck, a car, or a motorcycle?" "Would you like to be older, younger, or the same age?" "Do you prefer whole apples, apple juice, or applesauce?"

Thank you for your help.

PEOPLE SORT: THREE GROUPS

SUMMARY OF ACTIVITY

Students sort people into three groups.

Time: 30 minutes

Setting: A space with room for students to move around comfortably

Materials:
- Masking tape or three markers
- Copycat page for each student (see the home learning suggestion)

Subjects: Science, math, fine arts, social studies

Key Words: Most, least, more, less, fewer

RELATED CALIFORNIA FRAMEWORK CONCEPTS

Different kinds of living things have characteristics and behaviors by which they can be described, identified, sequenced, and classified. (*Science Framework Addendum*)

There are groups to which individuals belong. (Adapted from *History-Social Science Framework*)

OBJECTIVE

Students identify similarities and differences among themselves, based on three attributes.

BACKGROUND INFORMATION

Once students are able to sort objects into two groups, they are ready to sort objects—in this case themselves—into groups of three. It is more difficult to think of attributes that can be sorted three ways, but by moving beyond two groups students can learn more about a given set of objects. Students need opportunities to sort real objects into groups of three before they begin to sort pictures or graph symbols to represent three groups.

PREPARATION AND LEAD-UP

Choose a place large enough for students to move around in comfortably. Place three strips of masking tape (or some other marker) about 1.2 meters (four feet) apart.

Collect students' responses to the previous activity's home learning suggestion. Organize the responses so that those which form three groups can be used first. If students did not do the home learning suggestion, think of ways students can sort themselves into three groups.

PROCEDURE

1. Remind the students that they have been sorting living things into two groups using various attributes. Explain that sometimes it is more useful to sort things into three groups. This activity will explore ways that living things can be sorted into three groups.

2. Lead students to the area you have chosen for the activity. Tell students that they will sort themselves into three groups, according to your rule, so that students that are alike are grouped together.

3. Ask each student, "What color do you like best: red, blue, or yellow?" Have students line up behind the appropriate marker. Discuss the groupings (see the discussion questions).

4. Have the class reassemble then sort students using the following questions. "What fruit do you like best: apples, oranges, or bananas? Is your hair brown, black, or blonde? Are your eyes blue, brown, or green? How did you get to school: walk, bus, or car?" (You may get more than three groups here as a student may have ridden a bicycle. Use the opportunity to point out again that it is often difficult to sort ourselves into only a few categories.)

5. Continue the activity using students' ideas from the previous activity's home learning suggestion. If students are able, let them read or tell their idea to the class. Begin with those ideas that allow for three distinct groups. This will give students a chance to understand ways that groups of three can be formed. By the end students may be ready to understand that not all ways of categorizing are clear-cut. Stress that ambiguity is okay; in fact, it is more typical of how the real world works.

6. Teach students the following song as an illustration of the way three different animals move and where they live. Sing the song to the tune of "Frère Jacques."

Crawling beetle, crawling beetle, on the ground, on the ground.
Crawling, crawling, crawling.
Crawling, crawling, crawling.
All around, all around.

Hopping cricket, hopping cricket, in the grass, in the grass.
Hopping, hopping, hopping.
Hopping, hopping, hopping.
Very fast, very fast.

Buzzing bee, buzzing bee, in the air, in the air.
Buzzing, buzzing, buzzing.
Buzzing, buzzing, buzzing.
Everywhere, everywhere.

(Reprinted with permission from *Ranger Rick's NatureScope*, "Incredible Insects," published by the National Wildlife Federation, 1984.)

DISCUSSION QUESTIONS

(Ask after each sorting)

Which group has the most people? The least?
Does group X have more or fewer people than group Y? Than group Z?
Do any groups have the same number of people?
Does anyone fit into more than one group?

EVALUATION

Give students a "junk box" of similar objects—buttons, seeds, or pinecones. Ask students to sort the objects into three groups so that those that are alike are together.

EXTENSION IDEAS

- Have students transfer the results of some of the sorting to graphs. Use the discussion questions to explain what the graphs mean.
- Have students try sorting each other into groups of four. Alternatively, students can try to sequence a set of objects, for instance from smallest to largest.

HOME LEARNING SUGGESTION

(Use as lead-up to the next activity)

Send home the "Three Animals" copycat page. Ask parents to have their child dictate two sentences, one that describes ways in which the three animals are alike and one that describes ways in which the animals differ.

Name ____________________

THREE ANIMALS

Ways in which the three animals are alike:

____

____

____

____

Ways in which the three animals are different:

____

____

____

____

COMPARING THREE LIVE ANIMALS

SUMMARY OF ACTIVITY

Students compare three animals—a snail, an earthworm, and a mealworm.

Time: 45 minutes

Setting: Classroom

Materials:
- Earthworm for each pair of students
- Mealworm for each pair of students
- Snail for each pair of students
- Small styrofoam meat tray or a milk carton cut to half its size for each pair of students
- Petri dish for each pair of students (optional)
- Hand lenses (optional)

Subjects: Science, language arts, fine arts

Key Words: Mealworm, earthworm, snail, alike, different

RELATED CALIFORNIA FRAMEWORK CONCEPTS

Different kinds of living things have characteristics and behaviors by which they can be described, identified, sequenced, and classified. (*Science Framework Addendum*)

Talking and listening are important ways by which people communicate with and learn from each other. (Adapted from *English-Language Arts Framework*)

OBJECTIVE

Students observe and make comparative statements about three live animals.

BACKGROUND INFORMATION

Students have compared living things according to likenesses and differences and have sorted objects according to a given attribute into groups of two and three. In order for students to apply what they have learned to the natural world, they need experiences with real animals. In this activity students compare animals in a less formal way than in past activities, focusing on those attributes that arouse their curiosity.

PREPARATION AND LEAD-UP

Earthworms, snails, and mealworms can be purchased at bait shops or found in most gardens. Mealworms are also sold at most pet stores. Collect or purchase an earthworm, a snail, and a mealworm for each pair of students. Allow students to share their home learning assignment from the previous activity. Post the sheets on a wall or bulletin board.

PROCEDURE

1. Have students gather around the live animals. Demonstrate how to handle each of the animals carefully, keeping hands slightly moist for handling the snail and the earthworm. Tell students that they must share animals with their partners, that they are not to move the animals from the designated work area, and that when the observation period is over you will ask students to share what they have discovered about their animal.

2. Divide students into pairs and assign each pair a work area. For comparative purposes, it is

usually best to distribute all three animals at the same time to each pair of students. You may decide, however, given the nature of your students, that distributing one animal at a time is wiser. Allow students time to observe their animals.

3. Have students stop (you may want them to move to another area of the room) and share what they have discovered. Record words or phrases that summarize or generalize their statements. Discuss their observations (see the discussion questions).

4. After the lab, have students help clean up. Students should also return the animals to the appropriate environments in the classroom.

DISCUSSION QUESTIONS

What did you find out about these three animals?
How does the earthworm feel?
How does the snail move?
How does the mealworm act when you pick it up?
In what ways are the three animals alike?
In what ways are they different?
In what ways are any or all of the animals like you?

EVALUATION

Have students draw a picture of one of the animals. Students can then dictate a statement that describes an observation they made.

EXTENSION IDEA

Set up a learning station with magnifying lenses, petri dishes, and meat trays. Students can use this equipment to learn more about the animals. When students have studied the animals further, challenge students to move like an earthworm, mealworm, and snail.

HOME LEARNING SUGGESTION

(Use as lead-up to the next activity)

Send home with students the following letter and copycat page. The latter is to be completed by students with help from another family member and should be returned the following day.

Sample Letter

Dear Parent:

Please help your child complete the attached copycat page. If there is an animal living at your house that is not listed, write the name of the animal on the line after the word "other" and have your child draw a picture of the animal. If you have more than one kind of animal at your house, have your child circle all of the animals that you have.

We will be using this information to make a class graph of what animals live in our homes. Once our graph is assembled, we will compare the different ways pets eat, move, sleep, and protect themselves. This activity enables students to learn more about the diversity of living things and about different ways that living and nonliving things can be classified.

Thank you for your help.

Name ______________________________

WHAT LIVES AT MY HOUSE

Circle each kind of animal that lives at your house.

Dog 

Hamster 

Cat

Rat 

Fish 

Guinea Pig 

Bird 

Rabbit 

Other ____________________

____

____

____

PET GRAPH

SUMMARY OF ACTIVITY

Students develop a graph of animals they have at home and describe each animal.

Time: 30 minutes

Setting: Classroom

Materials:
- Graphing board
- Completed copycat page from the previous activity
- Animal pictures from previous activity's copycat page (enlarge the page and cut out the animals)
- Tape or glue

Subjects: Science, math, language arts, social studies

Key Words: Alike, different, most, least, same as

RELATED CALIFORNIA FRAMEWORK CONCEPTS

There is great diversity among living things. (*Science Framework Addendum*)

Concrete, pictorial, and symbolic graphs can be created and interpreted. (Adapted from *Mathematics Framework*)

Talking and listening are important ways by which people communicate with and learn from each other. (Adapted from *English-Language Arts Framework*)

OBJECTIVE

Students count, describe, and compare various household pets.

BACKGROUND INFORMATION

Young children need opportunities to develop language skills. In this activity students generate descriptive words that help them compare animals with which they are most familiar—their pets—accurately and in detail. By focusing on ways that animals eat, move, protect themselves, reproduce, and regulate their body temperature, students begin to think about and express verbally the diversity among animals.

PREPARATION AND LEAD-UP

Have students bring to class their home learning assignment from the previous activity. Prepare a graphing board with pictures of animals to represent the kinds of animals that students are likely to have as pets (the animals on the copycat page can be enlarged and cut out).

PROCEDURE

1. Explain that students are going to make a record of the kinds of animals they have at home by placing cutout pictures of their pets onto the graphing board. Take a quick census of the kinds of animals students have in their homes by counting raised hands as you name each animal.

2. Have students attach animal cutouts to the graph with tape or glue, one cutout for each individual animal, then as a class discuss the results (see the discussion questions). Summarize by telling students that they have a variety of animals living in their homes. (If students do not have pets, ask them which pet they would most like to have.)

3. Ask students to consider one kind of pet at a time and generate words to describe that animal. If appropriate for your class, record the words on the chalkboard under the name of each kind of animal. Begin grouping the descriptive words by asking students what words describe how the animal gets food and eats it, moves, protects itself, has babies, and keeps warm or cool. You may want to add some of the descriptions from the activity "Animal Pantomimes."

4. Remind students that animals are different from each other in the way they get food and eat it, move, protect themselves, reproduce, and keep warm or cool. Point out that students have generated words that describe these differences.

DISCUSSION QUESTIONS

What kind of animal does our class have the most of? What kind of animal does our class have the least of?

How many of each kind of animal do we have?
What does your family need to do in order to take care of your pet? Why is this important?
What do you like about your pet?
Why do we have pets?
Why do some people not have pets? Why is this okay?

EVALUATION

Use the above discussion questions to assess students' understanding of the concepts "most," "least," and "same as."

EXTENSION IDEA

Have the class find out more about animals. Take students to the library and let them look at books about animals in general or about one kind of animal.

HOME LEARNING SUGGESTION

(Use as lead-up to the next activity)

Have each student tell his or her parent what living thing he or she would like to be, other than a person, and why. Ask parents to write their child's response and see that their child brings it to class the following day.

ALIVE VERSUS NOT ALIVE

SUMMARY OF ACTIVITY

Students discuss their conceptions of alive versus not alive (inert).

Time: 15 minutes
Setting: Classroom
Materials:
- Butcher paper

Subjects: Science, language arts
Key Words: Alive, not alive

RELATED CALIFORNIA FRAMEWORK CONCEPTS

Living things have characteristics by which they can be described and distinguished from nonliving things. They take in food, give off wastes, grow, respond to stimuli, and reproduce their own kind. (*Science Framework Addendum*)

Different kinds of living things have characteristics and behaviors by which they can be described, identified, sequenced, and classified. (*Science Framework Addendum*)

Living things change from day to day, season to season, year to year. (*Science Framework Addendum*)

Talking and listening are important ways by which people communicate with and learn from each other. (Adapted from *English-Language Arts Framework*)

OBJECTIVE

Students identify and discuss the characteristics of living versus nonliving things.

BACKGROUND INFORMATION

Children's conceptions of what is alive change as children grow older. The change indicates intellectual development, not merely access to additional information.

In this activity students think about what it means to be alive. The teacher's role is to facilitate discussion, not lead students to the characteristics by which adults define aliveness. If students have a difficult time responding at first, you will have to guide the discussion carefully so that you do not end up providing answers.

PROCEDURE

1. Have students share their responses from the previous activity's home learning suggestion. Students can briefly discuss why they would like to be one kind of animal and not another kind.

2. Ask students how they know whether something is alive. If students need a little prodding, ask, "Is a leaf alive? Is a car? Is the moon? How do you know?" Let the discussion run its course with you merely acting as a listener and facilitator.

3. If appropriate, put the following chart on the chalkboard or butcher paper. As students' thinking progresses, add their words to the appropriate column.

Alive	Not Alive

4. Use the chart (or your memory of the discussion) to summarize the characteristics students agree upon as describing things that are alive (for example, living things eat, move, reproduce, and protect themselves). This chart will form an operational definition for students, although there may not be a consensus (that is okay—use this information to become more aware of how your students' thinking varies).

DISCUSSION QUESTIONS

How do you know if something is alive or not alive?
Do living things move?
Do they eat?
Do they reproduce?
Can a fence move? Is it alive?
Does a tree eat? Is it alive?
Are you alive?

EVALUATION

The chart of characteristics living things share demonstrates whether students understand the difference between living and nonliving things.

EXTENSION IDEAS

- Have students collect samples of nonliving things. These can be shared with the class.
- Use storybooks to introduce real and pretend (fantasy) animals. Have students compare the two and discuss similarities and differences.
- Have students list all of the living things in the classroom. Discuss the results.
- Give each student a large piece of paper, divided into two sections labeled "Alive" and "Not Alive." Have students cut out pictures from magazines and glue them under the appropriate heading.

HOME LEARNING SUGGESTION

(Use as lead-up to the next activity)

Ask parents to help students identify and list all of the living things found in their homes. Students should bring their lists to class the following day.

MEET A TREE

SUMMARY OF ACTIVITY

Students observe, explore, and compare trees.

Time: 45 minutes

Setting: Outside (preferably in a grove of trees)

Materials:
- A bell, whistle, or some other signal to indicate when to regroup
- Copycat page

Subjects: Science, math, language arts

Key Words: Alive, not alive

RELATED CALIFORNIA FRAMEWORK CONCEPTS

There is great diversity among living things. (*Science Framework Addendum*)

Different kinds of living things have characteristics and behaviors by which they can be described, identified, sequenced, and classified. (*Science Framework Addendum*)

Human beings get information about things by seeing, hearing, touching, tasting, and smelling. (*Science Framework Addendum*)

Using common words to express ideas fosters the ability to speak, write, and read. (Adapted from *English-Language Arts Framework*)

OBJECTIVE

Using their senses, students observe, compare, and describe trees.

BACKGROUND INFORMATION

Small children may not understand that plants are alive since plants don't behave like people and animals. This discrepancy can be a starting point for discussion that allows you to explore developmental differences in your students' thinking. The activity "Comparing Three Living Things" continues the process.

PREPARATION AND LEAD-UP

This activity may be most effective if only half the class participates at a time. The activity could be done concurrently with the activity "Looking at Levels" (step four). For both activities you will need to find a grove of trees (three or more) on or near the schoolgrounds.

PROCEDURE

1. Discuss the previous activity's home learning suggestion. Remember for future reference if any students mention plants as living things.

2. Take the class outside to the grove of trees. Give students five minutes or longer to use their senses of smell, touch, hearing, and sight to "get acquainted" with at least three trees. Encourage students to observe individual trees in different ways. (For example, ask, "How does the tree look when you are sitting? When you are lying on your side? When you are lying on your back?" Unless appropriate, do not let students climb in the trees.)

3. Have the class regroup. Ask students if anyone would like to volunteer to choose a particular tree and describe it, using his or her senses. Summarize students' descriptions by making comparative statements. You may want to structure students' comments by asking students to complete the sentence, "The tree is ______________ ."

4. Measure each tree by seeing how many students, holding hands, it takes to form a tight circle around the tree. Compare the measurements of the trees.

5. Ask students whether they think the tree is alive. Do not refute their responses but ask students to "prove" their answers by telling how they know whether the tree is alive.

DISCUSSION QUESTIONS

What did you notice about your trees?
How were your trees alike? Different?
Are trees alive? Why or why not?
Are other plants alive?

EVALUATION

Use the discussion questions to assess students' thinking.

EXTENSION IDEAS

- Divide the class into groups of three. Give each group a tree-related event to act out, for example, a gentle breeze, a forest fire, a windstorm, a squirrel running up the trunk, a gentle rain, a person planting the tree, or birds nesting in the branches.
- Have students plant a tree on the school-grounds. Students can set up a schedule to water and look after the tree.

HOME LEARNING SUGGESTION

(Use as lead-up to the next activity)

Ask students to observe a tree and record what living things they see. Give each student a copycat page and instruct them to bring the page (filled out) to class the following day.

SOURCE OF ACTIVITY

Project Learning Tree, "Plant Personification." Washington, D.C.: The American Forest Council, 1977.

Copycat Page

Name ______________________________

TREE OBSERVATION

Draw the living things you see at different levels of a tree.

Draw pictures of animals and plants (like moss or lichen) in branches above your head.

Draw pictures of animals and plants at eye level.

Draw pictures of animals and plants at the base of the tree.

LOOKING AT LEVELS

SUMMARY OF ACTIVITY

Students go on a walk around the schoolgrounds to observe the diversity of animals living there.

Time: 45 minutes

Setting: Outdoors, classroom

Materials:
- Butcher paper
- Crayons

Subjects: Math, science, art

Key Words: Sky scanners, eye-level lookers, ground crawlers

RELATED CALIFORNIA FRAMEWORK CONCEPTS

There is great diversity among living things. (*Science Framework Addendum*)

Different kinds of living things have characteristics and behaviors by which they can be described, identified, sequenced, and classified. (*Science Framework Addendum*)

Living things have adaptations that enable them to live in their particular habitat. (*Science Framework Addendum*)

OBJECTIVE

Students observe, record, and classify living things outdoors.

BACKGROUND INFORMATION

Students may be surprised to find an abundance of living things around the school. Even an urban school can be a rich laboratory for studying animals in their natural environments. This activity allows students to observe and record living things that live near the classroom.

Some students are not used to learning outdoors. They need structured observation time to help them focus. That is one of the purposes of this activity. Beginning teachers may want to refer to the section titled "Out-of-Class Activities," in the chapter for beginning teachers for more information.

PREPARATION AND LEAD-UP

Choose a route around the schoolgrounds or the immediate neighborhood. The route should take students about 10 minutes to walk.

Prepare a large piece of butcher paper as follows:

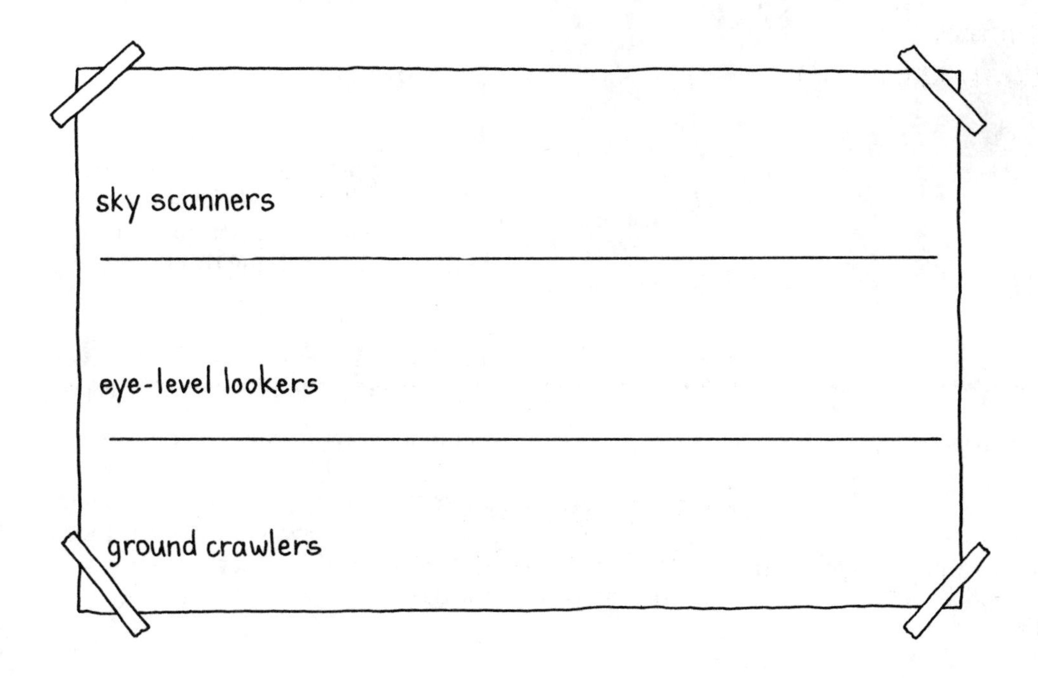

PROCEDURE

1. Remind students that yesterday they looked at trees and thought about how trees are alike and different. Have students share the results of their home learning assignment from the previous activity.

2. Explain that students will be going on a short walk to see the different kinds of living things that live around their school. Tell students that to make sure they are good observers, you will divide the class into three groups. Each group will be expected to look for living things at one particular level along the way.

3. Assign one-third of the class to be "ground crawlers." These students are to look for living things on the ground (make it clear that students do not really crawl but they are to look for living things that live on or close to the ground). Assign one-third of the group to be "eye-level lookers." These students will look for living things at eye-level. Assign one-third of the group to be "sky scanners." This group will look for living things in the sky. Ask students to give an example of the living things they might see at each level.

4. Take the class on a walk around the schoolgrounds. It is not crucial that students look only at their assigned level but remind them to focus on that level and to remember what they observe. If possible, have an adult with each group and keep the groups slightly separate so they can focus on their assigned level.

5. Back in the classroom, post the butcher paper with the three levels. Ask students to give examples of living things they observed at their assigned levels. Have students draw pictures of these things on the butcher paper. This may be managed most easily if you cut the levels apart (cut horizontally) and let each group draw in a different area of the room. Afterwards, tape the levels back together for discussion.

DISCUSSION QUESTIONS

What animals did you see at each level?
Were there any animals that were seen at every level? At two levels?
Looking at the whole chart, what animal did we see the most of? The least of?
What kinds of things were animals doing when you observed them?
Did anyone include plants (or anything else) as living things? Where did you see them?

EVALUATION

Give students the copycat page "Tree Observation" from the previous activity "Meet a Tree." Tell them to draw one to three animals that were seen at each level on the walk around the school and to show what the animals were doing. Encourage students to include any plants that were observed.

EXTENSION IDEA

Take students on a walk along a different route to observe living things in other parts of the schoolgrounds. Alternatively, conduct the activity at a different time of the year to see whether the number and kinds of living things observed varies.

HOME LEARNING SUGGESTION

(Use as lead-up to the next activity)

Send home with students the copycat page "Comparing Three Living Things." Ask parents to have their child dictate two sentences, one sentence that describes a way the three things are alike and one sentence that describes a way the three things are different from each other.

Name ____________________________

COMPARING THREE LIVING THINGS

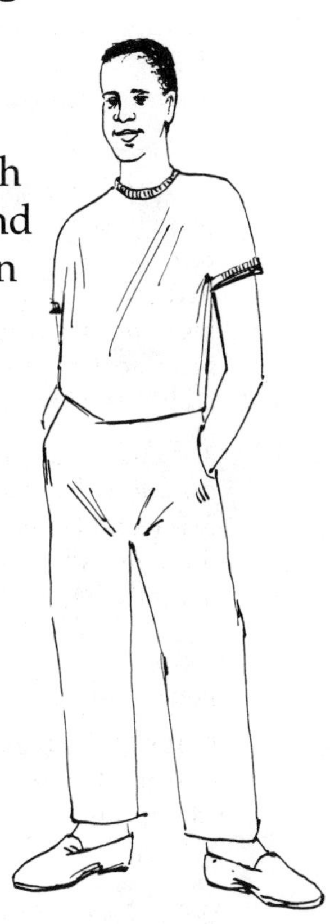

Dear Parent:

For tonight's home learning assignment, please talk with your child about these pictures of an animal, a plant, and a human. Have your child dictate a sentence (or more) in answer to the two questions below.

Thank you.

How are these three things *like* each other?

____

____

____

____

How are these three things *different* from each other?

____

____

____

____

COMPARING THREE LIVING THINGS

SUMMARY OF ACTIVITY

Students compare three living things—a plant, a live animal, and a human—and discuss ways that they are alike and different.

Time: 30 minutes

Setting: Classroom

Materials:
- A plant
- A live animal

Subjects: Science, math, language arts

Key Words: Alike, different

RELATED CALIFORNIA FRAMEWORK CONCEPTS

Different kinds of living things have characteristics and behaviors by which they can be described, identified, sequenced, and classified. (*Science Framework Addendum*)

Talking and listening are important ways by which people communicate with and learn from each other. (Adapted from *English-Language Arts Framework*)

OBJECTIVE

Students observe, compare, and record similarities and differences among a plant, an animal, and a human.

BACKGROUND INFORMATION

In the three previous activities students had opportunities to articulate and clarify their thinking about what is alive. In this activity students look at three different live things—a plant, a "wild" animal, and a human. For comparative purposes, each is identified as representing a subgroup of living things; however, remind students that humans are animals but differ from other animals in profound ways.

PREPARATION AND LEAD-UP

Bring to class a plant and a live animal different from the live animals used earlier in this unit. Pill bugs (sow bugs) are good to use because they are easy to find. Pill bugs live in dark places in a garden and can be collected by placing half of a hollowed-out orange peel in an area of damp soil (they should congregate underneath the peel within 24 hours).

PROCEDURE

1. Have students sit in a circle. Ask for volunteers to share results from the previous activity's home learning suggestion.

2. Remind the class that plants are alive. They grow, breathe, get "food" (from soil and sun) and water, and reproduce. Pass the plant and the live animal around the circle.

3. Display the plant, the animal, and a human (you or a student) for students to observe. Ask, "What are some of the ways that the three living things are all alike? What are ways that they are all different?"

4. Make three columns on the board and label them "Plant," "Animal," and "Person." Ask students to identify characteristics of each and record responses in the appropriate column.

DISCUSSION QUESTIONS

Can we describe each living thing by its color? Size? Shape? Texture? Action or behavior?
How does each living thing breathe? See? Hear? Eat? Sleep? Move? Make sounds?
How do we handle each living thing?
How do we care for each living thing?

EVALUATION

Have students draw a human, a plant, and an animal. Students can then dictate to you or to an aide one way the three living things are alike and one way they are different.

EXTENSION IDEA

Have students draw a Plantanimalperson—a creature that is part plant, part animal, and part human. Discuss the characteristics of this creature.

HOME LEARNING SUGGESTION
(Use as lead-up to the next activity)

Ask parents to find a picture of their child when the child was an infant, a picture when the child was a toddler, and a picture from the past year. Encourage parents to discuss with their child how the child has changed. Ask parents to send the pictures to class with the student.

HOW WE HAVE CHANGED

SUMMARY OF ACTIVITY

Students bring in baby pictures of themselves and observe how they have changed over time. Students also discuss life cycles of living things and learn a finger play about the life cycle of a butterfly.

Time: 30 to 45 minutes

Setting: Classroom

Materials:
- Baby pictures of students
- Pictures of other living things in various stages of life
- Drawing paper
- Crayons

Subjects: Language arts, math, fine arts

Key Words: Change, grow, life cycle

RELATED CALIFORNIA FRAMEWORK CONCEPTS

Living things change from day to day, season to season, year to year. (*Science Framework Addendum*)

Individuals are aware that their needs and the needs of others grow and change. (Adapted from *History-Social Science Framework*)

BACKGROUND INFORMATION

In this activity students look at pictures of themselves at three different ages and discuss life-cycle changes of humans. The activity serves as a lead-up to the last activity, in which life cycles of plants are discussed.

PREPARATION AND LEAD-UP

Ask students to bring to class a picture of themselves when they were infants, a picture of themselves as toddlers, and a recent picture of themselves (if convenient you can take a picture of each student prior to the activity). If you feel this is too much to ask of parents, ask for one baby picture and have a current picture of each student on hand (perhaps a school picture). The pictures can be displayed for a few days prior to the activity.

PROCEDURE

1. Have students sit with their pictures in front of them. Instruct students to put the pictures in order, from youngest to oldest. Ask, "How have you stayed the same over time? How have you changed?" Give students a few minutes to look at their pictures and share observations with each other. Then ask for volunteers to share some of their observations with the class. Students may be excited to share their pictures, so allow plenty of time.

2. Discuss what kinds of changes happen to a person as he or she grows from a newborn baby to a toddler to a child to a grown-up. Ask, "Do we see these changes happen every day?" Explain that although some changes are evident on a daily basis, most changes happen gradually over several weeks, months, and even years.

3. Have the class sort all of the photos into three piles, putting the infant pictures in one pile, the toddler pictures in another pile, and the current pictures in the third pile (make sure students' names are written on the backs of their photos). Alternatively, tell students that you will save the pictures to use a few days later (see the extension idea).

4. Show students pictures of other living things (or, if possible, the real thing) at different stages of their life cycles. For example, you can show pictures of a caterpillar, cocoon, and butterfly or of an egg, tadpole, and frog. Tell students that living things go through different stages that vary in length of time. Some adult living things have babies that look very much like them, only smaller (for example, horses, cows, and people). Other living things change dramatically as they mature (butterflies and frogs, for instance).

5. Teach students the following finger play:

Words	Action
Ten little eggs,	Hold hands up, fingers straight.
All in a mound.	Join hands together in a ball.
Out come caterpillars crawling all around.	Extend and wiggle fingers.

(Continued next page)

Next they will sleep	Lay head to one side
and we know why.	on hands.
Soon they'll come	Hold hands up,
out as butterflies.	fingers straight.
	Wave fingers.

(Reprinted with permission from *Ranger Rick's NatureScope,* "Caterpillar Finger Play," published by the National Wildlife Federation, 1986.)

DISCUSSION QUESTIONS

How have you changed as you have grown older?
Will you continue to change? How?
How have your pets changed?
How do plants change?
Are the changes in humans, other animals, and plants noticeable every day?

EVALUATION

Pass out drawing paper and ask students to draw two pictures of themselves, one labeled "then" and one "now." Explain that the "then" picture can be of themselves at anytime during their past while the "now" picture is how they look today.

Underneath the pictures students can complete these sentences through dictation:

I used to be ______________________

But now I am ______________________

EXTENSION IDEA

Display photographs of students or pictures of people in magazines at different stages of life. Ask, "Can you put these pictures in piles so that those that are alike are together? How did you decide which ones go together? Can you choose five pictures and line them up from youngest to oldest? What changes do you see in the pictures as people grow older?"

HOME LEARNING SUGGESTION
(Use as lead-up to the next activity)

Have students draw pictures of at least three people in their family, lined up from youngest to oldest. Students should bring the pictures to class the following day.

LIFE CYCLE OF A PLANT

SUMMARY OF ACTIVITY

Students examine the changes a plant goes through during its life cycle by observing a seed, a seedling, and a mature plant.

Time: 40 minutes

Setting: Classroom

Materials:
- One seed, seedling, and mature plant of the same species for each pair of students
- Containers for seeds
- Magnifying lenses
- Paper
- Copycat page

Subjects: Science, math, fine arts

Key Words: Seedling, mature

RELATED CALIFORNIA FRAMEWORK CONCEPTS

Living things change from day to day, season to season, year to year. (*Science Framework Addendum*)

By sequencing objects, their relationships can be described. (Adapted from *Mathematics Framework*)

OBJECTIVE

Students observe and form a sequence of plants at different stages of the plant life cycle.

BACKGROUND INFORMATION

Classifying objects sequentially requires an understanding of the ordered relationship among a set of objects. If students have no experience classifying objects by sequence, you may want to give them opportunities to do this with familiar objects before doing this activity. Since kindergarten and first-grade students tend to classify objects according to perceptual cues, this activity allows students to observe visible differences among plants in different stages of the life cycle.

PREPARATION AND LEAD-UP

Gather the materials.

PROCEDURE

1. Have students share their drawings from the previous activity's home learning suggestion. Discuss ways in which people in the pictures are the same and ways in which the people differ.

2. Divide students into pairs. Tell students that you will give each pair a seed, a seedling, and a plant of the same kind. Students will observe their seed, seedling, and plant and put them in order from youngest to oldest. Remind students to handle these living things carefully.

3. Distribute seeds, seedlings, and plants and have students observe them. Pass out magnifying lenses so that students can take a closer look.

4. Have students sequence their plants in different ways (for example, youngest to oldest, smallest to biggest, hardest to softest, lightest to darkest, and dullest to shiniest). Partners can discuss ways to sequence the plants until they agree on a way. After they agree, partners can draw a picture of one sequence.

DISCUSSION QUESTIONS

What did you notice about your seed? About your seedling? About your plant?

Was it easy to put them in order from youngest to oldest? From smallest to biggest? From hardest to softest? From lightest to darkest? From dullest to shiniest?

Do the seed, seedling, and plant tend to stay in the same order when you re-sort them or does their order change sometimes?

EVALUATION

Instruct students to draw or find pictures of various living things and sequence them in order from youngest to oldest.

EXTENSION IDEA

- Try a guided imagery activity. Tell students (ellipses indicate a pause), "Imagine you are a little seed that has just been planted in the ground . . . You are lying under the deep, rich earth and you begin to feel the earth growing damp around you . . . It has begun to rain and you are getting your first drink of water . . . After the rain stops, you feel the earth warming up gradually, and slowly, slowly you begin to grow . . . You form a little sprout that comes out of the seed and begins to push up against the earth above you and toward the warmth . . . As you grow you break through the top of earth and you can now feel the sun shining down on you . . . Now you are growing in two directions . . . Above the earth, you grow taller . . . Now two little leaves begin to uncurl near the top of your stem . . . Below the ground, you begin to form roots which will anchor you to the soil so that you don't fall over as you get taller . . . More rain comes . . . More sun shines on you and a breeze is in the air . . . You begin to grow outward as well as upward . . . More leaves are forming and now you even have a flower . . . Suddenly, the breeze becomes a wind and blows the seeds from your flower . . . Soon you cannot get the water you need and it becomes too hot for you to survive . . . Slowly, slowly you begin to wilt and die . . . but remember that your seeds have been spread far and wide and will soon be sprouting themselves!"

HOME LEARNING SUGGESTION

(Use as follow-up to this activity)

Send home with each student a seed from a plant that is easy to grow (like grass, a radish, or a carrot). Ask parents to help their child plant and care for the seed so that students can observe a living thing change and grow over time.

Homes and Habitats

First and Second Grades

Introduction to the Unit

Every living thing—people, other animals, and plants—requires a special place to live that satisfies the organism's particular needs. The scientific name for that special place is "habitat." Ideally an organism's habitat includes all of the things it needs to survive—food, water, shelter, and space—and its suitability is determined by both living and physical factors.

In the first activity of this unit students compare animal, plant, and human "homes" and learn that each habitat meets the survival needs of its occupants. In the next two activities students examine their own habitat, finding other living things that share their home and surveying the different types of places found in their neighborhood.

The focus of the next four activities is on animal and plant habitats. In these activities students observe animals that inhabit a tree, study the living things found in various microhabitats, investigate some of the nonliving factors that make one habitat different from another, and observe how an animal's coloration helps it survive in a particular habitat.

Students are then introduced to the idea that humans can manipulate their environment. Students investigate the impact of a wall, fence, or other human modification on the environment, compare houses from another culture to a house from their own culture, and explore different population densities in the classroom. In the final activity students are given the opportunity to effect desirable changes in their own habitat by modifying the classroom environment.

Resources

Busch, Phyllis S. *The Urban Environment.* Chicago, Ill.: J. G. Ferguson Publishing Co., 1975. These activities for students in kindergarten through third grade help them learn about the urban environment.

Nickelsburg, Janet. *Nature Activities for Early Childhood.* Menlo Park, Calif.: Addison-Wesley Publishing Co., 1976. This book for parents and teachers involves them with their children as they explore a plant or animal.

For Students

Busch, Phyllis S. *At Home in Its Habitat: Animal Neighborhoods.* New York: The World Publishing Co., 1970. This book describes the places where animals live and where they find safety and protection for themselves and their families. It compares human habitats and animal habitats and includes many photographs.

Entwistel, Theodore Roland. *Animal Homes.* New York: Random House, 1987. This book contains wonderful depictions of the homes animals live in.

Skorpen, Liesel Moak. *We Were Tired of Living in a House.* New York: Coward-McCann Inc., 1969. This is a story about children who try living in different places only to find that their house is the best place to live.

UNIT TIMELINE ■ Participation in Activity □ Ongoing observation and study

Page	Activity
41	Everybody Needs a Home
45	Your Habitat Survey
49	Neighborhood Places
52	Tree Habitat Survey
55	Observing Microhabitats
59	Habitat High-Low
63	Birds and Worms
67	Walls and Fences
70	Dwellings
72	Too Close for Comfort
74	It's Your Space

Week: 1 2 3 4

EVERYBODY NEEDS A HOME

SUMMARY OF ACTIVITY

Students look at pictures of places where animals and plants live. They draw pictures of human homes and compare their own needs with the needs of other animals.

Time: 30 minutes

Setting: Classroom

Materials:
- Pictures of animal, plant, and human homes
- Paper for drawing
- Crayons

Subjects: Language arts, art, science

Key Words: Survival, survival needs, habitat, home

RELATED CALIFORNIA FRAMEWORK CONCEPTS

Living things need special kinds of food and a special place to live. (*Science Framework Addendum*)

All animals need food, water, air, and a place to live. (*Science Framework Addendum*)

Living things get things they need from each other and from the environment. (*Science Framework Addendum*)

Visual art media can be used to translate ideas, feelings, and values. (Adapted from *Visual and Performing Arts Framework*)

Talking and listening are important ways by which people communicate with and learn from each other. (Adapted from *English-Language Arts Framework*)

OBJECTIVE

Through guided imagery and art, students express similarities and differences about the places where people, other animals, and plants live.

BACKGROUND INFORMATION

Humans, other animals (including pets, farm animals, and wild animals), and plants share basic survival needs, specifically food, water, shelter, and space. Every living thing needs a home but that home is not just a "house" like people live in. Homes for animals are often big areas and are outdoors; plant "homes" are areas that provide the right amount of sunlight, water, and soil to meet the needs of a particular plant. The scientific name for an animal or plant's home is "habitat." A habitat has everything an animal or plant needs to survive.

Humans build houses, apartments, trailers, and other kinds of shelter in which to live. Animals don't need a home that looks like a house but they do need some kind of shelter. Animal shelter might be underground, in a bush, among rocks, or inside the bark of a tree.

The main purpose of this activity is for students to understand that everybody needs a home. "Home" is bigger than a "house" and is more like a "neighborhood" that provides everything needed for survival.

PREPARATION AND LEAD-UP

Gather pictures of homes of people, other animals, and plants from calendars, books, or magazines. You might have students help you collect the pictures.

PROCEDURE

1. Take your students on imaginary excursions, using guided imagery. Have the students relax and close their eyes, then guide them by describing a scene, like this (ellipses indicate a pause): "Close your eyes and imagine that you are a small bird . . . Think about what it feels like to be a bird . . . You have feathers all over your body . . . You have a beak . . . Imagine that you don't have arms but you have wings . . . You are flying among trees and bushes . . . You are looking for something to eat . . . You spot something delicious on the bush so you land and eat it . . . Think about what it is you are eating . . . Now imagine that you are thirsty and you go to look for water . . . Imagine that you find a puddle of water in a field and you drink from it . . . Now imagine that you are going back to your bird home . . . Think about what your bird home looks like and where it is . . . Make yourself comfortable in your home . . . When you are ready, open your eyes."

Ask students about their experiences. "What did it feel like to be a bird? Where was the bird's home you imagined? What was it like? How did you get your water? How did you get your food?"

2. Have students close their eyes again and imagine that they are a flower. "Your petals and leaves are reaching toward the sun . . . Your roots are reaching deep into the ground . . . Think about what it feels like to be a flower . . . Where you live is your home . . . Think about what it feels like in your flower home . . . Think about how the ground around you feels . . . Look around you . . . Are there other plants or animals living near you? . . . Now imagine that you are thirsty . . . Imagine that your roots reach for water in the ground and through your roots you drink as much water as you need . . . Now imagine that you are hungry . . . Imagine that you reach up for the sun with your leaves and with power from the sun your leaves are able to make all the food you need . . . When you are ready, open your eyes."

Ask students about their experiences. "What did it feel like to be a flower? Where was your flower home? What was it like? How did you get your water? How did you get your food?"

3. Have students close their eyes and envision their own home. "Imagine that you are just getting home from school . . . Imagine walking through the door and into your house . . . Think about what it feels like to be home . . . Imagine that you are hungry and that you look for something to eat . . . Think about where you find your food . . . Now imagine that after you eat your snack you are thirsty . . . You get a glass of water . . . After you have finished your glass of water, make yourself comfortable in a chair . . . When you are ready, open your eyes."

Ask students about their experiences. "What does it feel like to be in your home? How do you get your water? How do you get your food?"

4. Ask students to point out similarities and differences among the animal, plant, and human homes they have envisioned. Discuss how every living thing needs food, water, shelter, and space in its home. Emphasize that although homes are different, everyone needs a home.

5. Show students pictures of different places where people, other animals, and plants live. Talk about how "home" is actually bigger than "house"; in some ways it is more like "neighborhood." The neighborhood where all of the survival needs of an animal are met is called a "habitat."

6. Ask students to draw a picture of where they live. Have students include in their drawings the things they need in order to live where they do (for example, a place to obtain and keep food, a place to sleep, and a place to play). Ask students to point out the things they need to live that are included in their drawings.

7. Tell students that over the next few days they will be taking a closer look at their own habitat. They will then look at the habitats of other living things.

DISCUSSION QUESTIONS

Why do people need homes?
What do homes provide for you?
What do homes protect you from?
Why do animals need homes?
What do homes provide for animals?
What do homes protect animals from?

EVALUATION

Give students cut-out pictures of animals from magazines or calendars and pictures of different habitats (such as forests, grasslands, oceans, deserts, and marshes). Have students match the animals with their habitats; for example, a camel in the desert, whales in the ocean, or a deer in the forest.

EXTENSION IDEAS

- Teach students "The Habitat Song" (scoring appears on page 44). Talk about plants and animals that live in the habitats described in the song.

THE HABITAT SONG
("Have to Have a Habitat . . .")
By Bill Oliver

Chorus:
Habitat, habitat; have to have a habitat
Habitat, habitat; have to have a habitat
Habitat, habitat; have to have a habitat
Have to have a habitat to carry on

The ocean is a habitat, a very special habitat
Where the deepest water's at, where the biggest mammal's at
Where our future food is at; it keeps the atmosphere intact
The ocean is a habitat that we depend on

Chorus

The forest is a habitat, a very special habitat
Where the tallest trees are at, where a bear can scratch her back
Keeps the ground from rolling back, renews the oxygen, in fact
The forest is a habitat that we depend on

Chorus

The river is a habitat, a very special habitat
It's where the freshest water's at, for people, fish, and musk-rats
But when the people dump their trash, the river takes the biggest rap
The river is a habitat that we depend on

Chorus

People are different than foxes and rabbits
Affect the whole world with their bad habits
Better to love it while we still have it
Or rat-a-tat-tat our habitat's gone

Chorus (repeat and fade)

- Read *Animals Should Definitely Not Wear Clothing,* by Judith Barrett. Have students create absurd situations involving animals that live in habitats not suited to their needs (for example, an elephant in a mouse's hole or a dolphin in a puddle). Have students draw and label pictures of the situations. As a class, discuss why the situations are inappropriate and why it is important for living things to live in their natural habitats.
- Students make clay models of animal homes. Compare them to places where people live. What are animal and people homes made of? How are they similar or different? What is their purpose?

HOME LEARNING SUGGESTION

(Use as follow-up to this activity)

Send a note home to parents asking them to spend 15 minutes with their children looking for places where animals live in their yard or neighborhood. Point out to parents that animals can be found in unlikely places like on walls or fences, underneath windowsills, or in the cracks of sidewalks. Be sure to stress to parents and students that they not disturb the animals or their homes. Next day in class discuss with students what they found and have them draw a picture of an animal home they discovered.

RESOURCES

For Students

Barrett, Judith. *Animals Should Definitely Not Wear Clothing.* New York: Macmillan Publishing Co., 1970. This amusing story illustrates ways that things suitable for people are not suitable for animals.

"The Habitat Song" by Bill Oliver available through Live Oak Records & Tapes, 515 E. 40, Austin, Tex., 78751 or "Audubon Adventures," National Audubon Society, RR 1, Box 171, Sharon, Conn., 06069.

SOURCE OF ACTIVITY

Adapted from *Project Wild,* "Everybody Needs a Home." Boulder, Colo.: Western Regional Environmental Education Council, 1985.

THE HABITAT SONG
Refrain: Hab - i - tat, hab - i - tat, have__ to have a hab - i - tat. Hab - i - tat, hab- i - tat, have
__ to have a hab - i - tat. Hab - i - tat, hab - i - tat, have__ to have a hab - i - tat. You
have to have a hab - i - tat to___ car - ry on._
Verse
1. The o - cean is a hab - i-tat, a
Verse: 2.
3.
ver - y spe-cial hab - i - tat. It's where the deep-est wa-ter's at, it's where the big-gest mammal's at. It's
where our fu-ture food is at, it keeps the at-mos-phere in-tact. The o-cean is a hab - i - tat that
we de-pend on._
Verse 4.
Verse:
(The) 4. Peo-ple are dif-ferent than fox - es and rab - bits, af - fect_
___ the whole world with their_ bad_ hab - its.__ Bet - ter to love it while we
___ still_ have it, or ra - ta - tat - tat, our hab - i - tat's gone.

YOUR HABITAT SURVEY

SUMMARY OF ACTIVITY

Students conduct a survey of the living things that live in their own homes.

Time: Three 30- to 40-minute periods over three days

Setting: Classroom

Materials:
- Small (2" by 2") squares of construction paper
- Large sheets of paper for graph
- Glue
- Crayons
- Duplicated letters for parents
- Sandwich bags

Subjects: Science, math, social studies, language arts

Key Words: Habitat, share

RELATED CALIFORNIA FRAMEWORK CONCEPTS

All animals need food, water, air, and a place to live. (*Science Framework Addendum*)

Living things need special kinds of food and a special place to live. (*Science Framework Addendum*)

Data derived from surveys and experiments can be collected, organized, and interpreted. (Adapted from *Mathematics Framework*)

Creating concrete, pictorial, and symbolic graphs can help us interpret data. (Adapted from *Mathematics Framework*)

The same kinds of living things often live together in groups. (*Science Framework Addendum*)

Usually several kinds of living things live with or near each other. (*Science Framework Addendum*)

OBJECTIVE

Students graph the living things that share their homes and propose ways the organisms get the things they need to survive.

BACKGROUND INFORMATION

Every living thing has a particular habitat that helps that organism survive. Usually many different kinds of organisms share some aspects of a habitat. For example, in a grasslands habitat one can find many types of grasses as well as rabbits and rodents that live among the grasses. In this activity students observe the types of organisms that share their own habitat and think about where the organisms get the things they need to survive.

PREPARATION AND LEAD-UP

Cut three different colors of construction paper into small squares (2" by 2"). You should have approximately 5 to 15 squares of each color per student.

PROCEDURE

Day One

1. Review with students what a "habitat" is—the place an animal or plant lives. Ask students, "Do other living things share your habitat with you?" Tell students that they will be looking for living things that share part of their habitat, which is their house.

Hand out construction paper squares, all one color, and direct students to draw pictures of the people that live in their house, including themselves (each person should be drawn on one square). Have students count the number of people with whom they share their habitat. Help students begin to make individual graphs of their own habitats by gluing the picture squares onto larger pieces of paper. Label the graphs "Living Things That Share My Habitat." Students will add to their graphs in the next two days.

2. Do the activity for day one that is described in the home learning suggestion.

Day Two

3. In class have students add pictures of the animals they found in and around their homes to the

graphs they began the day before. Discuss with students their findings. "Where do the animals live? How and where do the animals get the things they need to stay alive? Do people share anything with the animals? Do you like having these animals in your habitat? How do we keep animals that we don't like away from our own habitat?"

4. Do the home learning suggestion for day two.

Day Three

5. In class have students add pictures of the plants they found to their graphs. Discuss with students their findings. "How do the plants get the things they need to stay alive? Where did the plants come from? Do you like having these plants in your habitat?"

DISCUSSION QUESTIONS

Which are there more of in your habitat: people, other animals, or plants?

Which do you like sharing your habitat with? Why?

Do you get any of the things you need to stay alive from the people, other animals, or plants that share your habitat?

What would your habitat be like if you did not have any other living things sharing it?

EVALUATION

Have students draw a picture of one of the living things that shares their habitat. Students should indicate in the picture how that living thing gets what it needs to live.

EXTENSION IDEA

To help students observe their habitat more closely, have them survey sounds in the school environment by listening for as many sounds as they can hear in two or three minutes. Ask students to name the sounds they heard. Which sounds were loud? Which sounds were quiet? Which sounds were human-made? Which were made by other living things? The teacher can tape record 10-second segments in various habitats (for example, near a busy street, on a construction site, or from a backyard) and have students try to identify where the tapes were made. Students might bring in tapes they have recorded at home for other students to guess where they were made. Sounds students might record include a car revving up, a toilet flushing, a shower running (with singing), a door slamming, or popcorn popping.

HOME LEARNING SUGGESTION

(Use as part of this activity)

Day One

Explain to students that their task will be to count and draw pictures of animals that live in or around their habitat, like pets, bugs, birds outside their window, or squirrels that live in a tree near the building. Ask students to draw on separate squares of paper a picture of each animal they find. If students observe a lot of one kind of animal (for example, 10 ants), ask them to draw only one of that animal and indicate on the square the number they observe. Pass out paper squares of a color different than the color used to graph people plus a sandwich bag in which to carry the squares, and send them home with students along with the following letter to parents.

Sample Letter

Dear Parent:

We are studying homes and habitats in class. Please help your child observe and draw pictures of the different animals that together you find living in or around your home. I have sent home construction paper squares; help your child draw on separate squares a picture of each animal. If you observe a lot of one animal (for example, 10 ants), your child only needs to draw one picture of that animal but should indicate on the square the number observed. Animals you see might include birds or squirrels living in a tree outside your house, pets that live with you, or sow bugs that live under the doorstep. Your child will use these pictures in class tomorrow.

Day Two

Explain to students that their task will be to count and record the plants that live in or around their home. Pass out construction paper squares of a third color and sandwich bags in which to carry them, and send them home with students along with the following letter to parents.

Sample Letter

Dear Parent:

Please help your child observe and draw pictures of the plants that together you find living in and around your home. Help your child draw one plant on each square of paper that I have sent home. These pictures will be used by your child in class tomorrow. If you find many plants of the same kind (for example, 15 daffodils), your child only needs to draw one picture of that plant but should indicate on the square the total number found. Plants you find may include houseplants, flower pots, bushes, vegetable plants, or trees.

NEIGHBORHOOD PLACES

SUMMARY OF ACTIVITY

Students look for living places, working places, and playing places in their neighborhood.

Time: One 15-minute period and one 45-minute period, over two days

Setting: Classroom

Materials:
- Reproduced "Neighborhood Places" copycat page
- Paper
- Crayons

Subjects: Social studies, science, math, language arts

Key Words: Habitat, neighborhood, living places, working places, playing places

RELATED CALIFORNIA FRAMEWORK CONCEPTS

All animals need food, water, air, and a place to live. (*Science Framework Addendum*)

Living things get the things they need from each other and from the environment. (*Science Framework Addendum*)

Humans depend on many resources of their surroundings for the necessities of life. (*Science Framework Addendum*)

People are members of groups that use resources. (Adapted from *History-Social Science Framework*)

Data derived from surveys and experiments can be collected, organized, and interpreted. (Adapted from *Mathematics Framework*)

OBJECTIVE

Students observe and report the living, working, and playing places they find in their neighborhood.

BACKGROUND INFORMATION

Neighborhoods, especially city neighborhoods, serve a variety of functions. They usually have places to live, work, play, buy things we need, and obtain services such as fire and police protection, hospital care, and library resources. Within a neighborhood there may be spaces that serve a variety of purposes like spaces for walking, driving, playing, gathering, and finding solitude.

An animal or plant habitat is like a neighborhood. It provides all of the elements necessary for survival—food, water, shelter, and space.

In this activity students study the different functions of a neighborhood. They also think about the special places in neighborhoods that children seek out. Everyone—child and adult alike—has a special place that he or she feels comfortable in and is somehow emotionally attached to.

PREPARATION AND LEAD-UP

Make copies of the "Neighborhood Places" copycat page for each student.

PROCEDURE

Day One

1. Review with students what a habitat is, that it is more than just a house, that it is like a neighborhood. Tell students that to study their habitat they need to look at their neighborhood as well as their house. Discuss with students the things one finds in a neighborhood. Help students decide whether these are living places, playing places, or working places. Challenge them to see how many different places they can identify in their neighborhood.

2. Do the home learning suggestion described in this activity.

Day Two

3. Discuss the places students found. Discuss ways that these places help people obtain the things they need to stay alive. Talk about special places children seek out. Discuss whether these special places are inside or outside and whether they are private places or places for playing and sharing with friends.

4. Have students describe their special place by writing a story about it, by drawing a picture of it, or both.

DISCUSSION QUESTIONS

How do places in your neighborhood help you get the things you need to live?
How do places in your neighborhood make you feel?
What makes your special place special?
What attributes make it a good place to be?

EVALUATION

Students draw a picture of a working place, a playing place, and a living place in their neighborhood.

EXTENSION IDEA

Students work with partners building models of their ideal community. Use boxes with the sides cut down to about two inches as borders for the communities. Provide students with a variety of building materials such as cardboard, egg cartons, toilet paper tubes, wood blocks, pipe cleaners, drinking straws, empty thread spools, glues, rubber bands, paper clips, tree twigs, and string.

HOME LEARNING SUGGESTION

(Use as part of this activity)

Distribute the copycat page to take home and ask students to conduct an inventory of living, working, and playing places in their neighborhoods. Review what is meant by the words "living place," "playing place," and "working place." Use the following letter to ask parents to help students record the variety of places found.

SOURCE OF ACTIVITY

Adapted from O'Connor, Maura. *Living Lightly in the City*, "City Spaces, Special Places." Milwaukee, Wisc.: Schlitz Audubon Center, 1983.

Sample Letter

Dear Parent:

We are studying the kinds of things one finds in a neighborhood. Please spend 10 to 15 minutes with your child on a walk around three blocks of your neighborhood. During your walk help your child find and record the different types of places you find. "Living places" might include homes or apartment buildings. "Working places" might include libraries, office buildings, stores, or fire departments. "Playing places" might include parks, swimming pools, or backyards. Also please help your child think of a place in your home, yard, or neighborhood that is special to him or her.

Thank you for your help.

Name ____________________

NEIGHBORHOOD PLACES

Living Places	Working Places	Playing Places
______	______	______
______	______	______
______	______	______
______	______	______
______	______	______
______	______	______

This is my own special place:

TREE HABITAT SURVEY

SUMMARY OF ACTIVITY

Students observe and record information about the animals that inhabit a tree.

Time: 30 to 45 minutes

Setting: Outside area with several trees (schoolgrounds or nearby park)

Materials:
- Butcher paper
- Crayons or marking pens
- One pencil for each pair of students
- One data sheet for each pair of students
- One clipboard or hard writing surface for each pair of students
- One hand lens for each pair of students (optional)
- Construction paper (optional)

Subjects: Science, math, art

Key Words: Species, habitat

RELATED CALIFORNIA FRAMEWORK CONCEPTS

All animals need food, water, air, and a place to live. (*Science Framework Addendum*)

Living things need special kinds of food and a special place to live. (*Science Framework Addendum*)

Animals live in a variety of environments: oceans, fresh water, forests, deserts, tundra, and so forth. (*Science Framework Addendum*)

Living things get things they need from each other and from the environment. (*Science Framework Addendum*)

Usually several kinds of living things live with or near each other. (*Science Framework Addendum*)

Data derived from surveys and experiments can be collected, organized, and interpreted. (Adapted from *Mathematics Framework*)

OBJECTIVE

Students observe and record the living things they find on a tree and explain how the tree provides living things with what they need to survive.

BACKGROUND INFORMATION

This activity allows students to look closely at a tree, which is one habitat that provides the things some animals and plants need to survive. A tree is the habitat of many tiny animals that spend their entire lives in the tree's leaves or bark. It can also be the habitat of plants that grow on tree trunks and branches, such as algae, moss, and lichen. Although larger animals like birds, squirrels, and raccoons collect nuts or fruit from trees for food or use branches for nesting or shelter, trees are only a part of the their habitat. They go elsewhere to gather other food, hide from predators, and raise their young.

Many kinds of insects and other small bugs can be observed crawling on the tree bark and leaves. Oftentimes galls can be seen growing on leaves, stems, twigs, and other plant points. Galls are formed when a chemical excretion from a female insect or newly-hatched larvae is put onto the tree. The chemical causes the tree to grow a bulb around the larvae, keeping larvae safe from predators and giving them a readily-available food supply—the inside wall of the gall. Galls are most common on oak and willow trees.

Evidence of another type of insect larvae, called leaf miners, can be observed by looking carefully at leaves. Leaf miners cause leaves to have white or pale green spots that look like a winding path, fingerprint, or paint splatter. By holding the leaf up to the light, leaf miners can be seen inside. Leaf miners usually are the larvae of moths, flies, or beetles.

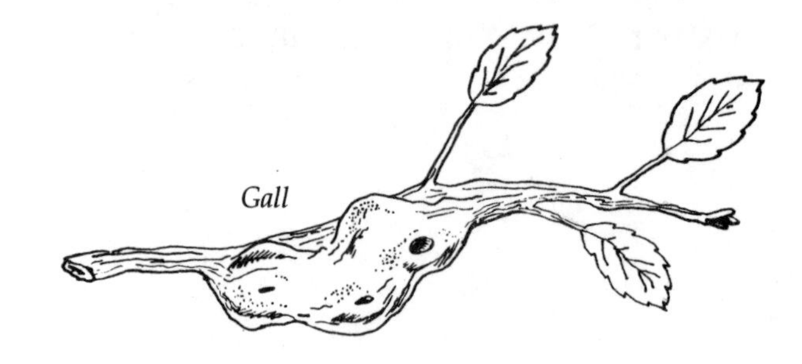

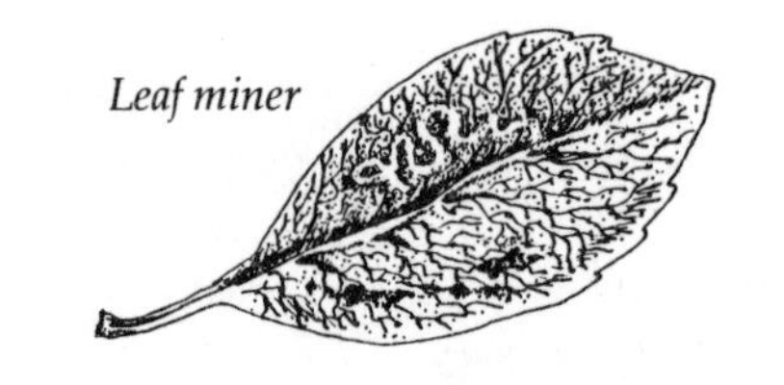

Borings in the bark, tent caterpillar nests, and bird and squirrel nests are other evidence of animals that live in trees. Leaves that have been chewed also indicate animals are present.

PREPARATION AND LEAD-UP

Make a data sheet such as in the illustration for each pair of students. Inside the classroom, draw a large outline of a tree on butcher paper. Allow students to practice using the hand lens.

Ask students for suggestions on how to study living things without harming them. Use their suggestions to emphasize that care must be taken when studying plants and animals. Make sure students understand that plants and animals can be held only temporarily for observing, then should be returned unhurt to their original spot. Ask volunteers to act out the desired behavior for the class.

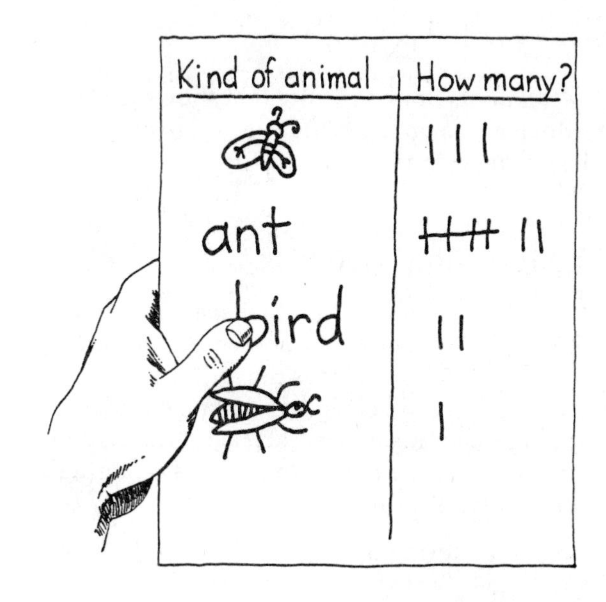

PROCEDURE

1. Introduce students to the activity by saying, "We have been studying our own habitat. We've looked at the kinds of animals that live in our habitat and at the different ways we get the things we need—in working spaces, living spaces, and playing spaces. Today we will be observing the plants and animals that live in a different habitat —a tree. A tree is a fairly small habitat compared to our own habitat, so to see the different things that live in it we will have to be very careful observers. We will pretend that we are on a safari. We must search in small nooks and look way up into the branches, underneath leaves, and around the tree trunk to find as many living things as we can."

2. Pair students with partners and pass out data sheets and crayons. Explain to students that they will draw a picture of each kind of animal they see and next to the picture they will record the number of each kind of animal they observe.

3. Take the class to an outside area with several trees. Remind students to be careful not to harm the plants and animals they observe.

4. Assign each pair of students a tree to observe. Have students look for evidence of animal inhabitants (like insects, birds, and mammals). Students may use hand lenses for closer observation.

5. Inside the classroom, discuss with students their observations. Generate a list of the animals observed by students and help students label the pictures they drew (do not feel like you must know each animal's specific name; generic names for animals like "brown bird," "insect," or "worm" are okay). Have students draw onto pieces of paper the animals they found or cut out shapes from construction paper. Place the animals on the tree outline you have prepared so that they are in the same area they were found on the live tree; for example, students might put a blue jay in the branches and an ant on the trunk.

DISCUSSION QUESTIONS

What kinds of animals did you observe?

Which kinds of animals were most likely to be found in branches?

Which kinds of animals were found in the trunk of the tree?

Which animals did you observe the most of?

How were animals using the tree?

How does the tree help other living things get the things they need to survive?

Do you think the tree is being helped or harmed by the animals? Why do you think so?

Did you notice any plants living on the tree (like moss or lichen)?

EVALUATION

Have students draw a picture that shows one way in which a tree provides the survival needs of other living things.

EXTENSION IDEAS

- Repeat this activity in another season (be sure to save the students' data sheets and tree drawing for comparison). Does the season affect the number and kind of animals on the tree? Encourage students to suggest reasons that different animals were found. In what ways might the season affect animals?
- In spring, during the nesting season, it is sometimes possible to entice birds to build nests nearby by providing bird houses or by hanging nesting materials in a prominent place. Possible nesting materials include string not more than two inches in length, excelsior (fine, curled wood shavings used for packing material), straw, cotton, and twigs. An alternative is to bring a nest to class for students to observe close-up; you might be able to borrow one from a museum or nature center.

HOME LEARNING SUGGESTION

(Use as follow-up to this activity)

In class help students make simple bird feeders. For each student punch two holes at one end of a toilet paper tube, roll the tube in peanut butter and then in bird seed, then tie a piece of string or yarn through the holes so that the feeder can be hung in a tree. Be sure to discuss the responsibilities and implications of making birds dependent upon a feeder for food. Ask parents to help students hang the feeder in a spot near their home where they can observe and record the number of birds that come to the feeder.

SOURCE OF ACTIVITY

Gall illustration adapted from: Bakker, Elna. *An Island Called California*. Berkeley, Calif.: University of California Press, 1971.

OBSERVING MICROHABITATS

Nature is to be found in her entirety nowhere more than in her smallest creatures.

—Pliny

SUMMARY OF ACTIVITY

Students study "planets" (or microhabitats) to find out what lives in them, and compare their planets with others.

Time: 30 to 45 minutes

Setting: Any outdoor environment around the school

Materials:

- One cardboard or construction paper "window" for each pair of students (see preparation and lead-up)

Subjects: Science, language arts, art

Key Words: Habitat, microhabitat, planet, alive, not alive

RELATED CALIFORNIA FRAMEWORK CONCEPTS

Living things need special kinds of food and a special place to live. (*Science Framework Addendum*)

Living things get things they need from each other and from the environment. (*Science Framework Addendum*)

Animals live in a great variety of environments: oceans, fresh water, forests, deserts, tundra, and so forth. (*Science Framework Addendum*)

Data derived from surveys and experiments can be collected, organized, and interpreted. (Adapted from *Mathematics Framework*)

Talking and listening are important ways by which people communicate with and learn from each other. (Adapted from *English-Language Arts Framework*)

OBJECTIVE

Given two microhabitats, students describe similarities and differences between the two.

BACKGROUND INFORMATION

A small habitat is called a microhabitat. A dead log or piece of wood that has been lying on the ground for a while can be a microhabitat. Many tiny animals live in the wood. Some make their home in it, using the wood for food, while others feed on the wood eaters, and still others use the wood for shelter but go outside for food.

Another microhabitat may be found under a stone or on a milkweed plant. A crack in the pavement is a microhabitat for plants; it is like an oasis in the desert where roots can go into the soil and find water.

Insects and other small creatures that live in microhabitats live under the same rules as larger forms of wildlife like bears or deer. Learning about these more easily found animals can lead to a better understanding of all animal life, including human life.

PREPARATION AND LEAD-UP

Select an outdoor study site, ideally with a variety of microhabitats (for example, a grassy area next to pavement). Determine the boundaries.

Prepare cardboard "windows" for observing the environment around the school, one window per pair of students. From cardboard or construction paper cut a frame that is approximately one inch wide and borders a window that is approximately one foot square (see the illustration), or bend a wire clothes hanger into a square about nine inches per side.

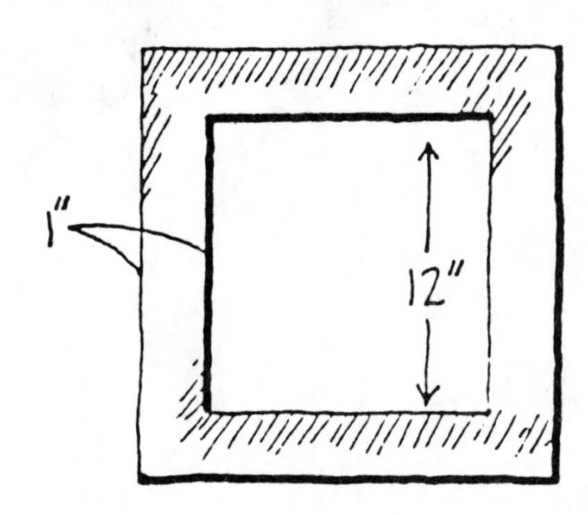

PROCEDURE

1. Introduce the activity by telling students that they will work in pairs as teams of scientists. As scientists they will use windows to look closely at a previously unexplored planet. Divide the class into pairs and pass out windows.

2. Take the group outdoors and point out the boundaries. Instruct each team to choose *one* spot on the ground to place their window and to examine what they see in their window. Remind students that the space within their window is their planet. Tell students that they are to get to know their planet as well as they know their neighborhood.

3. Allow the students approximately 10 minutes to examine their planet. As they are working, mingle and ask students questions like, "What can you tell me about your planet? What kinds of living things are you finding on your planet? What are the physical features of your planet that are the most noticeable? What might you name your planet? What would it be like if you were small enough to live on your planet?"

4. Bring the class back together *but instruct students to leave their windows exactly where their planets are.* If it is a windy or breezy day, you may want students to anchor their windows with a stone or other heavy object. Have students sit in a circle and ask them to share some things they found out about their planet. (Keep this brief as it is only an introduction to the next step.)

5. Pair up the pairs so that students are now in groups of four. Instruct each pair to take their new partner-pair to their planet and show them some of the things they discovered about their planet. Reiterate some of the questions posed before and ask students to share the answers with their partner-pair. When they have finished visiting one planet, students visit the other partner-pair's planet.

6. Gather the group back together, collecting their windows. Ask students what they saw on other planets that was the same as or different than what they found on their own planet. Explain to students that their planets were small microhabitats. Discuss with students the kinds of things that made the habitats different from each other (see the discussion questions). Tell students that the next day they will be learning more about factors that make habitats different from each other.

7. Students might draw pictures and dictate or write a short story describing what it would be like to live on their planet.

DISCUSSION QUESTIONS

Did all the planets look the same? If not, how were they different?
Did the same kinds of things live on all the planets?
What would it be like if you were small enough to live on your planet?
What was the habitat like of the living things you found?
Are all habitats the same?
What kinds of things make habitats different from each other?

EVALUATION

Give each student a large piece of drawing paper with two large, overlapping circles. Ask students to draw in one circle at least one thing from their planet that they *did not see on the other planet,* to draw in the other circle at least one thing from the other planet that they *did not see on their own planet,* and where the circles overlap to draw at least one thing that they saw on both planets.

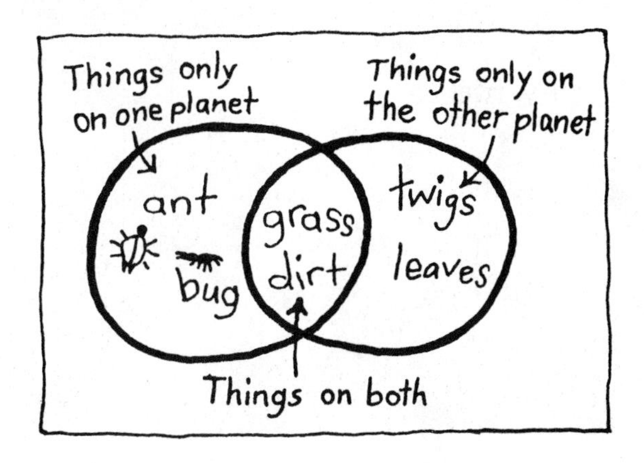

EXTENSION IDEAS

- Repeat this activity having students explore different "planets" in another environment. Students can compare these to their two planets.
- Have students make sun prints or rubbings of their microhabitats using only nonliving objects. The group can try to predict the kinds of plants and animals that might live in the habitat. Be sure that students return the objects to where they were found.
- Show students pictures of animals that live in a particular habitat, then as a class develop a list of other animals that share the same habitat. For example, crabs, sea anemones, snails, sea stars, and limpets all live in a tidepool habitat; rattlesnakes, lizards, mice, rabbits, and coyotes live in a desert habitat; pigeons, house finches, cats, and rats live in an urban habitat.

HOME LEARNING SUGGESTION

(Use as lead-up to the next activity)

Review the following vocabulary terms with your students: sunlight, moisture, heat, and wind. Explain to students that areas that have a lot of sunlight are sunny while areas that have relatively little sunlight are shady. Likewise, areas with a lot of moisture are wet while areas with little moisture are dry; areas with considerable heat are warm while areas with little heat are cool; and areas with a lot of wind are windy and with little wind are calm. Ask students to think of ways that these things might affect habitats. Make copies of the "Places In and Around My Home" copycat page and send it home with students.

RESOURCE

For Students

Russell, Helen Ross. *Small Worlds: A Field Trip Guide.* Boston, Mass.: Little, Brown and Company, 1972. This small but informative book describes animals that live in microhabitats and things to look for in finding them.

Name ______________________________

PLACES IN AND AROUND MY HOME

Dear Parent:

We are studying how different physical factors can affect habitats. Please spend 10 minutes helping your child find and record the places in and around your home that have the most and least amount of sunlight, moisture, wind, and heat.

Thank you.

The place with the *most* sunlight is:

The place with the *least* sunlight is:

The place with the *most* moisture is:

The place with the *least* moisture is:

The place with the *most* wind is:

The place with the *least* wind is:

The place with the *most* heat is:

The place with the *least* heat is:

HABITAT HIGH-LOW

SUMMARY OF ACTIVITY

Students investigate different sites in an outdoor area to determine which sites have the highest and lowest amounts of sunlight, moisture, heat, and wind, as well as the most and fewest organisms, and to find out how habitats differ.

Time: 60 minutes

Setting: Outside area with a variety of conditions (shade, sunlight, wind)

Materials:
- Paper
- Coloring pens or crayons
- Index cards (as many cards as students)
- Bamboo skewers or sticks (the same number as students)
- Waterproof marking pens
- Boundary markers like string or stones to designate sites
- Noisemaker or horn to call group back together

Subjects: Science, math, language arts

Key Words: Habitat, factor, physical factor, moisture, temperature, wind, light, most, least, warm, cool, calm, alive, comfort, discomfort, wet, dry, damp

RELATED CALIFORNIA FRAMEWORK CONCEPTS

Living things get things they need from each other and from the environment. (*Science Framework Addendum*)

Weather affects plants and animals. (*Science Framework Addendum*)

Heat comes from a variety of sources, such as fire or the sun. (*Science Framework Addendum*)

Light comes from a variety of sources. The sun is the source of daylight. (*Science Framework Addendum*)

OBJECTIVE

Given five study sites, students indicate which sites have the most and least amount of sunlight, moisture, heat, and wind as a way to describe differences between the sites.

BACKGROUND INFORMATION

Habitats can be divided into two parts—the things that are alive and growing like animals and plants, and physical features like sunlight, moisture, heat, and wind. Although the living aspects of a habitat certainly affect an organism, this activity focuses on the nonliving, or physical, factors of habitats. Physical factors of a habitat include the amount of light, moisture, heat, and wind found in a specific area. These factors greatly influence the suitability of an area for particular organisms.

Humans are the only animals that employ devices like light meters, thermometers, and anemometers (wind speed instruments) to help improve the accuracy of their senses. By having students use their own senses to determine differences in light, moisture, heat, and wind, this activity will help students be more sensitive to the physical factors that influence habitats.

PREPARATION AND LEAD-UP

Prepare cards as shown in the diagram.

Choose a study area. Designate and mark five specific sites within the study area (these sites are the only sites students will investigate). Try to choose areas that are different from each other in terms of temperature, sunlight, moisture, wind, and numbers of organisms. For example, choose a windy spot and one where the wind is blocked.

Review the previous home learning activity or have students practice investigating environmental variables by distinguishing between hotter and cooler areas (near a radiator or window); distinguishing between shady areas; distinguishing between moist and dry areas; distinguishing between windy and calm places; and going on a hunt to categorize objects as living or nonliving.

PROCEDURE

(NOTE: This activity works best on days that are cloudy, breezy, or very warm or on dewy mornings.)

1. Introduce the activity to students by asking them, "If you could live in any place, where would you really like to live?" Have students draw a picture of the place where they would like to live. Discuss with students what living and physical factors make their place a desirable place to live. Ask, "What things do you like about the place you chose? Of the things you like about your place, which are living things? Which are nonliving things?"

2. Explain to students that they will be learning about some of the physical factors that make one habitat different from another. Ask students what kinds of physical things they think may make one habitat different from another. Tell them that they will be going on a hunt to find the spots in different habitat areas that have the most and least heat, the most and least moisture, the most and least sun, the most and least wind, and the most and fewest living things.

3. Divide the class into pairs. Designate a different environmental factor for each pair to investigate. Give each pair of students a "most" marker and a "least" marker for the environmental factor.

4. Each pair of students should go to each of the sites to determine which site has the most and which has the least of its factor. For example, a pair of students studying sunlight will decide which site is the most sunny and which site is the least sunny. Make sure that students understand that the only sites they will investigate are the ones that have been designated by the teacher. After deciding which site has the most and which has the least for the factor (such as sunlight), students should mark their choices.

5. When all pairs have set their markers, call the class together. Visit each site to see how many markers of each type are at the site. Ask students, "What senses did you use to decide which sites had the most and the least for each factor?"

6. Ask students to think of a spot in the study area where they would like most to be, where they would be the most comfortable, and where the environmental factors are most inviting. Challenge students to find their "spot."

7. Discuss the spot selection with students and ask if they would choose the same spot on a rainy

day. Suggest that other animals live in "spots," or habitat areas, of their own. Discuss with students different habitats and spots that animals prefer. Begin by discussing the animals they found in this activity. "Are there any other animals that have spots they prefer?" (Use examples that students may have observed already, such as cats like to lie in the sun, sow bugs like to be under the shade of stones, slugs prefer moisture, and lizards like to be on warm, sunny rocks.) "What animals like the same kinds of places you do?"

8. Remind students of the pictures they drew in the "Neighborhood Places" activity. Ask, "Do any nonliving factors make that place special? Is it sunny? Full of shade trees? Snug and warm?"

9. Review with students today's activity, which was to study some of the factors that make habitats different from each other. Tell students that they have also looked at some of the reasons why animals and plants prefer one habitat over another—wind, sunlight, moisture, and temperature. Explain that tomorrow students will study another reason why an animal might prefer one habitat over another.

DISCUSSION QUESTIONS

What senses did you use to decide which was the most and least of each factor?

What environmental factor do you think is most important? Why?

EVALUATION

Ask students to draw a picture of the spot they selected in the study site during the activity and have them indicate the physical factors that were found in the spot.

EXTENSION IDEAS

- Repeat the activity at a different time of day. Compare the results.
- Have students draw pictures of animals that live in the different study sites. Are the animals the same? Different? Why?
- Have students study the plants around a building to determine whether the number and size of plants vary in places around the building. Students can investigate the physical factors of moisture, sunlight, temperature, or trampling that may affect plants.

HOME LEARNING SUGGESTION

(Use as follow-up to this activity)

Ask parents to help their children find examples of different ways that people control the amounts of wind, sunlight, moisture, and temperature in their homes. For example, fans and draft dodgers control wind; windows, skylights, shades, and draperies control sunlight; humidifiers and flood pumps control moisture; and heaters, air conditioners, and planting or not planting trees are ways to control the temperature.

SOURCE OF ACTIVITY

Adapted from *Outdoor Biology Instructional Strategies* (OBIS), "Sensory Hi-Lo Hunt." Developed by Lawrence Hall of Science, University of California. Nashua, N.H.: Delta Education, 1982.

Sample Letter

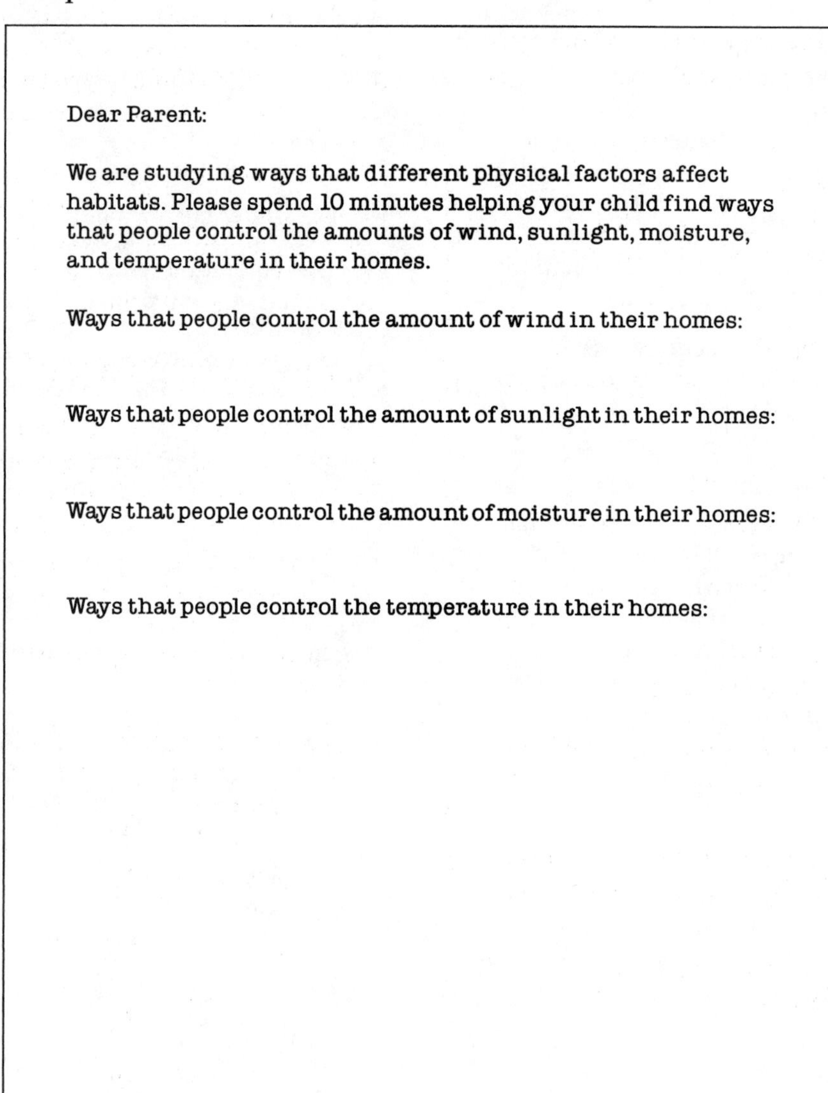

Dear Parent:

We are studying ways that different physical factors affect habitats. Please spend 10 minutes helping your child find ways that people control the amounts of wind, sunlight, moisture, and temperature in their homes.

Ways that people control the amount of wind in their homes:

Ways that people control the amount of sunlight in their homes:

Ways that people control the amount of moisture in their homes:

Ways that people control the temperature in their homes:

BIRDS AND WORMS

SUMMARY OF ACTIVITY

Students hunt for a variety of colored "worms" in two habitats and compare results.

Time: 30 to 45 minutes

Setting: Two different outdoor or indoor sites, such as on lawn and on soil or on carpeting and on linoleum

Materials:
- Four colors of toothpicks, 50 of each color
- Cardboard, styrofoam, or foam-core board
- Tape
- Pen

Subjects: Science, math, language arts

Key Words: Camouflage, adaptation, habitat, hiding, coloration, survive

RELATED CALIFORNIA FRAMEWORK CONCEPTS

Living things have adaptations that enable them to live in their particular habitats. (*Science Framework Addendum*)

Data derived from surveys and experiments can be collected, organized, and interpreted. (Adapted from *Mathematics Framework*)

Creating concrete, pictorial, and symbolic graphs can help us interpret data. (Adapted from *Mathematics Framework*)

OBJECTIVE

Through a simulation activity, students compare the survival abilities of different-colored "worms" in two separate habitats.

BACKGROUND INFORMATION

An animal's coloration can provide camouflage, serve to signal and attract mates, or, as in the case of some brightly colored fish, warn predators that the animal is poisonous. Many animals rely on their coloration to help them blend into their environment and thus "hide" from predators. Protective coloration can greatly increase an animal's chances for survival.

Although camouflage is similar to hiding, it is not the same as hiding. When people hide they are physically blocked by an object that keeps them from view. Camouflage enables an animal to blend into its surroundings without actually hiding.

In this activity students are introduced to the concept that an animal's coloration can provide camouflage. Students are also introduced to the idea that coloration which protects an animal in one habitat may not protect it in another habitat.

PREPARATION AND LEAD-UP

Punch holes in a foam-core board or cardboard to make a graph. Label the graph by indicating the colors of toothpicks. Distribute equal numbers of each color of toothpick in two different outdoor areas, for example, on dirt and on a lawn. Identify boundaries for each area (indoor areas can be used also—try to pick two areas that are different in background color, like a carpet and a tile floor).

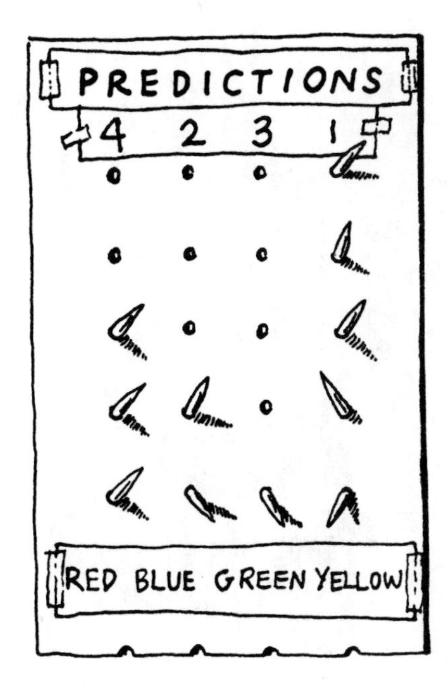

Read a book to your students about camouflage and hiding such as Diane Redfield Massie's *Chameleon Was a Spy*, Ruth Heller's *How to Hide a Butterfly and Other Insects*, or Heller's *How to Hide a Polar Bear and Other Mammals*. Discuss with students ways in which camouflage and hiding are

the same and also different. Tell students that animals need to hide to protect themselves from other animals.

PROCEDURE

1. Tell the class, "Today we are going to pretend that we're birds. It is early morning and we're hungry. We eat little worms that look like these (show several toothpicks including one of each color). In our world, morning is very short so when I say 'It's morning!' you'll want to gather food as quickly as possible." Take the class outside to one of the sites. Point out the boundaries.

2. Have students predict which one of the colors will be the easiest to find and which will be the hardest. Ask, "Which color do you think we will find the most of? The next most of? The third most of? The least of? Why do you think so?" On the graphing board, indicate the colors the students predicted they would find the most of and the least of by writing the numbers one through four (one indicating the most and four the least).

3. Say, "It's morning!" Allow students to gather toothpicks for about five seconds, then call the group back together. Have students stick their toothpicks into the graphing board so that toothpicks are lined up in rows according to their color. Discuss whether predictions made about the easiest and hardest to find worms were correct.

4. Repeat the activity in a different site. Discuss the results (see discussion questions).

5. Discuss with students whether an animal needs to be out of sight to be hidden. Review what is meant by the word "camouflage."

6. Review with students the physical factors that affect things living in a particular habitat. These factors—temperature, moisture, sunlight, and wind—also include coloration. Tell students that over the next few days they will learn about how people can change some factors of their habitat to try to make the habitat better.

DISCUSSION QUESTIONS

Which color worm did we find the most of in each habitat?
Which color worm did we find the least of?
Why did we find more of some colors?
Now pretend that you are a worm. If you are a green worm, which habitat would you want to be in so that you could hide from birds and survive best? If you live in a dirt habitat, which color would best hide you from the birds? (Note: It may be difficult for students to switch perspectives here. You might try having half the class "hide" the worms for the other half and then vice versa. The students hiding the worms may understand better the worms' perspective of which colors help hide them.)

EVALUATION

Give each student a colored worm and have the student find a "habitat" (spot) in the classroom where the worm is camouflaged.

EXTENSION IDEA

Have students color natural wood toothpicks using marking pens so that the toothpicks blend into a particular habitat like a lawn or carpet. Students may discover that variations in the patterns of different colors provide better camouflage than one color alone.

HOME LEARNING SUGGESTION

(Use as follow-up to this activity)

Give each student a natural-colored toothpick "worm" and ask students to modify their worm in some way so that it will be camouflaged to fit into a spot of their choice at home. Send home a note to parents like the one that follows on page 66.

RESOURCES

For Students

Heller, Ruth. *How to Hide a Butterfly and Other Insects.* New York: Grosset and Dunlap, 1985. This book illustrates insects that camouflage themselves.

Heller, Ruth. *How to Hide a Polar Bear and Other Mammals.* New York: Grosset and Dunlap, 1985. This book illustrates mammals that camouflage themselves.

Massie, Diane Redfield. *Chameleon Was a Spy.* New York: Scholastic Book Services, 1979. In this story a chameleon changes color to camouflage itself and becomes a spy for a pickle factory.

SOURCE OF ACTIVITY

Adapted from *Project Learning Tree,* "Bird 'n' Worms." Washington, D.C.: The American Forest Council, 1977.

Sample Letter

Dear Parent:

We have been studying ways in which camouflage helps animals remain unseen in their habitat. I have given your child a toothpick "worm." Please spend 15 minutes helping your child find a spot for the worm (like on the carpet, on the sofa, or on the bed), or help your child color the worm in some way so that it will be camouflaged. When you have finished, attach the worm to this sheet using tape or glue. Thank you.

Worm: (attach here)

Worm's spot: ____

____

WALLS AND FENCES

SUMMARY OF ACTIVITY

Students take a walk to examine walls and fences, then measure and record their observations.

Time: Two 30-minute periods over two days

Setting: Schoolyard or neighborhood

Materials:
- Butcher paper
- Crayons or marking pens
- Data sheet (depending on investigation) for each pair of students
- Hand lens or bug box (depending on investigation) for each pair of students
- Clipboard or other hard writing surface for each pair of students
- Pencil
- Flower press (optional)
- Simple bug key (optional)
- Simple common plant pictures (optional)

Subjects: Science, social studies, language arts, math

Key Words: Walls, fences, boundaries, change, modify

RELATED CALIFORNIA FRAMEWORK CONCEPTS

Animals live in a great variety of environments: oceans, fresh water, forests, deserts, tundra, and so forth. (*Science Framework Addendum*)

Data derived from surveys and experiments can be collected, organized, and interpreted. (Adapted from *Mathematics Framework*)

Ethnic heritages and the physical environment influence people's daily lives. (Adapted from *History-Social Science Framework*)

OBJECTIVE

Students record observations and evaluate their own predictions about walls and fences.

BACKGROUND INFORMATION

In the two previous activities students studied factors that influenced habitats and ways that an animal or plant is suited to its habitat. In this and the next two activities students are introduced to the idea that humans can manipulate their habitat.

In this activity students investigate the impact of a human modification—a wall or fence—on the environment. The activity uses the inquiry method of instruction—students ask questions about walls and fences, then search for the answers to the questions they generated. This approach requires that the activity be fairly open-ended as to questions the students will investigate.

Walls and fences are physical objects that humans construct to modify their habitats. These structures can add to the visual or aesthetic appeal of a habitat by creating wind breaks, providing shady places for plants, defining our territory, protecting people from what is inside or outside, and helping maintain the safety of the habitat by keeping out predators (like burglars) or wild animals. Students can readily understand the effect of these structures because they have probably experienced walls and fences that kept them out of an inviting area or kept them in some place.

Walls and fences affect our own environment and also provide a habitat for many types of living things; for instance, birds and cats sit on them, bugs crawl on them, and plants grow on them. Walls and fences can affect how sunlight and moisture fall on the surrounding areas; plants, for example, may grow better on one side of a fence than on the other side.

PREPARATION AND LEAD-UP

Find a safe walking route to examine different types of walls and fences. Take the class on an introductory walk along the route. Ask, "What are walls and fences for? How do walls and fences affect our habitat? Can you find a wall or fence you can see over? Through? Do all walls and fences look the same? Feel the same?"

Have students make rubbings of at least two different kinds of walls or fences. Start a mural of "Walls and Fences" using the rubbings and have students add to the mural over the next several days.

PROCEDURE

1. Tell students, "Yesterday, we took a walk to look at walls and fences. We found all kinds—some

tall, some short, some we could see through, some we couldn't see through. Today we're going to look at those same walls and fences more closely. What are some things we might find out?" Sample responses include: What plants grow on them? Do the same plants grow on each side? Is it sunnier on one side or the other? Is it windier on one side or the other? Are the numbers of animals the same on each side? What animals live on walls or around their bases? How tall is the wall or fence?

2. Help students choose two or more questions that they will investigate (alternatively, you may wish to select the questions). Allow students to predict what they will find.

3. To help students record their findings, it may be useful to design a simple data sheet like the one shown. Depending on the questions, the data sheet may be large enough for the entire class or smaller sheets for each pair of students.

4. Tell students, "In order to find out if our predictions are correct and to find any surprises, we will take along some hand lenses, bug boxes, butcher paper, and crayons" (or other materials needed to answer student-generated questions). Divide students into pairs and make sure each pair understands the procedure for recording its findings.

Kind of wall or fence	Plants on each	Animals on each
chain link	Ivy	—
Brick	moss dandelion	ants snail

5. Return to the same walking route. Allow ample time for examination of walls and fences. Circulate among students, asking them about the kinds of things they are finding out and if they have found anything that surprises them. If appropriate to what students are investigating, ask, "Why do you think this fence was built? Has it served any other purpose?" Help students record the things they find out.

6. Back in the classroom, discuss and record the results. For example, you might graph their findings as done in the illustration.

DISCUSSION QUESTIONS

Were our predictions correct?
What kinds of fences are more likely to have animals and plants living on them?
What are some of the reasons we like fences?
What are some of the reasons we don't like fences?
How do fences change people's habitats?
How do fences affect the habitats of other living things?

EVALUATION

Students draw a picture showing what they found out from their investigation.

EXTENSION IDEAS

- Have students draw a picture of a place they like. Have them draw it first with fences, then without fences. Ask, "Which do you like better? Why?"
- Discuss other kinds of boundaries (hedges, doors, invisible boundaries) and what they are for.
- Bring in a variety of building materials—bricks, wood, chicken wire, etc. Ask students what would be the advantages and disadvantages of each as a wall or fencing material.

HOME LEARNING SUGGESTION

(Use as follow-up to this activity)

Have students find a fence or wall at home, then record the kind and number of animals found in two different locations along the fence or wall.

DWELLINGS

SUMMARY OF ACTIVITY

Students draw a picture of a dwelling used in another culture and a dwelling from their neighborhood. They examine similarities and differences between the dwellings.

Time: One 30-minute period (lead-up) and one 60-minute period

Setting: Classroom

Materials:
- Pictures of dwellings from other cultures
- Drawing paper
- Crayons
- Story of child's life in another culture (optional)

Subjects: Social studies, science, math, art, language arts

Key Words: Modify, dwelling, alike, different

RELATED CALIFORNIA FRAMEWORK CONCEPTS

Ethnic heritages and the physical environment influence people's daily lives. (Adapted from *History-Social Science Framework*)

People are members of groups that use resources. (Adapted from *History-Social Science Framework*)

Visual art media can be used to translate ideas, feelings, and values. (Adapted from *English-Language Arts Framework*)

OBJECTIVE

Through art, students compare similarities and differences between a dwelling from another culture and a dwelling from their own neighborhood.

BACKGROUND INFORMATION

Unlike other animals, humans are able to live in nearly every type of climate and habitat. One of the most profound ways we are able to adapt to different environments is by building houses.

Our homes are our shelter. Homes help make our immediate environment habitable by sheltering us from rain, snow, heat, wind, and other elements. A home is a safe place to store food and helps protect us from predators like mosquitos and bears. A home is also a private place where we can shut out noise and neighbors and have a cozy place to sleep.

Houses from different cultures vary considerably but they usually have some things in common. Almost always they protect the occupants from the elements, and usually they have a place to cook and store food, a place to sleep, and a place to play.

In this activity students compare houses from another culture with houses from their own culture. Although different houses may look strange to us at first, when studying them we learn that houses in other cultures serve the same functions as our own houses. Differences occur because people build houses to suit their particular environment from the resources available to them.

PREPARATION AND LEAD-UP

Gather a selection of pictures of dwellings from other cultures. This may be done in connection with a social studies unit on foreign or Native American cultures. Some social studies textbooks contain suitable pictures.

Read a story about a child's life in another culture that includes information about the type of dwelling the child lives in.

PROCEDURE

1. Introduce the activity by reminding students that they learned one way people modify their habitat is by building walls and fences. Ask students what are some other ways people modify their habitats. Tell students that today they will be looking at how people can modify their habitats by building houses.

2. Show students pictures of dwellings from other cultures. Help students visualize the dwelling of a child from another culture as follows (ellipses indicate a pause): "Relax and close your eyes . . . Imagine yourself standing in front of one of the houses we've looked at today . . . Notice the shape and color of the house and where it is situated . . . Imagine yourself walking up to the house and touching it . . . Notice what the house is made of . . . And what it feels like . . . Now in your imagination walk into the front door of the house . . . Walk through all the rooms of the house . . . Pay attention to what the rooms are like . . . Where food is prepared . . . Where water comes from . . . Where the family sleeps . . . Where the children play . . . Now imagine how the family that lives in the house keeps warm in cold months . . . Or cool in hot months . . . Now bring yourself back to here . . . When you are ready, open your eyes."

3. Distribute a piece of paper and crayons to each student. Have students divide the paper in half. Explain that on one half of the paper students should draw a picture of the house they visualized and on the other half a picture of their own house or the house of a friend.

4. Have students describe differences between the two dwellings, and then similarities. Look at the materials used by other cultures and by our culture to build dwellings. Ask, "How are the houses alike? How are they different? What materials were used to build the houses? Where do people in other places get their building materials from? Where do we get ours from? How are each of the houses suited to the place where they are built?"

5. For each type of home discussed, have students describe where and how the functions of daily life like cooking, eating, bathing, and playing are carried out. Ask how these things are the same for each of the houses and how they are different. Remind students that even though other people's houses may seem strange to us, they are similar to our own houses because they provide the things people need to survive.

DISCUSSION QUESTIONS

How do our houses help us survive?

How do houses help us live in lots of different habitats?

EVALUATION

Students write a story about a day in the life of a child from another culture, describing how the child lives in his or her house.

EXTENSION IDEA

Define the terms "simple" and "complex" (something that is simple has only a few parts and something that is complex has many parts). Ask students which of the dwellings they have drawn has the most parts. Can they list or count them? (For example, a tepee has a door flap, a smoke flap, decorations, skins, poles, and pegs, while your house has a door, windows, chimney, steps, walls, roof, garage, stairs, and many rooms.) Ask, "Which dwelling is simpler? Which dwelling is more complex? What else do we have that is more complex? Is there anything we have that is simpler than that which earlier people had? Which is better to have—something simple or something complex? Why?"

HOME LEARNING SUGGESTION

Ask students to make a map of their house showing where they cook, eat, sleep, and play.

RESOURCE

For Students

Weil, Lisl. *The Houses We Build.* New York: Atheneum, 1985. This book illustrates some of the dwellings people throughout the ages have built in Europe and America.

TOO CLOSE FOR COMFORT

SUMMARY OF ACTIVITY

Students experience different population densities in the classroom and discuss the results.

Time: One 15-minute discussion period and one period of time for "experiment" (duration determined by the teacher)

Setting: Classroom

Materials: None

Subjects: Social studies, science, language arts

Key Words: Crowded, population, space, spacious, roomy, adequate

RELATED CALIFORNIA FRAMEWORK CONCEPTS

People are members of groups; there is cooperation and conflict within and between groups. (Adapted from *History-Social Science Framework*)

Animals need food, water, air, and a place to live. (*Science Framework Addendum*)

OBJECTIVE

After participating in a simulation activity, students express the impacts of crowding.

BACKGROUND INFORMATION

Every living thing needs a certain amount of space in its habitat in order to survive. The phrase "carrying capacity" refers to the number of living things an area of land or water can support at any given time. The same area will have different carrying capacities for different life forms. For example, the carrying capacity of an area of land will not be the same for golden eagles as it is for robins—eagles require much more space than robins. The carrying capacity is usually limited by some aspect of a species' habitat requirements such as the availability and quality of food, water, shelter, and space. Carrying capacities can be affected by both natural and human factors like natural disasters, fluctuations in rainfall, or the building of a dam.

If too many animals live in an area, they will not find enough food and will have to compete for habitat space. If there are too few animals living in an area, they may have difficulty finding mates for reproduction or predators may reduce their numbers significantly.

In this activity students are introduced to the idea of space requirements by experiencing the effects of a classroom that is more crowded than normal. People like to be near each other; we like to visit, have friends, and share things. However, we do not like being too crowded or living too close together.

PREPARATION AND LEAD-UP

Discuss with students whether the classroom is overcrowded. Ask, "What would it be like if we had 10 more students who had to use this room?"

PROCEDURE

1. Arrange student desks into a smaller than normal space (such as a corner of the room or one side

of the room). Tell students that they will be like animals that have large families and have to live in a place where space is limited. Students should spend a period of time (to be determined by the teacher) "living in a crowded habitat." This crowded situation should exist long enough so that students get over the novelty of sitting close together and begin to experience some stress.

2. After the experience, talk about it. "How did the crowded situation compare to the normal class situation? How were the situations alike? Different? Better? Worse? What were the problems associated with each? Was it harder to get along in the more crowded environment? Did people get in each other's way? Was it harder to concentrate?"

3. Talk about animals in the natural environment and have students hypothesize what problems might arise for animals in a community that is too crowded. Also ask, "What might it be like for animals that have too much room? What are examples of things that can happen to affect how many plants and animals can live in a habitat?"

DISCUSSION QUESTIONS

What are some other situations in which you have felt crowded?
How have you felt when you were in a traffic jam or standing in the lunch line?

EVALUATION

Students write a story or draw a picture about how they felt during the activity.

EXTENSION IDEA

Students conduct an experiment to see what it is like to be in a classroom that is less crowded than normal. If possible, arrange for half of the class to be in another classroom for part of the day and then switch. Discuss how this less crowded situation compared with the normal situation and with the crowded situation. How were the two situations alike, different, better, and worse? Were there problems when the classroom was less crowded?

HOME LEARNING SUGGESTION

(Use as follow-up to this activity)

Review with students: "Are there crowding problems where we live? How could we tell? What could we look for? Is there always room for you to sit on the bus? What is it like to shop in the store near you; do you have to wait in line a long time? Do your parents spend a lot of time in traffic jams on the way to work?"

Have students interview one or both parents about how long they spend commuting to work and the amount of time they wait in check-out lines at stores. Discuss with students their findings and have students draw a picture or write a story describing the results.

IT'S YOUR SPACE

SUMMARY OF ACTIVITY

Students discuss and try out ways of physically arranging the classroom.

Time: Two 45-minute periods spread over a week

Setting: Classroom

Materials:
- Butcher paper
- Crayons

Subjects: Social studies, language arts, art

Key Words: Arrangement, plan, science

RELATED CALIFORNIA FRAMEWORK CONCEPTS

Living things need special kinds of food and a special place to live. (*Science Framework Addendum*)

People are members of groups; communication, problem solving, and decision making in groups are important behaviors. (Adapted from *History-Social Science Framework*)

OBJECTIVE

Students devise, execute, and evaluate a plan for arranging their classroom.

BACKGROUND INFORMATION

Throughout this unit students have been learning about factors that make up and affect habitats and about ways that humans manipulate the environment. In this activity students are given the opportunity to effect desirable changes in their own habitat. By looking at their classroom, students think about what they like and do not like in their environment. They learn to consider other people's needs and feelings before making changes in the environment, then they actually make changes and evaluate the effects.

PREPARATION AND LEAD-UP

Establish your requirements for the classroom arrangement. Are there aspects you feel are necessary, like the location of your desk or space for focusing the whole class on a chalkboard? Determine in advance what you will and will not allow to be rearranged before discussing rearranging the classroom with the students. Be as flexible as possible.

PROCEDURE

1. Introduce the idea that we arrange our homes so that we can live comfortably and have space to do the things we enjoy doing. Discuss areas of the home we set aside for special uses (like a T.V. room, sewing room, or kitchen). Ask the class to consider what the classroom is used for. List the answers on the blackboard (possible answers include reading quietly, sharing, playing, and watching films). Ask, "How could we best set up the classroom so that we can comfortably get those things done?" (Now is the time to introduce any restrictions you may have on the physical arrangement.)

2. Divide the class into groups of three to five students. Have each group draw a picture of how it would like to arrange the classroom so that the class can get things done in a way that's comfortable for all. Ask students, "Where shall we put desks? Where will we hear stories? Where will we keep our personal things? Where will we do group work?"

3. Have each group share its picture with the class.

4. After all of the groups have had their turn, vote on which part of each group's plan the class will try (choosing at least one part of each plan). As the class decides on a class plan, the teacher should draw a big picture of the plan to see how it fits together. Alternatively, after the groups have shared their plans, the teacher can choose parts of different plans to try as a class, drawing a big picture of the plan for the class to see.

5. Rearrange the classroom according to the plan. Try living with it for one week. At the end of the week, have students reevaluate the plan. What is working? What is not working? How shall we modify our arrangement to make it work even better?

DISCUSSION QUESTIONS

What factors seem to be important in our classroom habitat?

How did changing our habitat make you feel? Why?

EVALUATION

Students write a story or draw a picture describing what they liked or did not like about the new classroom arrangement.

EXTENSION IDEAS

- Take a walk around the neighborhood. Ask students, "How do people use their space? Do they have yards? What are they used for? Do they have fences? Why? Do they have garages? Gardens? What can we find out about people just by looking at how they arrange their home environment?"
- Suggest to students that they work with their parents rearranging a room at home, if possible. Families can make the plans either on paper or on a model, discuss the plan as a family, then vote on the suggestions and carry out the desired changes.
- Study the school environment as a whole to see if there is some aspect that students could rearrange or improve (for example, trash cans could be moved closer to the lunch area, flowers could be planted in a bare spot, or litter could be picked up around the grounds).

HOME LEARNING SUGGESTION

(Use as follow-up to this activity)

Students revise maps they made of their house in the home learning suggestion of the "Dwellings" activity to indicate a better arrangement than currently exists. Students write a few statements explaining what makes the new arrangement better.

The Earth Supports Life

Second and Third Grades

Introduction to the Unit

The activities in this unit form a foundation of basic ecological concepts and build an understanding of human dependence on the earth. In the first two activities, students look at life in the earth (or soil) itself. The following three activities help students understand that all plants and animals (including humans) depend upon the earth for food. In the final four activities students look at other basic necessities provided by the earth, like water and shelter.

Advance Planning

Three activities ("Life in Soil," "Sow Bug Scavenger," and "Basic Necessities Microtrek") take place outdoors and you might want to arrange to have another adult assist you. Even though it is possible for one teacher to handle the class alone outside, it is much less hectic and much more enjoyable for everyone if there is another adult to help. It is also easier for students to get the assistance and guidance they need.

Some of the activities require materials that will need to be collected or assembled. For "Life in Soil" each pair of students will need a one-quart milk container. Let students know that they can bring in containers from home. For "Do Plants Need Soil?" each pair of students will need one clear plastic container with a cover, one plastic plate or yogurt lid, and two plastic vegetable bags. Again, students can contribute needed items from home. You may want to find one or more books to read to your students as part of "Creating a Food Chain." Suggested titles are listed at the end of the activity. For "Basic Necessities Microtrek" each pair of students will need a cardboard clipboard about 9 inches by 12 inches. Begin gathering the cardboard now. For "Earth Plays" you may want to use magazine pictures showing ways that the earth supports life. If so, you, a parent, or an aide should begin to collect the pictures now.

Classroom Food Chain

Students will learn about and diagram food chains in the activity "Creating a Food Chain," and will consider food relationships in a number of the other activities. An optional activity that would greatly enhance this unit is a classroom food chain, whereby students can observe live members of a food chain kept in the classroom. The food chain could be maintained throughout the entire unit (several of the activities contain discussion questions related to the classroom food chain). As students care for and observe living plants and animals, they can better appreciate the important concept of food chains. This will help students understand that all life is ultimately dependent on the earth. In addition, caring for other living creatures can help students empathize with them.

Two easily maintained food chains are algae → daphnia → guppies, and plant foods → crickets → anoles (a kind of lizard). A local pet store or aquarium supply shop will be able to provide information on feeding and housing needs.

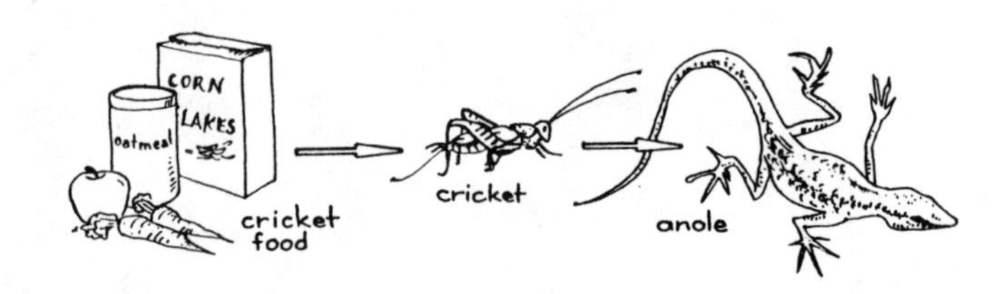

UNIT TIMELINE ■ Participation in Activity □ Ongoing observation and study

		Week 1					Week 2					Week 3					Week 4				
Page	**Activity**																				
80	Life in Soil	■																			
83	Sow Bug Scavengers		■	□	■	□	■														
88	Do Plants Need Soil?							■	□	■	□	■	□	■							
91	Do You Eat Plants?														■						
96	Creating a Food Chain															■	■				
102	The Beautiful Basics																	■			
104	Basic Necessities Microtrek																		■		
106	Earth Plays																			■	
108	Earth Books																				■

Even though a classroom food chain is a simple microcosm, it will require careful, ongoing care to maintain the plants and animals. A rotational system for feeding and cleaning duties is a good way to share the tasks among students.

Resources

Creatures in the Classroom. Portland, Ore.: Multnomah County Intermediate Education District, 1984. Care, feeding, and housing instructions for many common and uncommon classroom pets are contained in this large book.

Hampton, Carolyn H., and others. *Classroom Creature Culture*. Washington, D.C.: National Science Teachers Association, 1986. This collection of reprints on ways to keep and use animals in the classroom is from the magazine *Science and Children*.

LIFE IN SOIL

SUMMARY OF ACTIVITY

Students collect soil samples from a nearby area and search through them for animal life.

Time: 60 minutes

Setting: Classroom, schoolyard or park

Materials:

- A roll of plastic wrap
- Paper and drawing materials
- Scissors
- Construction paper and other materials to make a bulletin board
- Garbage can or other large bucket
- One empty milk carton (one-quart size) for each pair of students
- One small shovel or spoon for digging for each pair of students
- One magnifying lens for each pair of students
- One small plastic container with lid for each pair of students
- Two cotton swabs for each pair of students
- White butcher paper or newsprint
- One bug box (optional)

Subjects: Science, art, language arts

Key Words: Earth, soil, life

RELATED CALIFORNIA FRAMEWORK CONCEPTS

Animals live in a great variety of environments: oceans, fresh water, forests, deserts, tundra, and so forth. (*Science Framework Addendum*)

Artistic skills can be used to express and communicate responses to experiences. (Adapted from *Visual and Performing Arts Framework*)

OBJECTIVE

Students find and observe organisms living in soil and draw pictures of them.

BACKGROUND INFORMATION

Soil is composed of small pieces of weathered, broken rock (in the form of sand or clay particles) and bits of decaying organic matter (in the form of dead and decaying plant and animal parts). In addition, many kinds of plants and animals live in most soils.

Students are likely to find earthworms, beetles, and ants living in their soil sample. Students may also find snails, slugs, pill bugs, sow bugs, centipedes, millipedes, and spiders since all of these animals live right on the surface of the soil.

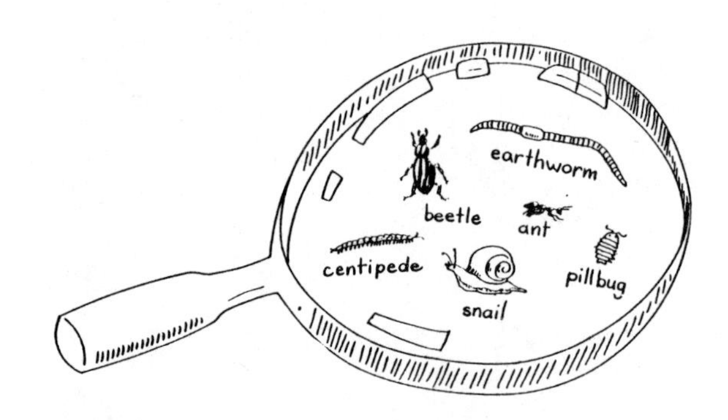

The soil used for this activity should be hospitable to animal life. It should be rich in organic matter (that is, have visible dead leaves and small twigs mixed in) and be damp. You will need to investigate nearby soils to find the best sites for students to collect their samples. The school maintenance department may be helpful in pointing out the most fertile soil on the school grounds. If you plan to go to a park, you will want advance permission from the parks department to collect soil samples. A vacant lot is another possibility, although the soil may be poor so you may find fewer visible life forms. If you do not have suitable soil nearby for students to collect, a gardener or nursery may be willing to provide enough soil for your students. You will probably need to bring the soil to class in this case; if so, divide the class into pairs and skip steps two through four.

PREPARATION AND LEAD-UP

Select the site where students will take soil samples or make arrangements to bring good soil to class (do not let it dry out). Gather the milk cartons and other materials that will be used to collect soil. Also gather materials for the bulletin board (see step six). If possible, arrange to have another adult available to help during this activity.

PROCEDURE

1. Tell students that today they will be looking for animals that live in the earth. Ask what animals live underground in the soil. Record suggestions on the chalkboard and save the list for use in step six.

2. Show students how they are to collect soil samples using shovels or spoons. It is important that students collect soil at least 15 centimeters (six inches) below the surface because that is where most soil organisms live. Demonstrate the way to cover milk cartons with plastic wrap, securing the wrap with a rubber band, to prevent soil and organisms from drying out. Describe the digging site.

3. Review the rules and proper behavior for working outdoors. Students should understand that they have a task to complete while outside; it is not playtime, even though it may be fun. Remind students to respect the environment. They should not harm plants and should only dig in the place where they are collecting their soil. If they see a soil animal while they are collecting, they should be sure to collect it, too, so they can look at it more closely in the classroom.

4. Divide students into pairs. Distribute the digging tools and milk cartons and have students write their names on their cartons. Take students outside and let them collect their samples.

5. Wet cotton swabs can be used to pick up most small organisms if students are uncomfortable picking them up with their hands. Demonstrate how to use wet cotton swabs and hand lenses. Distribute wet cotton swabs, butcher paper or newsprint, small plastic containers, milk cartons of soil, hand lenses, and bug boxes (if available). Each pair of students should dump its soil sample onto a piece of butcher paper or newsprint. Students should examine the soil carefully with the magnifying lens. If bug boxes are available, students can use these to more closely observe organisms they find. All organisms should be put into the plastic containers. When students are through looking at their soil samples, they should put them into a specially designated garbage can or other container so that they can be taken back outside later.

6. Hand out paper and ask students to draw a picture of the animals they found. Add the names of the animals to the list on the board so that students can label their drawings. Post students' drawings on the bulletin board.

7. Discuss students' findings and let the class know that for the next few weeks they will be studying some of the ways that living things get things they need from the earth. Write the phrase "the earth supports life" on the board and ask students what they think it means.

8. Discuss the need to return animals to their homes outside. Have the class return animals to their homes; students can return the soil at the same time (if the soil came from a nursery or another source, the class can place it carefully around the base of a plant or tree growing in or near the schoolyard).

DISCUSSION QUESTIONS

What living animals did you find in the soil?
What do the animals look like?
How do they move?
What might some of these animals eat?
Where might they get their water?
Did you find any parts of dead plants or animals in the soil?
What do you think happens to dead plants and animals in the soil?
Can you think of other kinds of animals, especially animals larger than the ones we found today, that might live underground in the soil? (Moles, gophers, gopher snakes, mice, and burrowing owls are several examples.)
Why should we return the animals to the place we found them? What do you think might happen if we didn't?

EVALUATION

Students name five organisms that live in the soil or underground.

EXTENSION IDEAS

- Make a bar graph listing the organisms students found in the soil. Have one student from each pair color in the appropriate number of squares to show how many of each kind of organism that pair found.
- If you have access to different types of soil, have students repeat the activity and compare the kinds and numbers of animals found in various soil samples. Try a sample with lots of leaf litter from under a tree, a sample of sandy or clayey soil, or a sample from a cultivated lawn. You can help students speculate on the reasons that some kinds of soil support more animals than other kinds.

HOME LEARNING SUGGESTION

(Use as follow-up to this activity)

Ask students to look for animals in the soil in their yard or neighborhood. Emphasize that students should get permission from a parent or other appropriate adult before they begin digging. Ask each student to bring in a drawing of one or more animals he or she found. You can add students' drawings to the bulletin board display in class.

RESOURCES

Nickelsburg, Janet. *Nature Activities for Early Childhood*. Menlo Park, Calif.: Addison-Wesley Publishing Co., 1976. The chapter "Looking for Things in the Ground" contains helpful suggestions for finding and learning about life in the soil.

Sisson, Edith. *Nature with Children of All Ages*. Englewood Cliffs, N. J.: Prentice-Hall, Inc., 1982. The chapter "Creatures Small and Spineless" gives general information about animal life that may be found in soil and suggests activities.

SOW BUG SCAVENGERS

Nature has no interest in the preservation of the dead; her purpose is to start their elements upon the eternal road to life once more.

—LOREN EISLEY

SUMMARY OF ACTIVITY

Students collect sow bugs or pill bugs and observe and record their feeding behavior.

Time: One 40-minute period and two 10-minute periods

Setting: Outdoors, classroom

Materials:
- Corrugated cardboard or several raw, hollowed-out potatoes
- Copycat page, one per student
- A clear plastic container with lid or a ziplock bag for each student
- Masking tape
- Wilted lettuce or soft fruit

Subjects: Science, language arts

Key Words: Sow bugs, pill bugs, scavengers, nutrients

RELATED CALIFORNIA FRAMEWORK CONCEPTS

Decomposers get their food from dead plants and animals and help return nutrients to the soil. (Adapted from *Science Framework Addendum*)

All animals need food, water, air, and a place to live. (*Science Framework Addendum*)

Living things get things they need from each other and from the environment. (*Science Framework Addendum*)

Soils are formed from particles of rock mixed with dead plant and animal matter. (*Science Framework Addendum*)

Writing enables us to communicate our ideas. (Adapted from *English-Language Arts Framework*)

OBJECTIVE

Students describe sow bug feeding behavior and generalize about what happens to decaying plant material in the soil.

BACKGROUND INFORMATION

Sow bugs and pill bugs are not insects. They are arthropods and are related to crabs and lobsters. Students will be able to see and feel their outer shell, a characteristic of arthropods (the primary characteristic separating sow bugs from pill bugs is that the latter—also known as "roly-poly" bugs—protect themselves by rolling into a ball or "pill").

Sow bugs and pill bugs are scavengers because they eat dead plant materials (they also eat fresh lettuce leaves, strawberries, apricots, and other soft fruits). Decomposers like bacteria and fungi are different from scavengers because they work at the microscopic level, breaking down decaying materials into their chemical constituents. Both scavengers and decomposers help by returning nutrients to the soil where they can be used again by growing plants.

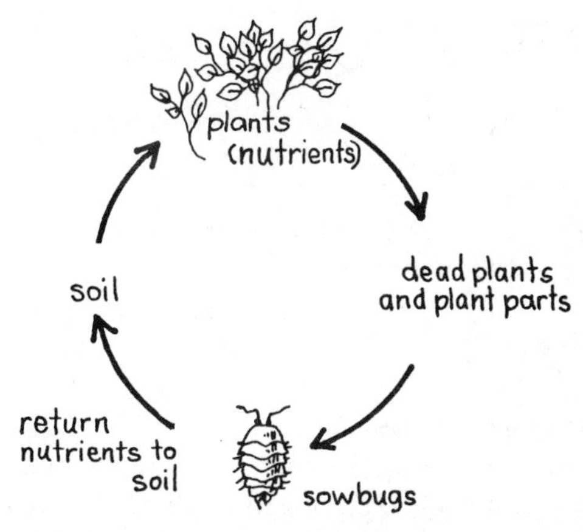

In this activity students keep sow bugs or pill bugs for five days to observe their ability to act as scavengers. Sow bugs are not very hardy in captivity so it is best to minimize their time in the classroom. You may want to start this activity on a Monday, scheduling the two other observation sessions on the following Wednesday and Friday. This way the sow bugs can be released before the weekend.

PREPARATION AND LEAD-UP

Gather the containers students will use to house their sow bugs (any closed, clear plastic container will do; plastic ziplock bags filled with air also make excellent containers). Students should open their bags or containers daily to prevent the buildup of moisture, which encourages the growth of mold. Students should not poke holes in their containers—there is more than enough air in even a small container to last small organisms for many days.

Decide how you want the sow bugs collected. Students can collect them on their own at home or the class can collect them together in the schoolyard. If students bring sow bugs from home, they can be stored in containers with damp decaying leaves or grass. If students will be collecting sow bugs at school, you should find out where sow bugs are most common (sow bugs prefer cool, damp, dark places). If you are having trouble finding sow bugs at school, you can lay down pieces of corrugated cardboard or a raw, hollowed out potato in a cool, damp spot. After a couple of days, sow bugs should have congregated underneath the cardboard or potato.

PROCEDURE

1. Review the animals students found in the previous activity. Explain that students will now study one particular soil animal—sow bugs (or pill bugs). Let students know that they will work in pairs and that each pair will keep several sow bugs for five days. Ask, "Where have you seen sow bugs before? Do you have any ideas about what they might eat?"

2. If students will be collecting the sow bugs, discuss where they should look (in shady areas under low growing plants, logs, stones, or decaying plant parts; among grass and weeds growing around the edges of buildings; in leaf litter; or under the cardboard or potato you set out). Make sure students know where in the schoolyard they will be allowed to search. Ask, "How can you handle the sow bugs gently? What should you do to make sure you don't harm any plants or animals while you are outside?"

3. Remind students that they will need to be quiet when they are near other classrooms and that they should treat the environment, plants, and animals with care. Make sure students know how they are expected to behave when they are out of the classroom.

4. Divide the class into pairs and give each pair a container. Each team should collect eight to ten sow bugs. If the sow bugs have been collected previously, distribute them to students at this time.

5. When students return to the classroom, each pair should use masking tape to label its container with the names of both partners. Students should also make sure there is moisture inside each container but no standing water (sow bugs drown easily). Distribute lettuce or fruit pieces to each pair and have students add these to their containers. Containers should not be kept in direct sunlight because sow bugs may get too hot and die.

6. Ask students, "What do sow bugs look like? What do they feel like? What are they doing? What kind of food did you put in your container?" Record on the board descriptive words students used.

7. Distribute the "Sow Bug Scavengers" copycat page. Ask students to use some of the words on the board to write about their sow bugs (how many there are, what they look like, what they are doing) and the food they added (the kind of food, number of pieces, color, and size). You may want to have volunteers read their observations to each other in small groups or to the whole class. Save and store these sheets for future use.

8. Over the next few days schedule two more observation and writing sessions. Again discuss with students what they see and make a list of their descriptive words on the board before they begin writing on their copycat pages.

9. Remind students to open their containers to prevent moisture buildup. If the containers become too dry inside, students can add a little water. Students should remove and replenish the sow bugs' food periodically, before it molds. Have students try different foods to see if the sow bugs have a preference. Students may be able to contribute food from home or from their own lunches.

10. After the class has recorded all of its observations, discuss what students found (see the discussion questions). Explain that there are nutrients in dead plants and animals and that scavengers like sow bugs help return the nutrients to the soil for plants to use (the next activity introduces the concept that plants rely on nutrients from the soil).

11. When the class is through, the sow bugs should be returned to their usual habitat. Remind students that sow bugs prefer cool, damp, dark places. Ask students to remember exactly where they found their sow bugs (for example, under a specific tree or in a certain crack along the bottom of the fence). Have students return the sow bugs to safe and healthy homes.

DISCUSSION QUESTIONS

What happened to the food that you put into your sow bug container?
Did the sow bugs seem to prefer certain kinds of food?
Based on your own observations, what happens when fruit falls uneaten on the ground?
What might happen when leaves fall? When a tree dies?
What do you think happens to animal bodies when they die?
Sow bugs are called scavengers because they eat dead plants. Other scavengers eat dead animals. Why are scavengers called the "garbage collectors of the forest"?
What would the forest be like if there were no sow bugs or other scavengers?
Which parts of our garbage do you think sow bugs would eat? How come?
What would they not be able to eat? Why?
What happens to the parts of our garbage that the scavengers and decomposers can't eat?

EVALUATION

Students write a story about how a sow bug helps return nutrients to the soil. Students can draw a picture illustrating the story.

EXTENSION IDEAS

- Teach the following song to your students (scoring appears on page 86). Ask, "What happens when things die?"

  DECOMPOSITION
  by Steve Van Zandt

  Chorus:
  Group 1 chants "DE-COMP—osition, DE-COMP—osition"
  Group 2 chants "Get D-O-W-N-N-N, break D-O-W-N-N-N-N-N"
  Group 3 snaps fingers above head and makes beetle crunchy click sounds with mouth (munch, munch, munch)
  (Suggest that Group 1 be deep voices, Group 2 be high voices)

  Is there waste? Well I don't know.
  One thing dies to let another grow.
  The circle we see most every day,
  The name that we call it is decay.
  Well come all you people gather round, break down, and listen to

  Chorus

  There are many kinds of bugs:
  Worms and snails and banana slugs.
  But they are useful to me and you:
  They help to make the soil renew.
  Well come all you people gather round, break down, and listen to

  Chorus

  Decomposition is a useful game.
  A tree drops its leaves but they don't stay the same.
  A bug chews them up and spits them back out,
  Making the soil for a new tree to sprout.
  Well come all you people gather round, break down, and listen to

  Chorus

- Keep earthworms in the classroom. Observe what happens to decaying leaves, coffee grounds, orange peels, lettuce scraps, and other foods that are placed in containers that house earthworms. Earthworms are more active at night (that's why fishermen call them "night-crawlers"), so keep their containers covered with black paper at all times when they are not being observed.
- Small organisms that have died in classroom colonies or been found dead outside can be put into vials or jars with wet sand so that the process of decay can be observed. First, fill vials about three-quarters full with sand. Add water until the sand is thoroughly moistened. Use a small stick to move sand away from the side of the vial so that the dead organism can be placed next to the glass so that it is visible. Encourage students to add dead plant parts, too. Students can make weekly observations for the next four or five weeks. They will notice mold and, if they open their vials, an unpleasant odor, which is evidence of bacterial decay.

* "A", "B", and "C" vocal parts are to be "layered" and sung all at once, with one group of singers taking each part.

HOME LEARNING SUGGESTION

(Use as follow-up to this activity)

Have students look around their yards and neighborhoods for evidence that dead plant parts (like flowers, leaves, fruit, needles, and bark) are decaying and returning to the soil. If possible, students should find a living specimen to compare to the decaying plant parts. For example, they may be able to find a living leaf or flower to compare to decaying ones they find on the ground. Students might make a drawing of a living plant part and its corresponding decaying part, and write a short description of each.

RESOURCES

Nickelsburg, Janet. *Nature Activities for Early Childhood.* Menlo Park, Calif.: Addison-Wesley Publishing Co., 1976. The chapter "Sow Bugs and Pill Bugs" has information on keeping and using these animals in the classroom.

Hampton, Carolyn H., and others. *Classroom Creature Culture.* Washington, D.C.: National Science Teachers Association, 1986. The chapter "Terrestrial Isopods" contains information on trapping and housing sow bugs and pill bugs.

For Students

Van Zandt, Steve. Original *Banana Slug String Band* recordings are available from Steve Van Zandt, P.O. Box 717, Pescadero, Calif. 94060. These fun, lively songs are about caring for and enjoying the earth.

Name ____________________

SOW BUG SCAVENGERS

Date	Observations: Sow Bugs	Food

DO PLANTS NEED SOIL?

SUMMARY OF ACTIVITY

Students plant seeds in soil and on a paper towel, then make a series of drawings to illustrate what happens to their seeds over a two-week period.

Time: One 30-minute period and three 15-minute periods

Setting: Classroom

Materials:
- Butcher paper
- Radish seeds
- Potting soil or other rich soil
- Newspaper
- Cans or pitchers for watering
- Crayons or other drawing materials
- Masking tape
- One piece of 11-inch by 17-inch paper per student
- One paper cup or other small container for each pair of students
- One plastic plate or plastic lid for each pair of students
- Two paper towels for each pair of students
- Two pieces of masking tape, about 10 centimeters (four inches) long for each pair of students
- Two plastic vegetable bags for each pair of students

Subjects: Science, art

Key Words: Soil, seeds, nutrients, observation, earth, support

RELATED CALIFORNIA FRAMEWORK CONCEPTS

Soils provide water and nutrients to plants. (*Science Framework Addendum*)

Most plants grow in soil. (*Science Framework Addendum*)

All plants need water. (*Science Framework Addendum*)

Green plants need light. (*Science Framework Addendum*)

Artistic skills can be used to express and communicate responses to experiences. (Adapted from *Visual and Performing Arts Framework*)

OBJECTIVE

Students plant and prepare seeds according to a teacher demonstration, illustrate what happens to the two sets of seeds by drawing a sequenced set of pictures, and identify effects of soil on growing seeds.

BACKGROUND INFORMATION

In the previous activity students were introduced to the idea that nutrients are returned to the soil by scavengers and that these nutrients are used by growing plants. This activity emphasizes that plants need soil to grow.

Plants take up water and nutrients from the soil through their roots. The major nutrients plants need are nitrogen, phosphorus, and potassium. Other nutrients needed in smaller amounts for most plants include calcium, magnesium, and sulfur.

Soils are made up of organic matter (decaying plant and animal matter called humus) and inorganic matter (sand, silt, and clay). Organic matter usually provides the majority of nutrients plants derive from soils and helps retain soil moisture. In general, the more organic matter soil has, the more fertile it is.

During this activity engage students in discussion about things plants need besides soil. The four basic needs of plants—soil, water, sunlight, and air—will be reviewed again in the activity "Creating a Food Chain."

A week after students have planted their radish seeds, they should be able to see a clear difference between the seeds grown in and out of soil. As the activity progresses, students may suggest other lines of investigation, or ask questions that could lead to other studies (such as testing what happens if some plants are not watered or are kept in a dark closet). Encourage this questioning and try to allow for further investigation.

NOTE: Some plants are able to grow without soil. Algae, duckweeds, pond lilies, and other floating plants are adapted to take their nutrients from water. Mistletoe and other parasitic plants send their roots directly into another growing plant to obtain nutrients. Hydroponics is a method of growing vegetables and other plants without soil; the plants are supported so that the roots grow into a bath or pool of water. Hydroponically-grown plants grow and produce because the water contains a special formula of nutrients that takes the place of soil nutrients.

PREPARATION AND LEAD-UP

Decide where plants will be kept during the activity. The spot should receive some natural light each day but little or no direct sunlight.

For each student, draw on 11-inch by 17-inch paper two rows of four boxes. Students will make drawings in the boxes on the first day of the activity, the last day (one week later), and two days in between.

PROCEDURE

Day One

1. Ask students to think of any time they have planted seeds or have helped to take care of plants. "Have any of you ever grown a garden or taken care of house plants? Have you planted seeds? What do you think seeds need in order to grow into plants? Do plants need soil? Do you think seeds will grow without soil? Let's find out!"

2. Explain that students will plant five seeds in soil and let five seeds sprout on a paper towel. Ask students to predict what they think will happen to both sets of seeds.

3. Introduce the materials for planting and demonstrate the steps students will take. Fill the cup almost to the top with soil. Add five seeds and cover them with one centimeter of soil (a little less than half an inch). Then fold the two paper towels so that they fit onto the plate or lid to be used for sprouting. Place five seeds on the towels.

4. Water both sets of seeds. The soil and the paper toweling should be damp but not soggy (it is not necessary to make drainage holes in the bottom of the cups of dirt since the experiment will be over in a week). Place each set of seeds inside a plastic bag. The plastic bags should cover the seeds or soil but be loose enough to allow air to circulate. The bags will prevent the seeds from drying out between waterings.

5. Divide the class into pairs. Have students spread newspaper over their work areas. Allow time for students to plant and water both sets of seeds. Students should use masking tape to label their cups and plates with the names of both partners.

6. Distribute the paper (with boxes drawn on it) and drawing materials to each student. Explain that they will make drawings of both sets of seeds to keep track of what happens. Let students know that at the end of this activity you want them to use their drawings to answer the question, "Do plants need soil?" Have students make their first drawings in the two left-hand boxes. Collect and store the drawings.

During the Week

7. Twice during the next week allow time for students to water, observe, and draw their plants. Students may notice the seeds on the paper towel sprouting before they notice anything happening in the soil. Ask, "Does this mean the seeds in the soil are not growing yet? What do you think might be happening under the soil?"

A Week Later

8. Give students time to make a final drawing of both sets of plants. By this time the seeds growing in soil should be taller and healthier. Ask, "Why do you think the seeds in the soil grew more? What might be in soil that plants need?" This discussion can lead back to sow bugs and other organisms returning nutrients to the soil. Point out that students were able to watch the earth (soil) supporting life as they watched their seeds sprout and grow. Ask what else seeds need to grow (water will be an obvious answer; introduce the idea that plants also need sunlight and air).

NOTE: The plants probably won't develop radishes. They tend to get "leggy" when grown indoors. Your students may want to continue caring for their seedlings, however, to see what happens.

DISCUSSION QUESTIONS

What was different about how these two groups of plants were grown and cared for?
What kinds of things do plants need?
Has anyone seen someone fertilizing plants (at home, in a garden, or on a farm)?
What does fertilizer do for the plants?
How is the soil we used for our seeds like the earth?
Do the plants in our classroom food chain need soil? What for? (See the introduction to the unit. If you have an aquatic food chain, students will notice that the algae do not need soil. Algae get needed nutrients from water. Decaying plants and animals add nutrients to the water.)
Do the animals in our classroom food chain need soil? Why?
Where else have you seen the earth helping plants to live?
How do we get our nutrients?

EVALUATION

Students write about why plants need the earth to grow.

EXTENSION IDEAS

- Invite a local gardener or house plant enthusiast to visit the class. Students can interview the guest about how he or she grows plants from seed and how basic needs of plants are supplied. The guest may also be able to bring some plants for students to look at (or taste). You may want to brainstorm a list of questions to ask the visitor before he or she arrives.
- People sometimes choose to grow seeds without soil. The class can try to grow bean sprouts in glass jars. Do not add soil. Rinse the sprouts daily with water (they should always be damp). Ask students to predict how the sprouts will look after several days. After three to five days, have students taste the sprouts. (Mung beans or lentils sprout well and are edible. Mung beans are the familiar bean sprouts of Chinese food, although yours probably will be shorter than those found in supermarkets and restaurants. The class can make a Chinese meal using the bean sprouts they have grown.)

RESOURCE

For Students

Back, Christine. *Bean and Plant.* Morristown, N. J.: Silver Burdett and Company, 1984. This book describes in pictures and words the life history of beans from seed to the dinner table and back to the soil again.

DO YOU EAT PLANTS?

SUMMARY OF ACTIVITY

Students are introduced to plant foods that contain many nutrients and provide energy.

Time: 45 minutes

Setting: Classroom

Materials:
- Fresh fruits, vegetables, nuts, and other plant foods
- A live plant or a poster showing major plant parts
- Index cards
- Plates
- "Do You Eat Plants?" copycat page, one per student
- "Your Dinner" copycat page, one per student

Subjects: Science, language arts

Key Words: Root, stem, leaf, bud, flower, fruit, seed, energy, nutrients, food

RELATED CALIFORNIA FRAMEWORK CONCEPTS

Animals depend on plants for food. (*Science Framework Addendum*)

OBJECTIVE

Students list examples of foods they eat that come from plants and realize that plants are an important source of food for people.

BACKGROUND INFORMATION

Since we depend on plants for nutrients, calories, and some of our protein, and since plants depend on the soil to supply nutrients, water, and a place to anchor roots, we also depend on the earth. (Food is only one need supplied to us by the earth; water, fuels, minerals—in fact just about everything we use—can be traced back to one or more sources in the earth.) The earth does support human life, although the path between us and the earth is sometimes indirect.

Many students will be surprised at the variety of foods they eat that are derived from plants. Fruits and vegetables are obvious, but students probably don't know that breads, macaroni, crackers, cookies, breakfast cereals, and pancakes are made with grains. Pizza is made from tomatoes and grains. Taco shells are made from ground corn. French fries are made from potatoes. Meat is ultimately "made" from plants; before people eat cows and chickens, these animals eat plants (in the next activity students will make food chains where the concept that "people eat animals that eat plants" will be introduced).

Here are some foods that represent different plant parts:

Roots Carrots, radishes, turnips

Stems Bean sprouts, bamboo shoots, broccoli stalks

Leaves Lettuce, spinach

Flowers Broccoli (the top of a broccoli "tree" is actually clusters of small unopened flower buds), cauliflower

Fruit Apple, banana, orange, watermelon, dates, tomato (anything with seeds inside is a fruit), grains (kernels of wheat, rice, corn, and other grains look like seeds but are really fruits; each kernel consists almost entirely of one seed)

Seeds Nuts, peas, beans, sesame seeds

PREPARATION AND LEAD-UP

Bring several fruits, vegetables, nuts, and other plant food to school. Cut fruits and vegetables into small pieces so that all students will be able to taste the samples. Save at least one uncut sample of each fruit or vegetable. Set the food on the plates.

Arrange stations around the room where students can see, handle, smell, and taste the food samples (remind students to wash their hands before beginning the activity). Each station should have only one kind of food, with the name of the food written on an index card. There should also be space at each station for students to record observations on their data sheets.

Make copies of the "Do You Eat Plants?" and "Your Dinner" copycat pages. The latter will be used in a home learning assignment.

PROCEDURE

1. Do not show students the food yet. Ask students, "Are you a plant eater? Who ate plants for breakfast? What kinds? Who brought plants for lunch? What kinds?"

2. Use a live plant or a plant poster to demonstrate the major parts of a plant. Give a few examples of foods that come from plants. The point of the activity is for students to realize how much they depend on plants for food, not to have them memorize plant parts, so make the demonstration brief.

3. Hand out the "Do You Eat Plants?" copycat page and go over each column to be sure students understand what is expected of them. In the first column students are to copy the name of the plant. In the second column they are to describe the look and smell of the food, using as many appropriate words as possible. In the third column, students just need to answer yes or no to the question, "Have you ever eaten this food before today?" In the fourth column students should guess what part of the plant they are eating: root, stem, leaves, flowers, fruit, or seeds.

4. Explain how you want students to move from station to station. Remind them that they should eat only one sample of each food, and that they should not handle any other food samples. If students will be allowed to touch and hold the whole foods, let them know that now.

5. When students are done with their copycat pages, discuss each food item and take a vote on what plant part students think each is. Give the correct answers.

6. Introduce students to the notion that we eat some plants not only because they taste good but because plants store lots of things, like vitamins and minerals, that we need to stay healthy and grow. Ask, "What are some other plants we eat? Can you think of foods you eat that are made from plants?" You may need to give a few examples like bread and pizza.

7. After lunch, for the next day or two, ask students questions about what they have been eating. "Who is eating roots? Who is eating seeds? Who is eating something from a tree? Who is eating ground, baked seeds?"

DISCUSSION QUESTIONS

Why do we need to eat plants?
What things do we get from plants that our bodies need?
Besides humans, can you think of other plant eaters?
Who ate cow, pig, or chicken for lunch?
Besides people, can you think of other animal eaters?
Who has eaten sunlight before? (Use this question as an opportunity to help students realize that plants need the sun to live and make their food —and ours!)
Who has eaten soil? Water?
Which animals in the classroom food chain depend on plants? Which ate sunlight? Soil? Water? (See the introduction to the unit.)

EVALUATION

Students cut 10 pictures from magazines to show foods they eat that come from plants. Students can then make collages or a bulletin board with the pictures.

EXTENSION IDEAS

- Have students make vegetable prints to record some of the plants we use as food. Students can also cut vegetables into interesting shapes (for example, cut cabbages or brussel sprouts in half and green peppers in rings).
- Try some of the activities in the folio *Using Wild Edible Plants with Children,* available from the University of California at Berkeley's School of Education. Collecting, preparing, and eating wild plants can reinforce people's connection to the earth as the source of food.

HOME LEARNING SUGGESTION

(Use as lead-up to the next activity)

Send home with students the copycat page "Your Dinner." Ask parents to help students make a list at home of everything they eat for dinner on a particular evening and record whether each food item is plant, animal, or both.

SOURCE OF ACTIVITY

Adapted from Jorgenson, Eric, Trout Black, and Mary Hallesy. *Manure to Meadow to Milkshake.* Los Altos, Calif.: Hidden Villa Inc., 1978.

RESOURCE

Sly, Carolie, and Molly Whiteley. *Using Wild Edible Plants With Children.* Berkeley, Calif.: Instruction Laboratory, University of California, 1979. This folder includes information, activities, and recipes for ten common wild plants. Also included is safety information about wild, poisonous plants.

Copycat Page

Name ______________________

DO YOU EAT PLANTS?

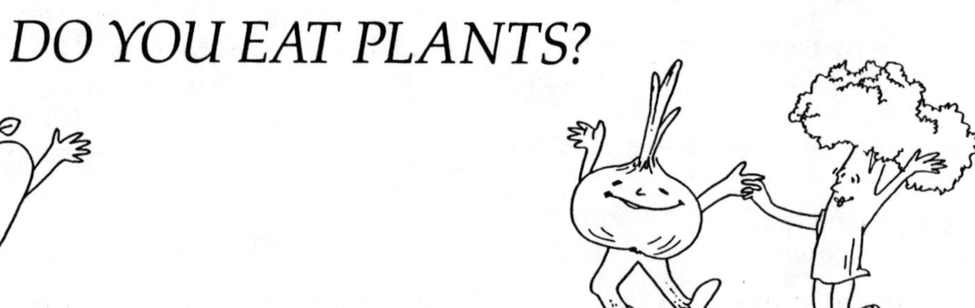

Name of Plant	How It Looks and Smells	Have You Eaten It Before Today?	Plant Part (root, stem, leaves, flowers, fruit, or seeds)

Copycat Page

Child's Name ______________________________

YOUR DINNER

Dear Parent:

Your child has been learning about some of the important plant foods we eat. Plants are important sources of nutrients (vitamins and minerals), energy, and protein. Sometimes it is not obvious that a food is really made from plants. For example, bread is made from grains and pizza is made from tomatoes (the sauce) and grains (the crust).

Other foods, like hamburgers and chicken, come from animals. Some foods are made from both plants and animals. For example, spaghetti (from grains) with tomato sauce (from tomatoes and perhaps other vegetables) and meatballs (from beef) is made from both plants and animals.

Your child should write down everything he or she ate for dinner tonight. You may need to help with spelling. Talk about whether each kind of food is made from plants, animals, or both. Your child should record this information on the chart below. This information will be needed during class tomorrow so please make sure it is returned on time. Thank you for your help and cooperation.

Name of Food	*From Plants*	*From Animals*	*From Both*	*Don't Know*

CREATING A FOOD CHAIN

SUMMARY OF ACTIVITY

Students list and analyze sources of food for people and animals, then illustrate a food chain for themselves and for another animal.

Time: Two 40-minute periods

Setting: Classroom

Materials:
- Paper
- Crayons or magazines, scissors, and glue
- "Food Chains for Me" copycat page, one per student
- "Basic Needs" copycat page, one per student

Subjects: Science, art

Key Words: Plants, animals, food chain, herbivore, carnivore, omnivore

RELATED CALIFORNIA FRAMEWORK CONCEPTS

All animals eat plants and/or other animals. (*Science Framework Addendum*)

Animals depend on plants for food. (*Science Framework Addendum*)

Living things get things they need from each other and from the environment. (*Science Framework Addendum*)

Artistic skills can be used to express and communicate responses to experiences. (Adapted from *Visual and Performing Arts Framework*)

OBJECTIVE

Students identify foods they eat from animals and plants, and graphically depict food chains for themselves and another animal.

BACKGROUND INFORMATION

Plants are the ultimate source of food for all animals, including people. Most people are omnivores, meaning they eat both plant and animal products. It is easy for students to see that they are eating plants when they eat a salad or an orange, but their dependence on plants may not seem so obvious when they are eating a piece of chicken.

A food chain is a simplified way of showing food relationships between plants and animals. Grass → cow → person is a food chain (when drawing a food chain, the arrows point in the direction the food energy is moving). A food chain can also include nonliving elements like sun, soil, air, and water. A food chain can be drawn to show that these four elements are used by a plant.

A food web illustrates the interrelationships between several food chains. Food webs more closely approximate the complexities of natural and human food chains. In this activity students are introduced only to food chains in the hope that a solid understanding of food chains will allow them later to grasp the more difficult concept of food webs.

If your class set up a classroom food chain (see the introduction to the unit), students can use that food chain in the second part of this activity. If your class did not set up a food chain, you will need to use a book or film to introduce students to an animal food chain (see the resources section for suggested titles). Do not feel that you need to know a complete food chain for any animal a student might suggest. What is important is that students understand that all food for us and other animals comes from plants and that these plants (and consequently we) depend on soil, water, air, and the sun.

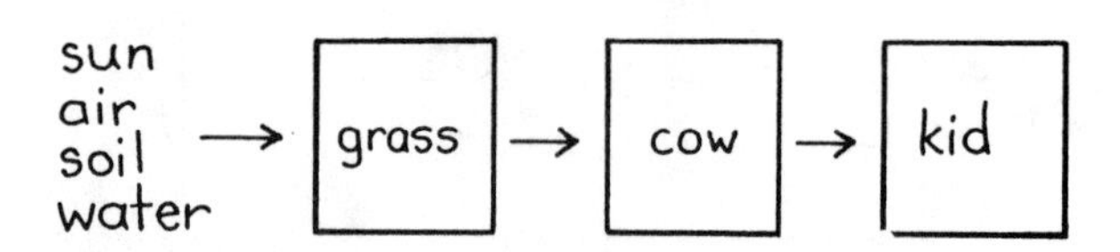

PREPARATION AND LEAD-UP

Gather books you will be reading to your students as part of this activity (four titles are suggested in the resources section). Any book that tells what an animal eats will be useful. If possible, find a book about a carnivorous animal—it will make for a more interesting food chain. Also, reproduce the copycat pages one per student.

PROCEDURE

Day One

1. Using the home learning suggestion from the previous activity, have students name foods they ate for dinner the night before. List these on the board and discuss the origins of these foods (save the list for step three). Ask, "Which of these foods come from plants? What plants are they from? Which come from animals? What animals are these foods from? What do these animals eat?"

2. This is a good time to show a film or read a book that illustrates human food chains. Students can discuss the information presented.

3. Choose one of the foods from the list made in the first step. Talk about a food chain while you diagram one on the board. For example, if you are making a food chain diagram for a person who ate a chicken that ate seeds, write on the board "Seeds are food for chickens." Then tell students that a shorter way to write this is "seeds → chickens." Introduce the term "food chain," which is a way of showing who eats what. Ask students what plant seeds need to grow. If students do not mention the four basics (soil, water, sunlight, and air) suggest those that they omit. Add these four plant needs to your diagram, as the following diagram shows.

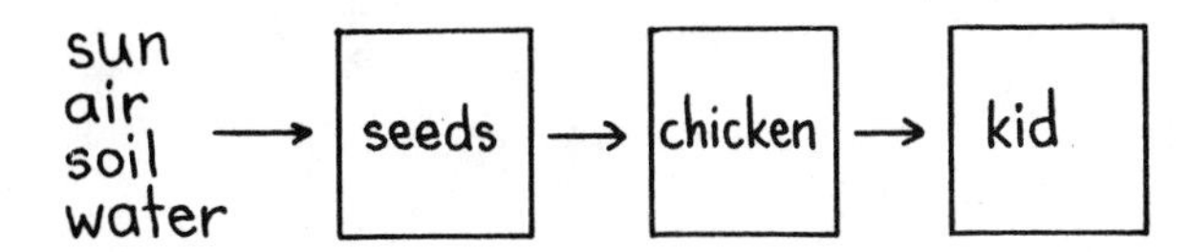

4. Use the arrow notation to diagram other food chains, repeating the words for the symbols to provide additional reinforcement. Point out that the arrows go in the direction that the food is going. In the example above, the chicken is eating the seeds.

5. Hand out the "Food Chains For Me" copycat page. Explain to students that they will be making two of their own food chains. Each food chain should start with the earth and the sun, on the left-hand side of the copycat page. Remind students that water, soil, and air are part of the earth and that plants need all of these things to grow, so these will be at the beginning of each food chain. Caution students to choose simple foods; lasagna, for instance, is hard to diagram because it is made from many ingredients.

6. When students have made their food chains, ask several volunteers to describe one of their food chains. Remind students that every food chain should begin with a plant. Have students look at the four words on the left of their copycat page (sun, water, soil, air) and discuss the needs of plants for these things. Ask whether we need these things, too.

Day Two

7. Review some of the food chains students made yesterday. Discuss the use of arrows to symbolize food moving through the food chain. Tell students that today they will illustrate another animal food chain.

8. If the class has a classroom food chain (see the introduction to the unit), ask students how to diagram it. Ask them about soil, water, sunlight, and air. Have students draw the food chain using pictures to represent everything, and including arrows and labels. If the class does not have a food chain, use a film or books to introduce students to a specific wild animal. In discussing the film or book afterwards, emphasize the animal's food sources. Diagram a food chain for this animal using arrows. If enough information was presented, you may be able to draw two or more food chains. Have students draw a picture of each part of the food chain, including arrows and labels.

9. Ask students to think of other animals that eat meat, other animals that eat plants, and other animals that eat both. Use or introduce the words herbivore, carnivore, and omnivore. Don't worry if you do not know what some animals eat (you may want to have students use an encyclopedia or other reference book to try to find out). Discuss our dependence on other animals, plants, soil, water, air, and sunlight. Ask, "Why do we need plants? How does the earth help us live?"

DIRT MADE MY LUNCH
by Steve Van Zandt

Chorus:
Dirt made my lunch, dirt made my lunch.
Thank you dirt, thanks a bunch
For my salad, my sandwich, my milk, my munch.
Dirt made my lunch.
Dirt is a word we often use
When we talk about the earth beneath our shoes.
It's a place where plants can sink their toes
And in a little while a garden grows.

A farmer's plow will tickle the ground.
You know the earth has laughed when wheat is found.
The grain is taken and flour is ground
For makin' a sandwich to munch down.

Chorus

A stubby green beard grows upon the land.
Out of the soil the grass will stand
But under hoof it must bow
For makin' milk by way of cow.

Chorus

DISCUSSION QUESTIONS

What do plants need?
Do we need these things, too? For what?
A wolf eats caribou and deer. How is a wolf dependent on plants? On soil? On the sun?
Are there any animals that do not depend on plants? On sunlight?
Are there any people who do not need plants? Sunlight?
Which, if any, of the basics (sun, water, air, soil) are kept from plants?
How would this affect our food? Other animals?
If all plants disappeared, could we survive by eating animals?
What else besides food do we get from plants? (Wood, paper, shade, etc.)

EVALUATION

Students write a "Recipe for a Food Chain," explaining what "ingredients" are required and putting ingredients into a proper sequence.

EXTENSION IDEAS

- Teach "Dirt Made My Lunch" to students. Ask, "How does dirt make your lunch?"
- Have students visit a pizza parlor; many pizza parlors will give free tours. Students can watch as vegetarian and pepperoni pizzas are made from scratch.
- Plan a trip to a bakery or some other place where food is made. Arrange to see the raw materials and find out where each came from. You can point out that many substances are added to keep foods from spoiling because they travel long distances. These substances are called additives. After the trip, students can bring in labels from prepared foods they have at home and look for listings of additives.
- If possible, visit a farm to observe what animals eat. You may be able to arrange in advance for students to help feed the animals.
- Bake bread or muffins so that students can see all of the ingredients that go into such foods. Discuss the origins of each of the ingredients.

HOME LEARNING SUGGESTION

(Use as lead-up to the next activity)

Send each student home with a "Basic Needs" copycat page. Students, with help from parents, should list basic needs of people, other animals, and plants. The following day in class students will use these lists to discuss basic needs.

RESOURCES

For Students

Freedman, Russell. *Rattlesnakes.* New York: Holiday House Inc., 1984. What rattlesnakes eat, how they hunt, and how they shed their skin are explained in words and illustrated with striking black and white photographs.

Lauber, Patricia. *Sea Otters and Seaweed.* Champaign, Ill.: Garrard Publishing Company, 1976. This book has a chapter on feeding and another on kelp forest ecology, as well as many photos of otters feeding.

Morris, Robert A. *Dolphin.* New York: Harper and Row, 1975. This "I-Can-Read-Book" tells of the birth and life of a dolphin, including what it eats and how it interacts with others in its pod.

Schnieper, Claudia. *On the Trail of the Fox.* Minneapolis, Minn.: Carolrhoda Books Inc., 1985. In addition to many photos, this book has information on the hunting and feeding behavior of foxes and describes other aspects of fox life.

Van Zandt, Steve. *Banana Slug String.* Original *Banana Slug String Band* recordings are available from Steve Van Zandt, P.O. Box 717, Pescadero, Calif. 94060. These fun lively songs are about caring for and enjoying the earth.

SOURCE OF ACTIVITY

Adapted from *Project Wild,* "What's for Dinner?" Boulder, Colo.: Western Regional Environmental Education Council, 1985.

Name ____________________

FOOD CHAINS FOR ME

sun

air

soil

water

Child's Name ______________________________

BASIC NEEDS

Dear Parent:

Please help your child list basic needs that people, other animals, and plants have. Encourage your child to think of as many things as he or she can that are absolutely necessary for survival. You may need to help with spelling.

List everything that you can think of that people, other animals, and plants need in order to survive.

People	*Other Animals*	*Plants*

THE BEAUTIFUL BASICS

SUMMARY OF ACTIVITY

The class generates a list of the basic necessities for people, other animals, and plants, then students make a collage of the basic necessities.

Time: 40 minutes

Setting: Classroom

Materials:
- Old magazines
- Scissors
- Glue
- Paper
- Crayons

Subjects: Science, language arts, health, art

Key Words: Basic needs, food, water, sun, soil, air, shelter, space

RELATED CALIFORNIA FRAMEWORK CONCEPTS

Living things get things they need from each other and from the environment. (*Science Framework Addendum*)

All plants need water. (*Science Framework Addendum*)

Soils provide the water and minerals that plants need. (*Science Framework Addendum*)

All animals need food, water, air, and a place to live. (*Science Framework Addendum*)

Water is essential to all life. (*Science Framework Addendum*)

Artistic skills can be used to express and communicate responses to experiences. (Adapted from *Visual and Performing Arts Framework*)

OBJECTIVE

Students identify basic needs shared by people, other animals, and plants, and explain how these basic needs are met.

BACKGROUND INFORMATION

Basic needs are those things a plant or animal needs to keep itself alive. Humans have the same basic needs as other animals, although when we think of our own basic needs, most of us would include things that are not absolutely essential to maintaining life, such as a refrigerator or a car.

In this activity basic needs include food, water, shelter, space, sunlight, soil, and air. All of these basic needs except sunlight are provided by the earth.

Students have considered their own food needs as they looked at plants and animals they eat. Students have also discussed the food needs of other animals and of plants.

Students made sure their sow bugs and plant seedlings had sufficient water. Students are also aware of their own need to drink water daily, as well as to use water for bathing, cleaning, and cooking.

Shelter provides refuge from the elements or from predators. For people, shelter may be a house, apartment, trailer, or other type of dwelling. Animals don't need to have a place that looks like a house. Their shelter may be underground, in a bush, under a rock, or in a cave.

Space is the territory needed to secure food for yourself and your offspring. Space needs vary tremendously from species to species. Some animals travel great distances in order to find food or a mate. Many other animals are able to live their whole lives in a relatively small area.

Students had to keep their seedlings in sunlight as the seedlings grew. Students probably do not know that plants need the sun's rays for photosynthesis, but they can understand that plants use sunlight as they make their own food. We depend on the sun indirectly because it helps our plant foods grow. We also need a little sun to shine on us in order for our bodies to manufacture enough vitamin D.

The seedlings grown by students grew better in soil than on the paper towel. Soil provides plants with nutrients and water. People and other animals therefore depend on soil to provide food.

People, other animals, and plants need air. Most plants use carbon dioxide and oxygen from air and give off oxygen as a by-product. People and other animals use this oxygen and give off carbon dioxide.

PREPARATION AND LEAD-UP

Gather old magazines for students to use in making their collages.

PROCEDURE

1. Tell students that they have been learning a lot about food and now they will concentrate on other important things living things need to survive. Review previous activities in this unit that touched upon basic necessities. Ask, "What did we need to do for the seedlings to make sure they survived?" (We planted them in soil, watered them, and made sure they got some sunlight.) "What did the sow bugs need to survive? What do the plants and animals in our classroom food chain need to survive?"

2. Ask students to take out their home learning assignment from the previous activity. On the board make three columns and label them "People," "Other Animals," and "Plants." Ask students to contribute ideas from their lists and record them in the appropriate column.

3. Have students look at each list and group related ideas together. For example, warmth and physical comfort could fit under the concept shelter. Narrow down lists to essentials for survival. All lists could include and be limited to food, water, shelter, space, sunlight, soil, and air.

4. Discuss the lists. If students do not come up with essentially identical lists for each group of organisms, you will want to question them further. For example, if they do not include soil as one of the basic needs for animals, use an animal they are familiar with to point out that it depends on soil for food.

5. Give students materials and instruct them to make a collage of their own basic needs. Students should refer to the list on the board and include in their collage pictures illustrating these things.

DISCUSSION QUESTIONS

How does the earth provide each of the basic needs?
In what way are plants' basic needs different from those of animals?
In what ways are the needs of plants and animals the same?
Do pets have the same basic needs as other animals?
How are each of these needs met?
What are some animals that need a lot of space to live in?
What do they need the space for?
What are some animals that need only a little space?
Why are they able to survive with so little space to live in?

EVALUATION

Each student lists four of the basic needs and tells how he or she meets those needs.

EXTENSION IDEA

Have students choose an animal and write a story about how that animal meets its basic needs. Students should refer to the class list of basic needs.

HOME LEARNING SUGGESTION

(Use as follow-up to this activity)

Have each student make a list of how a pet meets its basic needs. Students who do not have a pet can make the list for a friend's or neighbor's pet.

SOURCE OF ACTIVITY

Adapted from *Project Wild*, "The Beautiful Basics." Boulder, Colo.: Western Regional Environmental Council, 1985.

BASIC NECESSITIES MICROTREK

SUMMARY OF ACTIVITY

Students search the schoolyard for evidence that food and shelter are available for plants and animals, then contribute to a class mural illustrating their findings.

Time: 45 minutes

Setting: Classroom, outdoors

Materials:
- Butcher paper
- Crayons or markers
- One cardboard clipboard with a sheet of paper stapled to it for each pair of students
- Pencil for each pair of students

Subjects: Science, math, art

Key Words: Basic needs, food, shelter

RELATED CALIFORNIA FRAMEWORK CONCEPTS

Living things get things they need from each other and from the environment. (*Science Framework Addendum*)

Artistic skills can be used to express and communicate responses to experiences. (Adapted from *Visual and Performing Arts Framework*)

OBJECTIVE

Students identify sources of food and shelter in the schoolyard available to plants and animals.

BACKGROUND INFORMATION

A chewed leaf, ants in a garbage can, dead insects in a spider web, and birds eating crumbs left after lunch are evidence of food, as is soil and sunlight, which is food for plants. Nests, gopher holes, ant hills, and holes in trees are evidence of animal shelters.

As students discuss their findings, emphasize that the earth is providing these basic needs. In some cases it may be difficult for students to understand the connection to the earth. Encourage students in what they do understand and expand as appropriate from there. Keep in mind that this unit introduces some fundamental, complex concepts of ecology and is meant to serve as a foundation for future learning.

PREPARATION AND LEAD-UP

Decide where you want students to conduct the outdoor portion of this activity. If you can, arrange for the class to walk to a nearby park, creek, field, or orchard. Otherwise, decide which areas of the schoolyard students may use. Try to have another adult available to assist students while they are outside.

Staple a piece of paper onto each cardboard clipboard. These clipboards can be saved for other activities that involve writing or drawing outside.

PROCEDURE

1. Tell students that today they will investigate the schoolyard (or another place you have chosen) to look for evidence that plants and animals are meeting their basic needs. Let students know they will be concentrating on two of the basic needs—food and shelter. Ask, "What kinds of plants and animals live around the schoolyard? What kind of food might they find here? What kind of shelter might they find or make here?"

2. Divide the class into two groups, one group to look for food and one to look for shelter. Within each group divide students into pairs. Distribute the clipboards and pencils. One member of each pair will be the looker and the other will be the recorder. Students can record what they find with words, drawings, or both. Let them know that afterwards all students will add what they find to a large mural.

3. Review appropriate behavior for working outside. If you are going to be near the school building, remind students that other students are working quietly in class so students outdoors should not make a lot of noise. Also remind students not to harm any plants or animals they see. Show students the area you want them to work in and give the class a limited amount of time to conduct the investigation (10 minutes is good). Tell students they will need to work quickly and efficiently to find as much information as they can.

DISCUSSION QUESTIONS

What kinds of food did you find that animals could eat?
How does the earth provide this food?
What else might animals eat?
What sorts of shelter did you find animals using?
How does the earth provide this shelter?
What else could animals use for shelter?
Did anyone find anything unusual or surprising?

EVALUATION

Students name three food sources and three sources of shelter in the schoolyard (or wherever the activity was conducted) that are available for animals.

EXTENSION IDEA

Divide students into small groups and have each group find ants and observe their behavior. Ants can be found on sidewalks, near the cafeteria, around windows, on trees, and in flower beds. Included in students' observations should be evidence of how ants take care of their needs for food, shelter, and space. Have each group share its findings.

HOME LEARNING SUGGESTION

(Use as follow-up to this activity)

Have students look for sources of food and shelter for animals in their yards and neighborhoods. Students can write reports or the class can discuss the findings.

EARTH PLAYS

SUMMARY OF ACTIVITY

Students act out scenes to dramatize interactions between the earth and plants or animals.

Time: 30 minutes

Setting: Classroom

Materials:
- Magazine pictures or charade ideas written on strips of paper (see preparation and lead-up)

Subjects: Science, social studies, drama

RELATED CALIFORNIA FRAMEWORK CONCEPTS

Living things get things they need from each other and from the environment. (*Science Framework Addendum*)

Movement can be used as an external expression of an internal idea or feeling. (Adapted from *Visual and Performing Arts Framework*)

OBJECTIVE

Using pantomimes, students demonstrate the importance of the earth for all living things.

PREPARATION AND LEAD-UP

Collect magazine pictures that show people, other animals, and plants depending on the earth in some way. Alternatively, prepare written charade scenes (step two gives several suggestions).

PROCEDURE

1. Review ways that the earth supports life. Ask, "How does the earth help plants? People? Other animals?" If students think only of soil as the earth, ask them what other things are part of the earth and how these things help people, other animals, and plants. Tell students that today they will act out scenes that show how the earth supports life.

2. Explain how to play charades (each group gets a picture or a written idea to act out, rehearses it for a few minutes, then acts it out for others to try to guess what is happening). Divide the class into groups of three to four students. Give each group a scene to act out and allow a few minutes for rehearsal. Scenes you might use include:

Deer grazing in a field.
Bees and butterflies getting nectar from flowers.
Rabbits eating fresh spring leaves.
A coyote catching a rabbit.
Seeds falling on a sidewalk (where they don't grow) and on soil (where they do grow).
A farm family planting crops.
Watering a garden.
A family eating dinner.
Children playing and having fun in the mud.
Washing dishes.
Someone planting trees.
A group of workers digging a well for water.
People cutting trees to use for firewood.
People building a wooden house.
People making bricks from mud to build a house.

You may want to allow students to make up their own scenes of how the earth supports life, and to act these out for the class.

3. Invite each group to perform its scene for the class and have other students guess what is happening. As a matter of courtesy, ask students to allow performers to finish before anyone makes any guesses. After each scene is acted out, discuss how each person, other animal, or plant is depending on the earth (see the discussion questions).

DISCUSSION QUESTIONS

For each scene ask:

Who or what is depending on the earth?
What is each plant, animal, or person getting from the earth?
Can you think of any plant that doesn't need the earth to live? Any animal? Any person?
Does an astronaut in space depend on the earth? For what?

EVALUATION

Ask students to pretend they are a plant or animal, and have them write about how they need the earth. You may want students to use a starter sentence such as "I am a ____________ and I need the earth because . . ."

EXTENSION IDEA

Read Byrd Baylor's *The Other Way to Listen* to the class. Ask students what they have "heard" the earth say to them.

HOME LEARNING SUGGESTION

(Use as lead-up to the following activity)

Have students make a list of at least four ways they depend upon the earth. Students should bring the list to school to be used with the next activity.

RESOURCE

For Students

Baylor, Byrd. *The Other Way to Listen*. New York: Charles Scribner's Sons, 1978. This is the story of one boy's magical connection to sounds of the earth.

EARTH BOOKS

SUMMARY OF ACTIVITY

Each student makes a book titled "The Earth Supports Life" that shows ways he or she and other living things depend upon the earth.

Time: Two 30-minute periods

Setting: Classroom

Materials:
- Crayons or other drawing materials
- Stapler
- Four pieces of butcher paper
- Two 8½-inch by 11-inch pieces of construction paper or one 11-inch by 17-inch piece of construction paper for each student
- Four pieces of 8½-inch by 11-inch drawing paper for each student

Subject: Science, language arts, art

Key Words: Support, depend

RELATED CALIFORNIA FRAMEWORK CONCEPTS

Living things get what they need from each other and from the environment. (*Science Framework Addendum*)

Writing enables us to communicate our ideas. (Adapted from *English-Language Arts Framework*)

Artistic skills can be used to express and communicate responses to experiences. (Adapted from *Visual and Performing Arts Framework*)

OBJECTIVE

Students show in pictures and words how the earth supports people, other animals, and plants.

BACKGROUND INFORMATION

Throughout this unit students have been learning about ways that the earth supports life. In this activity students are given the opportunity to synthesize what they have learned by drawing and writing about how people, other animals, and plants depend upon the earth to live.

PREPARATION AND LEAD-UP

Label each piece of butcher paper with one of these titles: "The Earth Supports People," "The Earth Supports Other Animals," "The Earth Supports Plants," and "The Earth Supports Life."

PROCEDURE

1. Ask volunteers to share ideas from their home learning assignment on ways that they depend upon the earth. List the ideas on the butcher paper titled "The Earth Supports People." (If students do not do so, point out ways we enjoy the earth without using it up such as playing baseball on the grass, listening to birds in the morning, smelling flowers, or swimming in a lake.)

2. Continue with the next two lists, recording student ideas for each. Post the last piece of butcher paper ("The Earth Supports Life") but leave it blank.

3. Tell students that they will each make a book titled "The Earth Supports Life." Distribute the construction paper for the book covers. If students will be using one large sheet, they should fold it in half now. Distribute the drawing paper. Have students put the paper inside the construction paper and staple their books together. Distribute drawing materials and have students write the title and their name on the front cover.

4. Ask students to begin writing and drawing in their books using the four headings on the butcher paper for their four pages. Tell students they may use ideas listed on the butcher paper or think of other ideas. On each page they should draw a picture and write a sentence or two. On the last page ("The Earth Supports Life") they can illustrate the heading any way they like, perhaps including people, plants, and other animals in the drawing. Students will probably need two sessions to finish their books.

DISCUSSION QUESTIONS

What living things need the earth to live?

Can you think of any living things that do not need the earth to live?

EARTH BOOKS *(Continued)*

Can you think of anything you do that doesn't depend on the earth?
What are some ways you enjoy or use the earth without using it up?

EVALUATION

Students' finished books can be used to evaluate their understanding of how living things depend on the earth.

EXTENSION IDEA

Arrange to display students' books in the library or another location at school. Students can discuss the reactions of other students to their books.

Caring For The Environment

Kindergarten Through Third Grades

Introduction to the Unit

People who care deeply for others and for the world around them are motivated to act in ways that benefit people and the environment. In order for children to appreciate and care for the environment, they must begin to realize that they care for people, other living things, and places. This caring for people and things can be cultivated and encouraged.

The first two activities in this unit introduce the notion of caring. Students discuss and draw pictures of things they care about and then through poster art encourage each other to take care of their classroom and school. In the next three activities the focus moves to the schoolyard as students investigate what animals live there, begin a project to improve the schoolyard for wildlife, and create wildlife emblems to convey their caring for animals. In the sixth activity students use magazine photos to again consider the effects of actions, only this time students are asked to think of alternative actions that would be less harmful to the environment. The final three activities give students the opportunity to make environmentally sound choices to show that they care for the world around them.

Advance Planning

For the activity "Picture the Effects" you will need to collect magazine photographs showing ways that people can harm the environment. For the activity "Recycled Art" you will need to collect an assortment of reusable, clean, and safe materials that students can use for an art project.

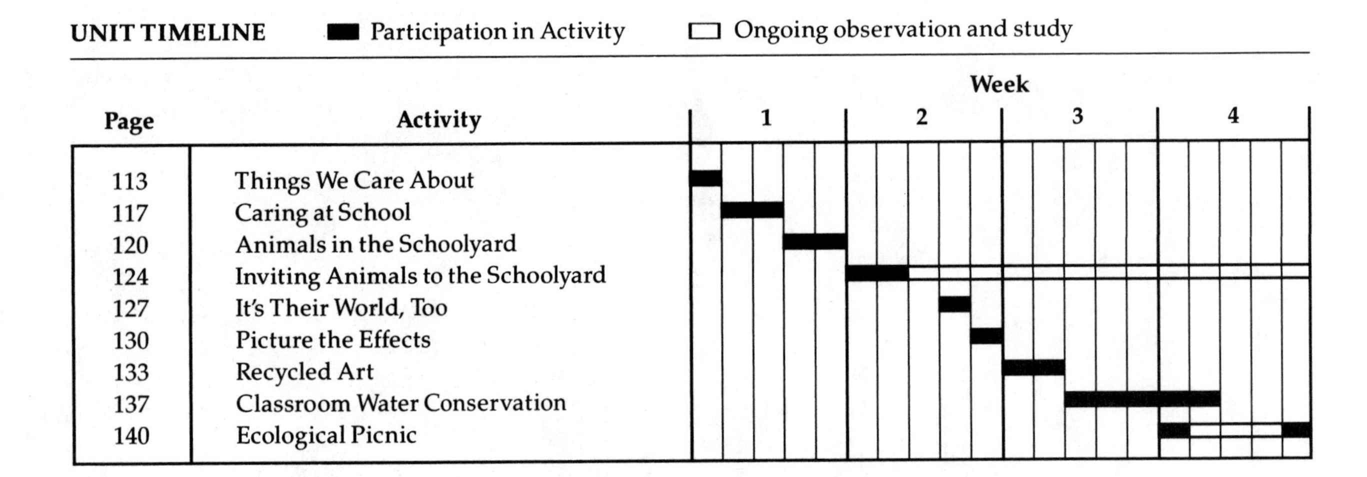

THINGS WE CARE ABOUT

SUMMARY OF ACTIVITY

Students draw a picture of someone or something they care about, then learn an ecological version of "It's a Small World."

Time: 30 to 45 minutes

Setting: Classroom

Materials:
- Paper
- Drawing materials
- Butcher paper

Subjects: Language arts, art, music, social studies

Key Words: Care, special, feelings, different

RELATED CALIFORNIA FRAMEWORK CONCEPTS

Art, music, and dance can influence and enrich group life. (Adapted from *History-Social Science Framework*)

OBJECTIVE

Students point out that everyone cares about certain people, places, and things.

BACKGROUND INFORMATION

This unit begins by asking students to think about things they care about deeply. Through discussion students discover (or you may want to point out) that each of us is different and that we have different opinions, lifestyles, and experiences. Let students know that there are no right or wrong answers; each student's answer is just as valid as any other. What is important is that students discover that all of them care.

PREPARATION AND LEAD-UP

You may wish to make a chart of the key words for this activity. Keep the chart posted and add new words as students hear them.

Write the song "It's a Small World" (see step four) on a separate piece of butcher paper.

PROCEDURE

1. Tell students that today they will talk about caring. Ask them to think for a minute about someone or something they care about. Have them first share their feelings with a partner, then ask for volunteers to tell the class about their special person or thing. You may wish to make a chart or a list ot "Things we care about" (you can save the chart and add to it during step one of the next activity, "Caring at School").

2. Discuss the different things that class members and others care about. Encourage students to be aware of the variety of things people care about and to notice that different people care about different things.

3. Hand out drawing supplies and have students draw a picture of the person or thing they care about. Ask students to include themselves in the picture (for older students, write a sentence starter such as "I care about . . . " on the blackboard). Save students' pictures so that you can compare them with pictures they draw later (see the evaluation section of "Ecological Picnic").

4. Let students know that over the next few weeks they will learn about caring for the earth and its life (people, animals, and plants). Teach students this version of "It's a Small World." Have the class sing it frequently and as students become more familiar with the words discuss the meaning of each verse.

Learn the song "It's A Small World," by Sherman and Sherman, Walt Disney, Inc. Then sing the additional verses by Hallesy and 1976 LeConte Lodge Summer Staff.

IT'S A SMALL WORLD

Chorus:
There is just so much water and so much air
And just so much land and food everywhere
There's so much we must share, oh it's time we're aware
It's a small world after all.

Chorus

So many people using up so much so fast
We cannot go on as we've done in the past
It is time to confess we have got to USE LESS
It's a small world after all.

Chorus

On this spaceship earth we are all a crew
And we've got to learn what we must do
It is time we're aware we use more than our share
It's a small world after all.

Chorus

DISCUSSION QUESTIONS

What kinds of things do we care about?
Why are there some things all of us care about?
Why are there some things some of us care about but not all of us?
How do you know if you care about someone? What does it feel like?
How do you know if someone cares about you? What does it feel like?
How do you know if someone else cares about something or someone?
Do you have a special place that you care about?
How do we treat things we care about?

EVALUATION

Students name or write about three to five things children and other people care about.

EXTENSION IDEAS

- Read *The Wheel on the School,* by Meindert DeJong, to the class. Have students look for ways the children in this story show they care.
- Read Rebecca Caudill's *A Pocketful of Cricket* to the class. Have students list things the boy cares about.
- Read *Miss Rumphius,* by Barbara Cooney, to the class. Ask students, "What does Miss Rumphius do to show she cares about people and the world? What could you do to show you care?"
- Have students interview one or more people (parents, siblings, students from other classes) and ask what person, place, or thing they care about.

HOME LEARNING SUGGESTION

(Use as follow-up to this activity)

On the copycat page that follows this activity students can record three things they care about and how they show they care. Send the following letter of explanation to parents.

RESOURCES

For Students

Caudill, Rebecca. *A Pocketful of Cricket.* New York: Holt, Rinehart and Winston, 1964. This story tells about sharing something special with others. A young farm boy finds a cricket, cares for it, and shares it with his classmates on the first day of school.

Cooney, Barbara. *Miss Rumphius.* New York: The Viking Press, 1982. This is a story of generations, travel, and the wish to do something to make the world more beautiful. Miss Rumphius plants lupines; her granddaughter isn't sure yet what she will do.

DeJong, Meindert. *The Wheel on the School.* New York: Harper and Row, 1954. In this novel children in a small school make their school building an inviting place for storks to nest. As the children learn the history of storks in their village, they find help and encouragement from some of their oldest neighbors and work together to bring back the storks.

Sample Letter

Dear Parent:

We are beginning a unit about caring for the environment and as an introduction I am asking students to think of people, pets, places, or other things they care about. Please talk with your child about the things he or she cares about and ask how your child shows he or she cares for each thing. Your child should complete the enclosed page and return it to class tomorrow. Ask your child to dictate endings for the sentences while you write down his or her words.

Thank you for your help.

Note: For older students you will want to modify the letter to indicate that the student should do the writing.

Name ______________________________

THINGS WE CARE ABOUT

What I Care About	*How I Show I Care*
I care about ____________________ .	I show I care by ________________ .
I care about ____________________ .	I show I care by ________________ .
I care about ____________________ .	I show I care by ________________ .

CARING AT SCHOOL

SUMMARY OF ACTIVITY

Students make and display posters with messages about caring for each other and their school, then observe any changes in their own and other students' behavior. Students also make caring awards to give to classmates and others.

Time: Three 30- to 45-minute periods

Setting: Classroom, school building, school grounds

Materials:
- Butcher paper
- Poster board, oak tag, or some other heavy paper, one piece per student
- Drawing materials
- Construction paper
- Scissors
- Glue
- Glitter, stencils, ribbon (optional)
- Posters with a conservation message (optional)
- Old magazines (optional)
- Black felt markers (optional)

Subjects: Social studies, language arts, art

Key Words: Environment, message, care, share, behavior

RELATED CALIFORNIA FRAMEWORK CONCEPTS

People can cooperate to preserve the beauty of our environment and improve the quality of life in it. (Adapted from *History-Social Science Framework*)

Art, music, and dance can influence and enrich group life. (Adapted from *History-Social Science Framework*)

OBJECTIVE

Students choose actions that improve their school environment for themselves and others.

BACKGROUND INFORMATION

The previous activity focused on students' personal feelings of caring. This activity expands the focus to the immediate environment of the student—the classroom, school buildings, and the schoolyard.

PREPARATION AND LEAD-UP

Inform the principal and other teachers that your students will be making posters to display around school. Obtain permission, if necessary, to hang the posters.

Cut out of construction paper the shapes students will need to make their own awards. Cut a center circle from white or light-colored paper to provide a good background for the students' writing and drawing. You may want to have extra materials on hand because many students will want to make more than one award.

Some local energy and water utilities distribute free conservation posters. If available, these posters offer good examples to students of ways to use art to convey an environmental message (see step four).

PROCEDURE

Day One

1. Ask for volunteers to share with the class one of the things they care about and how they show they care (if you began a "Things we care about" chart during the previous activity, you can add to it now). Encourage students to accept a variety of answers from their classmates and remember to thank all those students who offered to speak to the class.

2. Tell students that today they will think about ways to show they care for each other, their classroom, and their school. Introduce the word "environment" and ask students what they think it means. On butcher paper make a list titled "What Is the Environment?" Refer and add to the list throughout the unit (you will need to use the list again in the activity "Picture the Effects"). At some point students probably will develop the idea that the environment includes *everything* around them —people, plants, animals, water, air, streets, soil, cars, buildings, and climate.

3. Tell students that they will make posters showing ways they care for their school environment. Have the class develop a list of ways they care. Students will easily come up with "Don't litter." Help further their thinking by asking questions like, "How can we share with other people here? How can we share with plants and animals here? How can we care for the buildings, desks, and materials?" Encourage students to come up with many ideas and list ideas on a chart. Ideas don't need to be practical at this point so encourage creative thinking by accepting all ideas. In the next step ideas will be evaluated.

Day Two

4. Look over the list of ideas with students or read it to them and choose several ideas (three to five, depending on the age of the class) that seem practical, appropriate, and relatively easy to do. For each idea chosen have students suggest a message in the form of a saying, phrase, slogan, or short sentence. Write these on the board. (For second- and third-grade students you may want to discuss some of the things that go into making a good poster—a simple, catchy phrase, a rhyming phrase, large lettering and drawing, or the use of bright colors. If you have posters in the room, discuss what techniques were used by the artists.)

5. Give students the materials for making posters. Ask students to choose one of the messages on the board and make a poster illustrating it.

6. Hang the posters in the classroom or in places around school where students are likely to see them, like in the library, in the cafeteria, over drinking fountains, near the office, or in hallways.

Day Three

7. Discuss the effects of the posters. Ask students if they are following their own suggestions. Ask if they are noticing any changes in the behavior of other students in the class (see the discussion questions).

8. Tell students that they will make a caring award for someone they know who cares for the environment. Ask students for their ideas on what to draw or write, then demonstrate how students can put together the construction paper pieces to make their caring awards. Distribute the construction paper pieces and other materials. Let students glue, color, and decorate their award. (You may want to keep materials for the awards on a table for several days so that students can make additional awards if they want to.)

DISCUSSION QUESTIONS

What does the school environment include?
What does your home environment include?
What does a park, beach, or shopping mall environment include?
Did you follow your own suggestions? Why or why not?
Do you think most of the students in the class behaved differently after the posters were made? Why or why not?
Were any of the suggestions easy to follow? What made them easy to do?

Were any of the suggestions hard to follow?
What made them hard?
How did it feel to do something caring?
How did it feel to see someone else caring?
What is it like to try to change your behavior?
Why do you think it is hard for people to change their habits?

EVALUATION

Students write a story or draw a picture about themselves doing things that show they care for the environment.

EXTENSION IDEAS

- If you know or can contact another teacher in another part of the state, the nation, or the world, your classes can exchange environmental boxes. The box can include a class photo, drawings, a mural, photos of the nearby environment, stories, poems, and natural objects from the schoolyard and local community (these could be gathered on a class walk or field trip).

  Materials for the box can be collected during the unit. Choose student work that is the most original, poignant, or exemplary of the local environment. Keep in mind your audience; include things that will help students elsewhere learn about your local environment so that they can compare it to their own environment.

  When your class receives an environmental exchange box from another class, make a bulletin board or other display of the materials sent. Discuss the similarities and differences between your school and neighborhood environments and those of the other class. Send the other class thank you letters.
- Have students role play picking up litter, shaking hands with two neighbors, watering plants, walking to the store instead of driving in the car, and throwing away trash in the garbage can. Students can also act out messages from their posters.
- Have students work alone or in small groups to make a collage showing what is in their school, home, or community environment. If it is appropriate, you can have students divide their paper in half and include living things in their environment on one side and physical factors like houses, cars, streets, water, and sunlight on the other side.

HOME LEARNING SUGGESTION

(Use as follow-up to this activity)

Have students draw a picture of their home environment, including as many things as possible. If they are able, students can label everything in their pictures.

ANIMALS IN THE SCHOOLYARD

Nature, in her blind search for life, has filled every possible cranny of the earth with some sort of fantastic creature.

—DAVID CAVAGNARO

SUMMARY OF ACTIVITY

Students survey the schoolyard to observe and record wildlife and evidence of wildlife, then make a mural of wildlife in their schoolyard.

Time: One 45-minute period and one 30-minute period

Setting: Schoolyard, classroom

Materials:
- Three large pieces of butcher paper
- Three jump ropes
- Drawing materials
- Cardboard "clipboards," about 9 inches by 12 inches, one per student (optional)
- Paper (optional)
- Pencils (optional)

Subjects: Science, art

Key Words: Wildlife, domesticated animal, pest, evidence

RELATED CALIFORNIA FRAMEWORK CONCEPTS

Animals live in a great variety of environments: oceans, fresh water, forests, deserts, tundra, and so forth. (*Science Framework Addendum*)

OBJECTIVE

Based on outdoor observations, students recall and recognize wildlife living in the schoolyard.

BACKGROUND INFORMATION

Wildlife ranges in size from microscopic (like soil bacteria) to enormous (like whales). Occasionally wild animals are tamed or kept as pets, but for the most part they survive on their own. A good way to tell whether an animal is wild is to think about how the animal most often lives. If it depends largely on people to provide its food, water, and shelter, then the animal is domesticated. For instance, even though a few pigs live in the wild, most pigs in this country are cared for by people and thus are considered domesticated. (Occasionally, domesticated species escape and are able to live on their own in the wild, as feral pigs have done in an undeveloped state park in Santa Cruz County. A feral animal is one that is a member of a domesticated species but has become self-supporting and now lives independent of people.)

In talking about wild and domesticated animals you will probably want to discuss with students some local animals that are considered pests. Have students discuss why some animals are considered pests but not others.

Also, you will need to emphasize that students must look carefully to find animals or evidence of animals. Many schoolyards are not hospitable to animals so be prepared to find only a few species.

Encounters between people and animals can be confusing or frightening, as well as enjoyable. Many people, both children and adults, are afraid of insects, rodents, or other animals. Be prepared for some students to act fearful or timid (it is important that students gain knowledge and appreciation of the wildlife in their schoolyard as preparation for the following activity, "Inviting Animals to the Schoolyard").

PREPARATION AND LEAD-UP

Arrange to have at least one aide, parent, or older student with you for the outdoor portion of this activity.

Label pages of butcher paper with these titles (one title per page): "Ground Crawlers," "Eye-level Lookers," and "Sky Scanners."

If you will be using the optional cardboard clipboards in step eight, cut out the clipboards from cardboard boxes or other pieces of stiff cardboard. Either staple or paper clip a piece of paper to each clipboard.

PROCEDURE

Day One

1. As a review, ask students to name things that are part of the schoolyard environment. If students do not mention animals, ask them about any animals they have seen or know about. They may mention some animals considered pests. Ask students to think about why we consider certain animals pests and why we enjoy having other animals in the schoolyard.

2. Tell the class that after they learn about animals that live in or visit the schoolyard environment, students will begin a project that will help make the schoolyard a better place for some animals. First, though, students have to find out as much as they can about animals in the schoolyard.

3. Let students know that to search for animals they will need to look carefully. Ask students to think like animal detectives—where would they look? Some possibilities are on the bark of trees, on shrubs, along cracks in sidewalks, on telephone wires, among blades of grass on the lawn, in dirt and plant litter (especially in places that people usually don't walk), along the edges of buildings, under eaves, on walls, on fences, and in tree stumps.

4. Let students know that they should also look for any evidence of wildlife, of whether an animal has been there before. Ask students what kinds of evidence they might find (some possibilities are spider webs, bird nests, tracks in mud, chewed leaves, bird or rodent droppings, slug and snail slime, dead insects, and cocoons). Ask students whether they will be able to see all the animals that live in the schoolyard environment.

5. Let students know that you do not want any animals—no matter how small, scary, or icky—to be hurt or killed. There are some animals that make their homes on the school grounds and they shouldn't be disturbed.

6. Talk with students about the way you expect them to behave outside. They will need to be quiet walking past other classrooms. Let students know where on the school grounds you want them to look. Make sure they understand the rules and boundaries for this activity before they start searching for wildlife.

7. Assign students to three groups—"ground crawlers," "eye-level lookers," and "sky scanners." Explain that each group of students is to look carefully for animals at their assigned level, either along the ground, at eye-level, or above their heads.

8. Explain that the class will need to keep track of the different animals seen, so students will make drawings while they are outside. If students will be using the clipboards to make preliminary drawings, distribute these materials. Show students the large pieces of butcher paper they will use to make a permanent record of their sightings. Explain that each student is to draw on the group's piece of butcher paper the animals he or she sees, and that he or she will have time tomorrow to complete the drawings begun today.

9. Give each group a jump rope to hold on to. This will keep the group together and help it focus on the quest for animals. Take students outside and give them 10 to 15 minutes to make their observations and drawings. Encourage students to look in a variety of places around the school site. The more places they look, the more kinds of animals they will see.

Day Two

10. Distribute drawing materials and arrange a place for each group to work. Allow students time to complete their group drawings.

11. When the drawings are finished, discuss how the animals might get their food, water, and shelter (see the discussion questions). Talk about

ways to improve the schoolyard environment to make it a better place for wildlife. Talk about whether it is realistic for every place to be a good home for every kind of animal and why the schoolyard could never be the right place for certain animals (monkeys, elephants, and maybe even deer, if the school is situated in an urban area).

DISCUSSION QUESTIONS

What animals did you find?
Were you surprised by any of the animals you or your classmates found?
Where were the most animals found?
How many different kinds of animals did we see?
Why didn't we find more animals?
What kinds of food might be available on or near the schoolyard for the animals that were found living here?
How and where might these animals get water?
What kind of shelter might animals find and use on the schoolyard?
What kinds of things could we do to help make the schoolyard a better place for wildlife?
Would our schoolyard be a good place for an elephant to live? An eagle? A mountain lion?

EVALUATION

Students give three examples of wildlife (or evidence of wildlife), where animals might be seen, and how animals might get their food, water, and shelter.

EXTENSION IDEAS

- Read *Secret Neighbors: Wildlife in a City Lot,* by Mary Adrian, or Helen Ross Russell's *City Critters.* Both books describe the kinds of animals that might be found living in a city schoolyard.
- If you have access to a camera, take pictures of one of the more common animals found in the schoolyard—kids. Ask students why they should be considered a schoolyard animal and

what effect their presence has on the schoolyard environment.

- Have students write or dictate poems or stories from the perspective of animals that live in the schoolyard. You can start them out with "If I were an ant at (name of school), I would . . . "

HOME LEARNING SUGGESTION

Use as follow-up to this activity)

Students and parents might look for evidence of wildlife around their home. Ask each student to choose one kind of animal he or she enjoys having around and to list ways to encourage the animal to visit the student's yard. The following letter can be used (for older children you may want to indicate that the student will do the writing).

REFERENCES

For Students

Adrian, Mary. *Secret Neighbors: Wildlife in a City Lot.* New York: Hastings Publishers, 1972. These stories provide information about how wild animals survive in some not very wild places. The stories correspond with the seasons.

Russell, Helen Ross. *City Critters.* Cortland, N.Y.: Wilkins/Printers, 1975. This book has information on feeding behavior, habits, and history of a variety of city animals, from rats and roaches to squirrels and sparrows.

Sample Letter

Dear Parent:

Today in school we surveyed the schoolyard to see what kinds of animals live there. Tomorrow we will begin a project to make the schoolyard a better place for some of the animals we enjoy having around.

Please discuss with your child the animals he or she can think of that live around your house or neighborhood. Help name any other animals that your child didn't mention and list all of the animals on a piece of paper. Ask your child to pick one of those animals that he or she especially likes and to draw a picture of it on the same piece of paper. Then ask your child to think of ways to encourage that animal to visit your yard or neighborhood, and write down his or her responses.

Please have your child bring the paper to school tomorrow. Thank you for your help.

INVITING ANIMALS TO THE SCHOOLYARD

Unless someone like you cares a whole awful lot, nothing is going to get better. It's not.

—Dr. Seuss, *The Lorax*

SUMMARY OF ACTIVITY

Students carry out a project to make the schoolyard a more attractive place for wildlife, and observe and discuss changes they notice.

Time: Varies

Setting: Classroom, schoolyard

Materials: Depends on project chosen

Subjects: Science, other subjects (depending on project chosen)

Key Words: Wildlife, environment, care

RELATED CALIFORNIA FRAMEWORK CONCEPTS

Proper care of pets and domestic animals and behaviors affecting the welfare of wildlife involve personal responsibility and social policy. (*Science Framework Addendum*)

People can cooperate to preserve the beauty of our environment and improve the quality of life in it. (Adapted from *History-Social Science Framework*)

Animals live in a great variety of environments: oceans, fresh water, forests, deserts, tundra, and so forth. (*Science Framework Addendum*)

OBJECTIVE

Students develop ways to make the schoolyard more livable for wildlife.

BACKGROUND INFORMATION

In the previous activity students began to learn what animals live in or use the schoolyard. This activity has suggestions of simple ongoing projects that can make the schoolyard a more attractive place for wildlife. By trying to improve the schoolyard for local wildlife, students will also get to know their local environment better. Caring comes with knowing.

Three projects, building bird feeders, planting flowers, and caring for trees are described here. You may wish to have your students do one of these, or have the class come up with their own project.

Easy birdfeeders can be made by spreading peanut butter onto pine cones or empty toilet paper rolls, then rolling them in bird seed. A variety of seeds, suet, or berries will increase your chances of attracting more species of birds. Hang the feeders outside the classroom windows for easy observation. (You should never discontinue filling a bird feeder during winter, because birds may have come to depend upon your offerings at this time of year when other foods are scarce.)

Another project is to grow flowers to attract birds and insects. Many annual and perennial flowers, as well as shrubs, vines, and trees, attract wildlife by providing food and shelter. Three easy-to-grow annual flowers that can be planted from seeds are marigolds, zinnias, and impatiens. The seeds should sprout within a few weeks and can be started indoors. If there is no space to transplant them into the ground, let the plants continue growing outside in pots or other containers. Marigolds and zinnias provide nectar for butterflies and seeds that are eaten by finches and sparrows. These two flowers need a sunny location. Red and orange impatiens are best for attracting butterflies and hummingbirds. Impatiens grow well in partial shade.

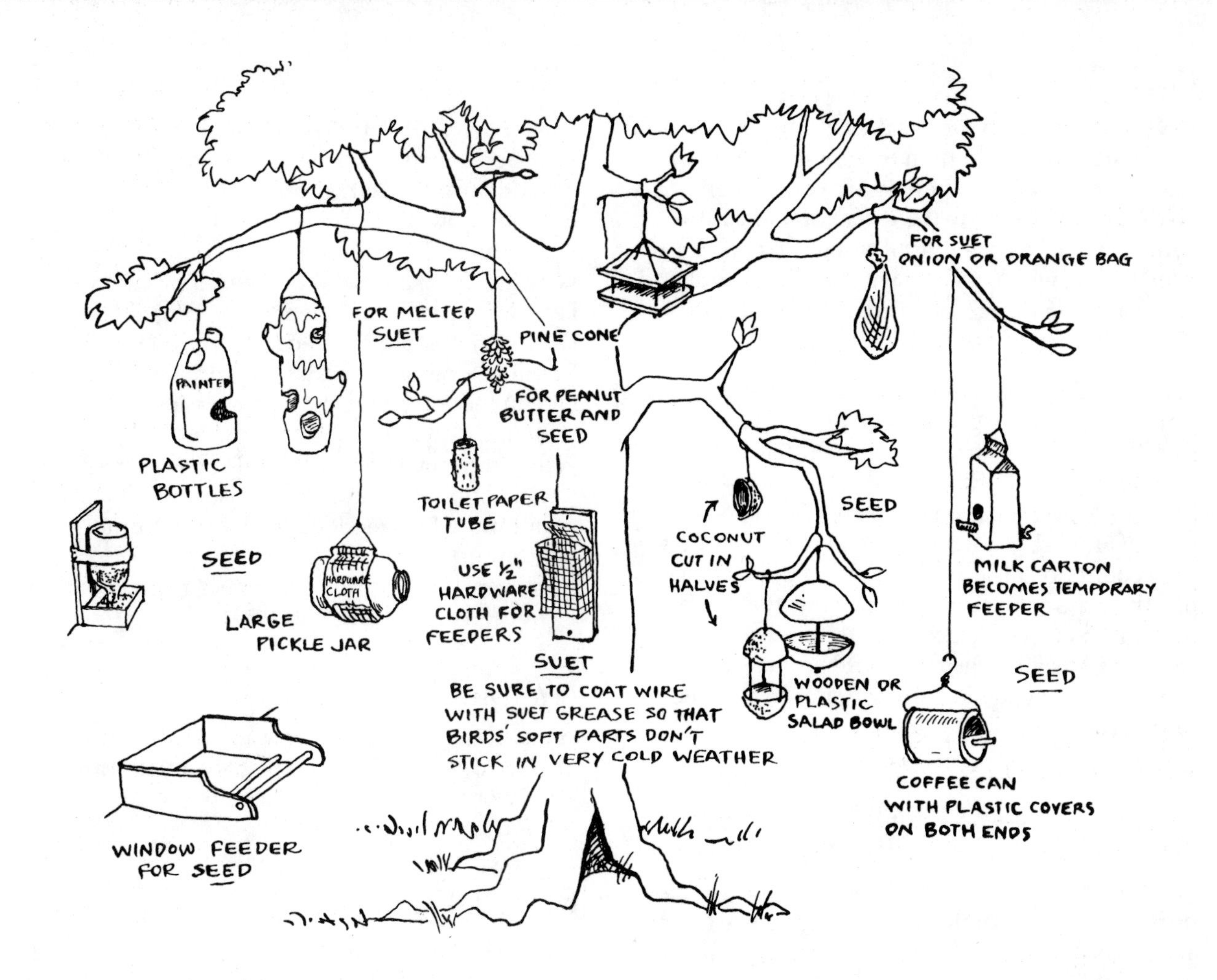

You may want to try growing native wildflowers. California poppies (the official state wildflower), tidy tips, evening primroses, and any other wildflower from your area should be planted in late fall or early winter in a sunny spot for springtime flowering. The area will need to be weeded several times so that grasses and other plants won't crowd out the wildflower seedlings. The seeds should be watered occasionally, especially if the weather is dry or warm.

Another possible project is to have students care for one or more trees, which provide food and shelter for birds, squirrels, and other animals. Students can start by investigating the trees in the schoolyard to see what kinds of animals use them. Birds may perch, build nests in the branches, or eat the seeds. Ants may climb the trunk and branches looking for food. Beetles may bore through the bark, eating as they go. Butterflies and bees may feed on the nectar of the flowers. Squirrels may hide in the branches to escape from people, cats, and dogs below.

Many animals depend upon trees, so we can help animals by keeping trees healthy. Choose one tree or several for the class to take special care of. Students can guess how far out the roots go and then water the tree roots. Students can also feed the tree bits of their lunch; for instance, they can turn their applecores into an elm tree by composting them at the base of the tree. Students can keep the area around the tree free of litter, too.

As students get to know the tree better, you may want to lead a thank-a-tree session. Students can thank the trees in the schoolyard or any other kind of tree they can think of. Let everyone express thanks for one gift (such as birds, butterflies, squirrels, shade, a place to climb, shelter, fruit, nuts, paper, and firewood).

PROCEDURE

1. Review and continue the discussion about wildlife in the schoolyard from the previous activity. Ask, "What kinds of animals did you find or find evidence of?" (Refer to the group drawings students made.) "What kinds of things do animals need to survive? In what ways does the schoolyard provide these things for animals? In what ways is the schoolyard not good for wildlife?"

2. Ask students to share their home learning assignment from the previous activity. If you want the class to decide on a project, ask, "How could we make the schoolyard a better place for wildlife?" List their ideas on the board. Then look at the list and ask students to choose a project that they could do. It is important that the project be one the class can accomplish and one that has a high rate of success (success in this case means that students are able to see wild animals using the project). If you have already chosen a project for the class, introduce it now.

3. Discuss how the project will benefit wildlife. Also discuss any potential problems for wildlife or people that could arise from the project.

4. Inform the principal and other teachers of the project. Check with the maintenance department and anyone else who might be affected by the project.

5. Discuss with students how to carry out the project. Decide what roles students will play and divide the work. You may want to enlist parent volunteers.

6. Have students observe and monitor any changes resulting from the project. Allow ample time for casually observing and discussing the project, wildlife seen, and anything unexpected that happens. Some of the discussion questions may be useful after the project has been going for several weeks or months.

7. If your class project does not work out as planned, be sure to discuss with students what they think happened. Encourage them to consider what they might do differently next time. If there is time and interest, you may want the class to implement the project again.

DISCUSSION QUESTIONS

How do you think this project might help wildlife?
Are there any potential problems for people or wildlife if we do this project?
Do you know of any wild animals that are considered pests?
Why are these animals considered pests?
How was wildlife affected by our project?
How were people affected by our project?
Did anything happen that you didn't expect?
Did our action encourage any animals that we hadn't expected?
Were there any bad or harmful consequences of our action? (For example, wasps may come to a hummingbird feeder and chase away the hummingbirds.)
If we were going to do this project again, what would you do differently? Why?

EVALUATION

Have students write or draw an answer to the question, "If you could do whatever you wanted, what would you like to do to help wildlife in our schoolyard?"

RESOURCES

Gardening With Wildlife: The Official Backyard Habitat Planning and Planting Kit. Washington, D.C.: National Wildlife Federation. This kit contains a book, calendar, and pamphlets, all providing information about what kinds of plants will attract what kinds of wildlife.

Schmidt, Marjorie G. *Growing California Native Plants.* Berkeley, Calif.: University of California Press, 1980. This book provides specific information on growing conditions necessary for many California native plants.

Sunset Western Garden Book. Menlo Park, Calif.: Lane Publishing Company, 1986. The recent edition includes information on growing California native plants.

SOURCE OF ACTIVITY

Sisson, Edith A. *Nature With Children All Ages,* "Feathered Friend: Birds." Englewood Cliffs, N.J.: Prentice-Hall Inc., 1982.

IT'S THEIR WORLD, TOO

SUMMARY OF ACTIVITY

Students design wildlife emblems and pencil banners and learn "Let It Be," a song by Malvina Reynolds.

Time: 30 minutes

Setting: Classroom

Materials:
- Copycat page, one per student
- Crayons, markers, colored pencils
- Scissors
- Tape
- Butcher paper
- Guitar (optional)

Subjects: Art, science, social studies

Key Words: Wildlife

RELATED CALIFORNIA FRAMEWORK CONCEPTS

People can communicate and cooperate to preserve the beauty of our environment and improve the quality of life. (Adapted from *History-Social Science Framework*)

Proper care of pets and domestic animals and behaviors affecting the welfare of wildlife involve personal responsibility and social policy. (*Science Framework Addendum*)

Art, music, and dance can influence and enrich group life. (Adapted from *History-Social Science Framework*)

OBJECTIVE

Students design wildlife emblems, drawing pictures of animals to convey a message about wildlife.

BACKGROUND INFORMATION

Animals belong to this world as much as we do. Although we consider some animals pests, some useful, and some beautiful, each has an existence separate and distinct from ours. Each animal contributes in some way to the rest of the world, for example, bees pollinate flowers, snakes eat rodents, and ants aid in decomposing dead plants and animals. In this activity students are asked to create pictures showing that animals are part of this world. After all, it's their world, too!

PREPARATION AND LEAD-UP

Make copies of the emblem sheets.

If possible, read to the class *The Lorax* by Dr. Seuss and discuss what plants and animals were part of the world and why the Lorax tried to help them.

Copy the words to "Let It Be" on a piece of butcher paper (see step four).

PROCEDURE

1. Ask students to think of other animals that share our world. Write "It's their world, too" on the board. Ask students what this means and why they think people should care for animals.

2. Tell students they will make wildlife emblems that say "It's their world, too." Students can use the emblems for decoration and to remind themselves and others that wildlife is important.

3. Distribute the emblem sheets and the coloring materials. Have scissors and tape ready so that students can cut out the emblems and tape them to their pencils and covered school books (if students have not yet covered their textbooks, this would be a good time for them to do it—have some large grocery bags available). Encourage students to take one or more of their emblems home to display there.

4. Teach students Malvina Reynolds' song, "Let It Be." Ask students what the words mean to them.

LET IT BE
By Malvina Reynolds

When you walk in the forest, let it be.
There's a flower in the wood, let it be.
There's a flower in the wood, and it's innocent and good,
By the stone where it stands, let it be.
Let it be, let it be.
It's so lovely where it is, let it be.

Tho' you want it for your own, if you take it from its place,
It will not be what it was when you loved it where it stood in the wood.
Let it be, let it be,
It's so lovely where it is, let it be.
It's a thoughtful child, innocent and wild, by the stone, by the reed,
Let it bloom, let it seed, let it be.

DISCUSSION QUESTIONS

What does "It's their world, too" mean?
What animals live in our neighborhood? In our county? State? In the world?
Why do you think we should care about animals?

EVALUATION

Students draw a picture or write a story about what the world would be like without animals.

EXTENSION IDEAS

- Read *Once There Was a Tree* by Natalia Romanova to your class. Discuss how the tree didn't belong to any one of the animals or to the man but to all of them.
- Read Byrd Baylor's *Hawk, I'm Your Brother* to your class. Ask, "Did the boy care about the hawk? How do you know?"

RESOURCES

For Students

Baylor, Byrd. *Hawk, I'm Your Brother.* New York: Charles Scribner's Sons, 1976. A boy finds and keeps a young hawk, then finally decides that the best way to care for the bird is to let it go.
Romanova, Natalia. *Once There Was a Tree.* New York: Dial Books, 1985. A tree stump attracts many different animals, including a man. Who does it really belong to? Translated from Russian.
Seuss, Dr. *The Lorax.* New York: Random House, 1971. This is a story, in unmistakable Dr. Seuss rhyme, of pollution, greed, and caring.

SOURCE OF ACTIVITY

Chargin, Claudia. *It's Your World.* Los Angeles, Calif.: Troubador Press, 1971.

IT'S THEIR WORLD, TOO

Here are three "save our wildlife" emblems to color and cut out. Use them to remind people to help protect our animal friends.

PICTURE THE EFFECTS

SUMMARY OF ACTIVITY

Students look at pictures of various human actions, discuss how these actions could harm the environment, and suggest alternative actions that would be less harmful.

Time: 30 minutes

Setting: Classroom

Materials:
- Photos from magazines and calendars (see preparation and lead-up)
- Butcher paper
- Drawing paper
- Drawing materials
- "What Is the Environment?" chart from the activity "Caring at School"

Subjects: Science, language arts, music, social studies

Key Words: Care, environment, harmful, waste, choice, reuse, alternative

RELATED CALIFORNIA FRAMEWORK CONCEPTS

People can work to preserve the beauty of our environment and improve the quality of life in it. (Adapted from *History-Social Science Framework*)

Conservation of resources is an ethical concern of individuals and societies. (*Science Framework Addendum*)

OBJECTIVE

Students suggest alternatives to common actions that harm the environment.

BACKGROUND INFORMATION

This activity asks students to think about how our actions affect other living things and the environment, and to consider some choices we can make that will be less harmful to the environment. Two choices that help protect the environment are not wasting resources and reusing things. These two conservation practices are addressed throughout the rest of this unit so it is important that they are represented in the photos you choose and that they are emphasized in the follow-up discussion.

PREPARATION AND LEAD-UP

For this activity you need at least as many pictures as students in the class. The pictures (preferably large and in color) should show some harm done by people to the environment. Look for magazine photos that show exhaust coming from a car, a truck driving through a stream, someone dropping garbage, photos of litter, a garbage dump, names carved into the bark of a tree, smoke from a factory, dirty water discharging from a factory, or floating debris in a river or lake. Pictures can be found in magazines like *National Geographic, Sierra, Time,* and *Newsweek*. You may want to mount pictures or laminate them. On butcher paper write these questions, "What is happening? How is the environment being harmed? What could people do that would not be so bad for the environment?"

If you will be using other adults to help with small discussion groups (see step three in the procedure), arrange for them to be there. You may want to make a copy of the discussion questions for them.

PROCEDURE

1. Tell students that today they will be thinking and talking about choices. Ask them to think about times they have been able to make a choice. Most students have probably had chances to choose what food to eat, what clothing to wear, what games to play. Ask students if they can think of times when they have made a choice that affects the environment (like putting trash into a garbage can or turning off the water while brushing their teeth).

2. Let students know that they will look at pictures of people doing different things and that you want them to think about three questions when they look at the pictures. Post the butcher paper chart with the three questions on it and the "What Is the Environment?" chart, then hold up one picture for the whole class to see. Have students answer the three questions and also the discussion questions, referring as needed to the "What Is the Environment?" chart.

3. This activity can be conducted with the whole class, in several groups supervised by adults, or (for older students) in pairs. If you are going to work with the whole class, continue discussing pictures. If you have other adults to help, divide the class into groups so that each adult has a group of students. Give each group a number of photo cards and allow about 10 minutes for discussion of each photo. For pairs, give each pair two or more photos. If you wish, students may write out answers to the three questions listed on butcher paper. Allow about five minutes for each picture. Then gather the class back together and discuss several pictures as a whole group.

4. End by having the whole class consider at least one picture that has to do with garbage. Let students know that tomorrow they will be using "garbage" for a special art project (see the preparation and lead-up to the activity "Recycled Art").

DISCUSSION QUESTIONS

Regarding each picture, ask students:
What is happening?
Does it harm wildlife? Plants? Air? Water? People? Other things in the environment?
Does the person's behavior seem okay or not?
Is the person having fun?
What do you like or not like about this picture?
What other choices does the person have that would not harm the environment?
Why do you think it is important to care about the environment?
What are ways you could keep from wasting things?
Why is garbage a problem for the environment?
What are ways you could reuse things so that you would throw away less garbage?

EVALUATION

Give students an open-ended question and have them draw or write a response. For example, ask students to pretend that they have come upon a stream littered with garbage. Have them draw a picture showing who or what might be harmed, then have students write about what they could do to improve the situation.

EXTENSION IDEA

Read *Isn't It a Beautiful Meadow?* by Wolf Harranth and Winifried Opgenoorth or *The Little Chestnut Tree* by Lisl Weil to the class. Ask, "What happened in the story that was harmful to the environment? How would you finish the story?" Both stories are open-ended so students can decide what they would like to happen next.

HOME LEARNING SUGGESTION

(Use as follow-up to this activity)

Ask students to draw a picture of something they know about or have seen that can harm the environment. Send students home with the letter on the following page (the letter should be changed for older students to indicate that the students will write their own descriptions with help from parents as needed).

RESOURCES

Foreman, Michael. *Dinosaurs and All That Rubbish.* New York: Thomas Y. Crowell, 1973. In his efforts to reach a much-admired star, a man fouls his own beautiful planet Earth. Once the man has gone into space, the dinosaurs reawaken to clean up his mess by stomping on freeways and dumping cars into smoking volcanoes. When the man returns, he is finally able to see the beauty of the Earth and that it belongs to everyone.

Harranth, Wolf, and Winifried Opgenoorth. *Isn't It a Beautiful Meadow?* New York: Oxford University Press, 1985. In this story a group of townspeople find a lovely meadow and treasure it. Step by step, they make "improvements" and suddenly the meadow looks like the town they left behind. They find another beautiful meadow nearby. What will they do this time?

Weil, Lisl. *The Little Chestnut Tree.* New York: Scholastic Book Services, 1973. This is a tale of a city crowding out an old tree. The book ends with a new beginning and encourages the reader to decide what happens next.

Sample Letter

Dear Parent:

Our class has been learning about things people do that are harmful to the environment and actions that people can take that are less harmful. Your child's assignment tonight is to draw a picture of something he or she has seen or knows about that can harm the environment. Ask your child to dictate to you what is happening in the picture and what could happen instead that would not be harmful. Please write this description on the drawing and have your child bring it to school tomorrow.

Thank you for your help.

RECYCLED ART

SUMMARY OF ACTIVITY

Students use materials that would have been discarded to create their own art project, then discuss other ways to reuse garbage.

Time: Two (or more) 30- to 45-minute periods

Setting: Classroom

Materials:
- Reusable materials (see preparation and lead-up)
- Scissors
- Glue
- Tape
- String

Subjects: Art, science, social studies

Key Words: Garbage, reuse, recycle, build, structure

RELATED CALIFORNIA FRAMEWORK CONCEPTS

Conservation of resources is an ethical concern of individuals and societies. (*Science Framework Addendum*)

Art, music, and dance can influence and enrich group life. (Adapted from *History-Social Science Framework*)

OBJECTIVE

After completing their art projects, students list kinds of "garbage" that can be reused and suggest ways to reuse them.

BACKGROUND INFORMATION

Garbage creates many problems. One problem is lack of landfill space (a landfill is a garbage dump). For some cities the landfill site is many miles away; the city of Berkeley, for example, trucks its garbage 46 miles to a landfill site near Livermore because the local site is filled to capacity. This means each garbage truck makes a 92-mile round trip to dispose of the city's waste.

Another problem is that throwing away garbage is really throwing away vital natural resources. Metals and glass can be reused, paper can be recycled, and organic wastes like kitchen scraps and wastes from food processing plants can be composted and returned to the soil as ferti-

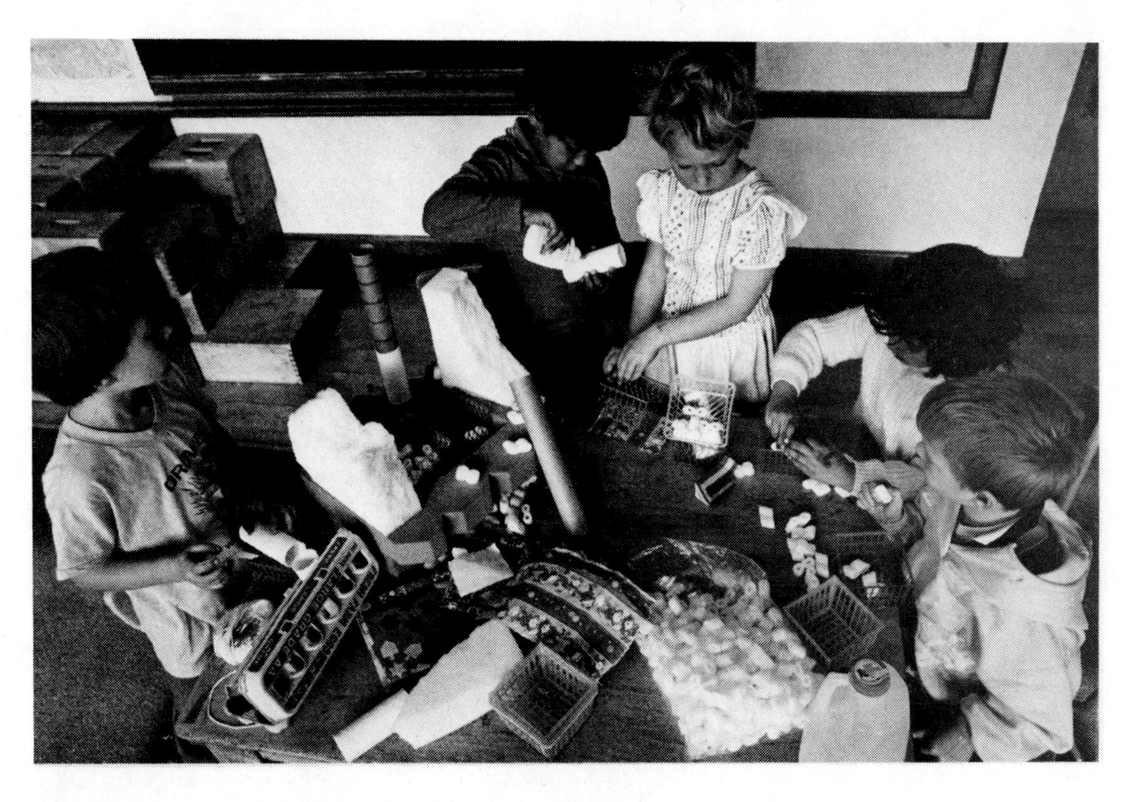

lizer. Garbage really is a waste; we could be reusing much of our garbage instead of wasting it.

The garbage problem young children most likely are aware of is litter. Litter can be ugly, unhealthy (rats and flies may breed in it), harmful to animals (a plastic six-pack holder can slowly choke a bird to death as the bird grows), and a fire hazard.

In this activity students reuse materials that normally end up in the garbage. Reusing and recycling garbage can help to reduce problems associated with garbage.

PREPARATION AND LEAD-UP

You need to accumulate a variety of reusable garbage for students to use in creating their art projects. The following letter can be sent to parents asking them to help collect things.

For the sake of variety and quantity you will probably need to supplement what your students bring. You may be able to find reusable materials in the school cafeteria, by asking the janitor or a high school shop or home economics teacher, or from some of the sources listed.

Gather all of the materials brought in and divide them so that each group of four students has its own box of reusables. Also, call the local sanitation district to find out where the landfill site for your area is (see step five).

Sample Letter

Dear Parent:

Your child will be learning about ways to care for and protect the environment. One way to take care of the environment is to reuse some of the things that usually are thrown away. I have planned an art project where students will do just this.

I am asking each student to bring to class one or more things that normally would be thrown away, which can be reused for the art project. Here are some of the things I have in mind:

- Cardboard tubes from paper towels or toilet paper
- Small pieces of scrap wood
- Leftover shelf paper or wallpaper
- Old wrapping paper and ribbons
- Sewing scraps
- Empty spools of thread
- Socks with holes
- Buttons
- Plastic lids
- Small boxes, including shoe boxes

You may be able to find interesting, reusable garbage at work also.

Please send reusable, clean, and safe materials to school with your child by [date].

Thank you for your help.

Material	Sources
Cloth	Fabric houses, upholstery shops, local tailors
Carpet or upholstery remnants	Interior designers
Paper	Printing shops, framing shops
Cardboard and shredded packing	Furniture stores
End roles of newsprint	Newspaper plants
Wallpaper rolls and sample books	Interior designers
Gallon cartons	Ice cream parlors
Bags and boxes	Department stores
Plastics (foam trays, meat wrapping acetate, wine bottle package)	Grocery stores
Plastics (x-rays, plastic tubing, old gloves)	Hospitals/doctors
Packaging	Electronics stores
Wire	Telephone company, electrical contractors
Wood	Lumber mills, hardware stores

PROCEDURE

1. Remind students that yesterday they saw pictures of garbage. Ask what they thought about when they saw the pictures. Discuss problems associated with litter and some of the benefits of recycling garbage.

2. Tell students that today they will be artists or builders (architects) and reuse garbage for art projects. Divide the class into groups of four, telling each group that it will get a box of materials to use and share.

3. Distribute the materials. You will probably need to allow at least two periods for building and maybe more if time and interest permit. When students are done, ask volunteers to share their projects with the class.

4. Talk about materials students used for their art projects and other materials that could be reused in other ways (refer to the discussion questions).

5. Ask, "Does anyone know where our garbage goes? Is there really such a thing as 'away'? Where is 'away'? Who has been to the dump? What was it like there? What did you see there? Did you see anything that could have been reused?"

DISCUSSION QUESTIONS

What materials did you like using?
What materials did not seem good for your project?
Can you think of other things you would have liked to reuse for your project?
If you hadn't used these materials for your art projects, what would have happened to them? Where would they probably be now?
What things do you throw away at home and at school?
Could any of these things be used for art projects?
Can you think of any other ways to reuse some of these things?
How does it help the environment to reuse things?
How does it help the environment if we make less garbage?

EVALUATION

Students name four items that usually are thrown away but could be reused. Invent one way to reuse each of these items.

EXTENSION IDEAS

- Read Paul Showers' book *Where Does All the Garbage Go?* to your class to learn more about garbage and recycling.
- Suggest to students who bring a bag lunch to school that they see how many times they can reuse one bag (the record number of reuses is over 30). Tell students that each day they bring lunch in a bag, you will stamp it with a rubber stamp so that they can keep track of the number of times they have used the bag. See who can use a bag the most times. Then see if someone can break the class record.

HOME LEARNING SUGGESTION

(Use as follow-up to this activity)

Have students look for and list things their family reuses. The following note to parents can be used (the letter will need to be modified for older students to indicate that they should write the list themselves).

RESOURCE

For Students

Showers, Paul. *Where Does All the Garbage Go?* New York: Thomas Y. Crowell, 1974. This book, which contains factual information about garbage and recycling, focuses on the story of a girl who decides to repair her yo-yo rather than throw it away.

SOURCE OF ACTIVITY

Environmental Awareness Through the Arts. Baton Rouge, La.: Louisiana Council for Music and Performing Arts, Department of Education, State of Louisiana, 1973.

Sample Letter

Dear Parent:

As part of our study of caring for the environment, the class has been learning about reusing things that are commonly thrown away. Please discuss with your child things that are reused in your home (like glass jars, paper bags, and plastic bags), then list those things below.

Thank you for your help.

CLASSROOM WATER CONSERVATION

SUMMARY OF ACTIVITY

Students monitor classroom water use for a week, then take action to reduce the amount of water wasted and to reuse wasted water.

Time: One 30-minute period, then 15 minutes a day on four consecutive days

Setting: Classroom

Materials:
- Dishpan
- 75 plastic party cups, eight ounces or larger
- Butcher paper or poster-sized graph paper
- Blue construction paper

Subjects: Science, math, social studies

Key Words: Water, conservation, reuse, waste, choice

RELATED CALIFORNIA FRAMEWORK CONCEPTS

Conservation of resources is an ethical concern of individuals and societies. (*Science Framework Addendum*)

Water is essential to all forms of life. (*Science Framework Addendum*)

People can communicate and cooperate to preserve the beauty of our environment and improve the quality of life in it. (Adapted from *History-Social Science Framework*)

Nonstandard units of measure can be used to measure volume. (Adapted from *Mathematics Framework*)

Data derived from surveys and experiments can be collected, organized, represented, and interpreted. (Adapted from *Mathematics Framework*)

OBJECTIVE

During a week of charting classroom water use and monitoring their own behavior, students act to conserve water in the classroom.

BACKGROUND INFORMATION

Water is considered a renewable resource but it is also an overused resource. Water use is a historical and ongoing political issue in California. Large water projects divert huge quantities of water from a number of rivers around the state, frequently removing enough water to change or destroy the habitat for fish and other wildlife. Untreated waste water returning to lakes, rivers, bays, or the Pacific Ocean pollutes water needed by people and wildlife. In some parts of the state water is pumped from underground sources that took thousands of years to form. In some places the ground is actually subsiding as water is withdrawn from underground reservoirs. Near the coast salt water is intruding into the underground water, making the water unusable for drinking or farming.

This activity emphasizes awareness of water waste and teaches students that they can make choices about their actions. For example, they can choose not to let the water run or choose to reuse wasted water.

To capture water that would normally go down the classroom sink, you need a dishpan or bucket that will fit under the faucet in the sink but still allow access to the water. To measure the captured water, use plastic party cups. After students have counted and graphed the day's catch, empty the cups and reuse them the next day.

Unless they have had concrete graphing experiences already, many young students will have difficulty understanding the meaning of the graph. Each day emphasize that the construction paper cups on the graph represent the real cups of water.

PREPARATION AND LEAD-UP

Make a graph on butcher paper similar to the graph pictured in the photo on the following page. Keep some extra butcher paper handy so that you can add another piece if needed (you will probably be surprised at how much water is wasted).

Cut rectangles one inch by two inches from construction paper to represent cups of water on the graph. Call your local water department to find

out the source or sources of local water. Call the local waste water treatment facility to find out how waste water is treated (see step six).

PROCEDURE

1. Discuss the importance of water for all living things (plants, fish, people, and other animals). Talk about how water is used, such as for drinking, for cleaning, and for transportation.

2. Remind students that one of the ways to help care for the environment is not to waste. Ask students to think about how they use water in the classroom. "Do you think you may be wasting water? What are some ways you use water that could be considered wasteful?" Tell students that they will keep track of how much water is wasted in the classroom.

3. Demonstrate the system for capturing water in the pan. Have several students show how to capture water while getting a drink or washing their hands. Explain that at the end of the day or whenever the pan is full, students will pour or scoop out the water into the plastic drinking cups. This way they can see how many cups of water were wasted each day. You may want to have students estimate at the beginning of the day how many cups of water will be wasted.

4. At the end of the day or whenever the pan is full, have several students help transfer water to the cups. Line up the cups so that everyone can see them and count how many there are. A student can graph the day's water use on the chart using the construction paper cups (for example, if there are 60 cups at the end of the day, students need to put 60 pictures of cups on the graph). Make sure the meaning of symbols on the graph is clear.

5. Ask students to think of ways to reduce water waste and to reuse the captured water (like watering indoor and outdoor plants, mixing up poster paint, or washing paint brushes). Emphasize to students that they should *not* drink the water or use it for any classroom pets (you may want to discuss possible health hazards of drinking waste water).

6. At some point during the week, let students know where their water comes from and where waste water (from sinks, toilets, agricultural use, and industry) goes.

7. As the week progresses and the class is wasting less water, point out to students that they are wasting less water because they are making choices about how to use water and are reusing water. Ask students how they think the environment benefits when they waste less water and when they reuse it.

DISCUSSION QUESTIONS

What are some of the ways we use water?
How do plants and other animals use water?
Could it be bad for the environment (plants, animals, rivers, and lakes) if we waste a lot of water?
How do we sometimes waste water in our classroom?
What are some ways we can use less water in our classroom?
Did you make some choices that helped the class use less water?
Why did we use less or more water today?
Where does the water go when it goes down the drain?
Does it really go "away"?
Is water clean when it goes down the drain?
How might this dirty water harm the environment?
What do we use water for at home?
How is water sometimes wasted at home?
What could you do to waste less water at home?

EVALUATION

Ask students to name three ways they sometimes waste water and three ways they can conserve or use less water.

EXTENSION IDEAS

- In addition to the graph suggested in this activity, have students make a bar graph or keep a tally of classroom water use. This will help students understand different ways data can be displayed.
- Have students make collages out of magazine photos to illustrate ways water is wasted or ways living things use water (the latter is especially appropriate for younger students).

HOME LEARNING SUGGESTION

(Use as follow-up to this activity)

The suggestion in the evaluation section could be given as a home learning assignment.

ECOLOGICAL PICNIC

The world can provide for every man's need, but not for every man's greed.

—Mahatma Gandhi

SUMMARY OF ACTIVITY

Students plan and enjoy a picnic using a minimum of disposable items, then sort and recycle as much of the picnic garbage as possible.

Time: Varies, generally 30 minutes for planning, 60 minutes for the picnic, and 30 to 45 minutes after the picnic

Setting: Classroom, outdoors

Materials:
- Typical lunch (see step one)
- Two buckets or large cans for picnic garbage
- One bucket with a tight-fitting cover for composting
- Sawdust or dirt (optional; see step eight)

Subjects: Science, social studies

Key Words: Reusable, garbage, choices, environment, ecological

RELATED CALIFORNIA FRAMEWORK CONCEPTS

People can communicate and cooperate to preserve the beauty of our environment and improve the quality of life in it. (Adapted from *History-Social Science Framework*)

Conservation of resources is an ethical concern of individuals and societies. (*Science Framework Addendum*)

OBJECTIVE

Following instruction and discussion, students pack a picnic lunch for themselves using as few disposable items as possible.

BACKGROUND INFORMATION

People use disposable products for picnics and other occasions because there are no dirty dishes left over and no utensils that need to be taken home and washed. Just toss the products away and they seem to disappear. But there really is no "away"; all garbage must go somewhere. Any garbage that is not recycled contributes to the local landfill or becomes unsightly litter.

This activity reinforces the idea that students can make personal choices about their actions. In this case they will be making choices that will minimize the amount of waste generated by a class picnic. After the picnic students will collect the garbage that remains and recycle or compost what they can.

PREPARATION AND LEAD-UP

Choose a site for the picnic (if you want students to help choose the site, see the extension ideas). Possible locations are the schoolyard, a vacant lot, a park, a playground, a ball field, a lawn, or the side steps to the school building.

If the weather is not suitable for an outdoor picnic, move it indoors. Push all of the desks aside and have the picnic in the middle of the classroom floor.

Label the buckets to be used for garbage during the picnic. The one with the cover should be labeled "Food." The other two buckets should be labeled "Cans" and "Other."

PROCEDURE

Day One

1. Decide upon a typical lunch that students might bring to school. Ask students to decide what items from the lunch would be thrown away. Ask if any of the pieces of garbage could be reused or recycled. Have students think of something that is reusable that could replace each disposable item (for example, silverware could be used instead of plastic spoons and forks).

2. Plan the picnic. Ask students for ideas about how they can pack a lunch that will produce the least amount of garbage. Explain that they will be making a friendship salad the day of the picnic and that they can contribute one or two pieces of fruit if they want to.

3. Send the following letter to parents telling them of the picnic and asking for volunteers.

Sample Letter

Dear Parent:

As the final activity in our unit on caring for the environment, we are planning an ecological picnic on ____*date*____ at ____*time*____ to be held at ____*site*____. We have discussed ways to pack a lunch so that there will be as little garbage left over as possible (for example, using cloth napkins instead of paper napkins, bringing reusable silverware or reusable plastic silverware, putting food in reusable plastic containers when possible, bringing juice or milk in a thermos). Please help your child pack an ecological lunch for the picnic.

We will recycle as much leftover garbage as we can. Cans and aluminum foil will be recycled. Leftover food that can't be saved will be composted.

We will make a friendship salad the morning of the picnic. Students will contribute the fruit. We will wash the fruit and chop it at school, then enjoy it for dessert at the picnic. If you can contribute to the friendship salad, please send one or two pieces of fruit with your child on ____*date*____ along with his or her ecological lunch.

Also, we need two or three parent volunteers to help make the friendship salad and supervise the picnic. If you can join the fun and help out, please let me know.

Thank you.

Day Two

4. On the morning of the picnic, discuss garbage and cleanup. Point out that some things will need to be thrown away even though the picnic was planned and choices were made so that there would be little garbage. Show students the buckets or cans you want them to use for all of the garbage at the picnic. Explain that one bucket is for recyclable containers, one is for leftover food that can't be saved, and one is for other garbage like paper and plastic. If there is water available at the picnic site, let students know that they can wash all dirty, reusable containers and utensils after the picnic.

5. One or more of the parent volunteers can help small groups of students wash and cut the fruit during the morning. Capture and reuse the water.

6. Remember to bring the three labeled buckets with you. Make sure students keep and sort their garbage after the picnic.

7. After lunch call the students together. Sing "It's a Small World," (see the first activity in this unit, "Things We Care About," for the words). Discuss what kinds of garbage are left over and what garbage isn't there because students made careful choices about what to bring. Make sure when the class leaves that no garbage is left at the picnic site.

After the Picnic

8. In the classroom put all of the food garbage from the picnic into the bucket for composting. You can layer the food with sawdust or dirt, if either are available. Make sure the cover fits tightly; open compost containers attract rodents and flies. Stir the mixture every three to five days for a couple of weeks. When most or all of it looks like dirt, use it. Add a little soil and plant flowers in it or mix it into the soil under a favorite tree. Let students know that compost is a kind of plant food; it contains many nutrients that plants use.

9. You or one of the parent volunteers can take the cans to the recycling center in your area. Discuss

with the students where the cans are going and why it is better for the environment to recycle cans rather than throw them away.

10. Discuss with students what they did during the picnic that was good for the environment and good for people. Let students express their ideas and feelings. Discuss savings of paper (trees), plastic, and money.

11. Distribute paper and drawing materials and have students draw a picture of the picnic showing themselves and others doing something good for the environment. Older students can label their own pictures; younger students will need to dictate a sentence or two.

DISCUSSION QUESTIONS

What do you usually throw away after a picnic?
How could you pack a lunch for a picnic so you would have little or no garbage?
Why do you think people might want to use something that could be thrown away, even if they know it just makes more garbage?
Why is garbage bad for people, plants, and animals?
What kinds of garbage were left over after the picnic?
What other kinds of garbage might we have had if we didn't plan an ecological picnic?
What choices did you and other class members make that were good for the environment? Good for people?
How can we turn a banana peel into a football? (Feed it to a pig.)
How can we turn an orange peel into a strawberry? (Compost it, then use the compost in a strawberry patch.)

EVALUATION

Have students repeat the first activity of the unit by drawing a picture illustrating things they care about. Compare each student's drawing with the one he or she made at the start of the unit to see if students have broadened their realm of caring.

EXTENSION IDEAS

- If you want your students to help choose the picnic site, plan a walk around the neighborhood to look at possible sites. Back in the classroom, discuss the positive and negative aspects of each site. Students can vote on where to picnic.
- Let each student thank the environment for some of the things we need, use, or enjoy. For example, "Thank you, tree, for a place to climb" or "Thank you, clouds, for rain." Get suggestions from students, then have everyone repeat "Thank you, _____, for _____."

Communities and Cultures

Third and Fourth Grades

Introduction to the Unit

All living things that share an environment are part of a community and all depend on each other in order to survive. The concept of community and the interrelationships between members of a community are introduced and built upon throughout this unit.

Beginning with the students' concept of their own community, the activities lead students to an understanding of both human and biotic (plant and animal) communities. The first two activities help students define the components of a human community. The next three activities look at ways that human communities and cultures differ in terms of how they use the environment. The unit then moves to a study of plant and animal communities. Students observe how ants in an ant colony interact, then investigate and compare two different biotic communities. The next two activities look at the interrelationships of members of a biotic community, focusing on food chain relationships and the roles of various community members. In the final activity students have the opportunity to synthesize all they have learned about communities in designing a community where people, other animals, and plants can live together in harmony.

Advance Planning

For the activity "Interviewing People Who Know" you will need to arrange with an older person in the community to visit your class. It would probably be best to do this before you begin the unit.

The activity "Establishing an Ant Community" involves setting up an ant farm in the classroom. You can use a commercially made ant farm or make one yourself (instructions for making an ant farm are included in the activity). If you buy an ant farm, information about ordering ants will be included. You will need to plan ahead as it may take six weeks for the ants to arrive. It may also be possible to find ants on your own, although during winter ants will most likely be scarce. The activity has information on finding and collecting ants. "Establishing an Ant Community" is an important activity because it allows students to observe an animal community in action. Several following activities refer to observations that students will have made. If it is difficult for you to obtain an ant farm and ants, do not be discouraged. The unit will still be valuable and exciting for your students, although you may need to make slight modifications to succeeding activities.

In the final activity, "The Ideal Community," students design communities where people and other living things can live harmoniously. If you decide to have students make models of their communities, you will need to collect a variety of "junk" materials for the models. You might write the following letter to parents asking for their donations.

Cooperative Learning Activities

To help build a sense of community in the classroom, cooperative learning activities have been included throughout this unit. Cooperative learning means that students work in small groups on a common task. Each group member is expected to

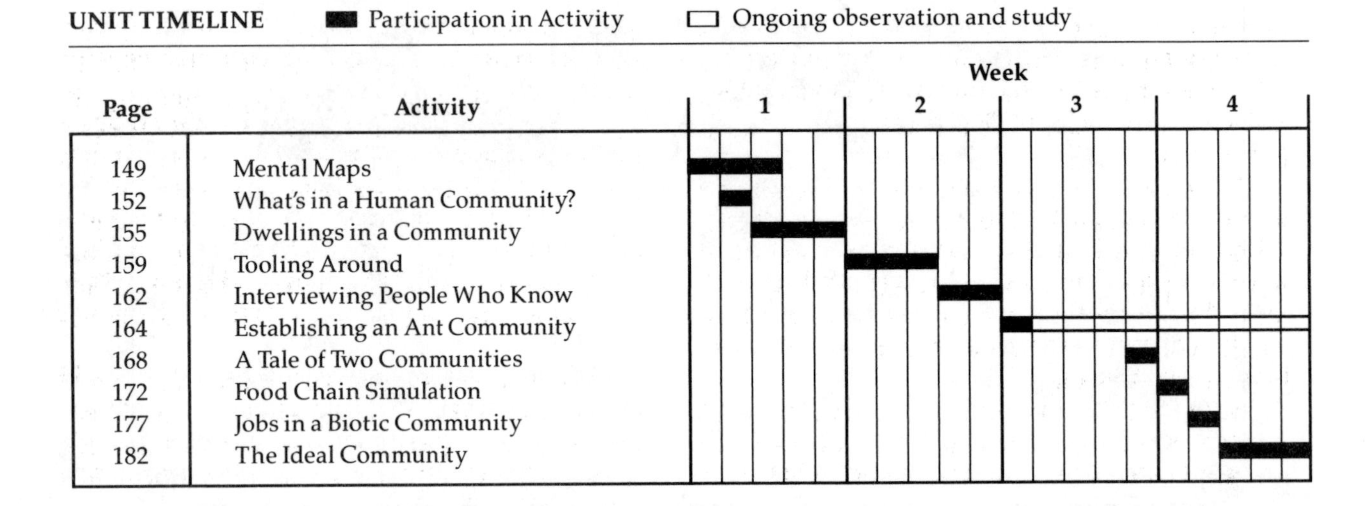

UNIT TIMELINE ■ Participation in Activity □ Ongoing observation and study

Page	Activity
149	Mental Maps
152	What's in a Human Community?
155	Dwellings in a Community
159	Tooling Around
162	Interviewing People Who Know
164	Establishing an Ant Community
168	A Tale of Two Communities
172	Food Chain Simulation
177	Jobs in a Biotic Community
182	The Ideal Community

Sample Letter

Dear Parent:

Over the next few weeks we will be studying communities and cultures. At the end of our study we are going to design "ideal" communities where people and other living things can live harmoniously. We will need donations of "junk" materials like berry baskets, toothpicks, toilet paper, paper towel rolls, margarine tubs, empty cereal boxes, popsicle sticks, styrofoam balls, pipe cleaners, pieces of heavy cardboard or masonite, and twigs or other natural materials. Please send materials to school with your child by ______ *date* ______.

contribute to the task and to help other members complete the task. During a cooperative learning activity students become important sources of information and ideas while acting as peer consultants to each other.

Cooperative learning activities may require a major role change for you and for your students. During these activities students and teacher share the role of providing and validating knowledge and ideas. The teacher takes on the important and difficult task of encouraging students to become active in their own learning.

Activities in this unit use a model called "Groups of Four" in which the class is divided into groups of four students, seated together. One of the goals of cooperative learning is that over time each student works with everyone else and benefits from everyone's ideas. Thus, assign groups randomly and change them regularly. Tell students that each group must follow these rules: (1) Students are responsible for their own work and behavior; (2) Students must be willing to help any other person in their group who asks for help; and (3) Students can ask the teacher for help only if they have a question that no one in the group can answer.

You may choose to change these rules or add others; whatever rules or expectations you choose, post them in the classroom and make sure students understand them. Students may not be accustomed to working cooperatively and may need your guidance. It takes practice, encouragement, and discussion for students to learn to work together successfully.

Resources

Chinery, Michael. *Animal Communities.* New York: Franklin Watts, Inc., 1972. This reference book contains pictures and information on animal language, parental care, family life, and the importance of communities.

Burns, Marilyn. "Groups of Four: Solving the Management Problems," *Learning,* September 1981, 46–51. This article gives information on managing cooperative learning "Groups of Four."

Strategies and Activities for Using Local Communities as Environmental Education Sites. Selected and developed by Charles E. Roth and Linda G. Lockwood. Columbus, Ohio: ERIC Clearinghouse for Science Mathematics and Environmental Education, Ohio State University, 1979. The activities described in this book encourage learning through involvement with the local community.

For Students

Environmental Action Coalition. *It's Your Environment: Things to Think About—Things to Do.* New York: Charles Scribner's Sons, 1976. Written especially for children living in or near cities, this book encourages young people to explore their environments and seek solutions to environmental problems.

MENTAL MAPS

SUMMARY OF ACTIVITY

Students sketch from memory a map of one area of their community and compare their maps to mental maps made by classmates and parents.

Time: One or two 45-minute periods

Setting: Classroom

Materials:
- Paper
- Pencils or marking pens

Subjects: Social studies, art, science, language arts

Key Words: Community, map, mental, landmark, north, south, east, west, left of, right of, in front of, behind

RELATED CALIFORNIA FRAMEWORK CONCEPTS

Communities—locally, nationally, and worldwide—are dynamic living and changing phenomena. (Adapted from *History-Social Science Framework*)

There is a great diversity within communities. (Adapted from *History-Social Science Framework*)

Visual art media can be used to translate ideas, feelings, and values. (Adapted from *Visual and Performing Arts Framework*)

OBJECTIVE

Given a particular area of their community, students compare their own observations about the area to those made by classmates.

BACKGROUND INFORMATION

A community consists of all the living things that share a location or environment. Members of a community (including humans, other animals, and plants) are bound together by their interactions with each other.

In this activity students work in groups of four to put down on paper the "mental maps" they have of their own community. A map is an abstract representation of an area and has certain elements emphasized and less important elements eliminated. A mental map is also an abstract representation but it is in an individual's mind. Each person has a different mental map of his or her own community depending on that person's experiences and what he or she considers important. This activity will help students think about their community and will enable them to see that people have different perceptions about the world around them.

Some students will want to make carefully designed maps while other students will be content with rough sketches. If your class tends to prefer "finished" products, you may want to allow additional time for students to produce maps of higher quality.

PREPARATION AND LEAD-UP

Choose an area of the community to be mapped. It should be an area familiar to all students (like the schoolgrounds, a local shopping mall, the local neighborhood, or the entire town if it is small). You may want to take students on a walking tour through the area to be mapped.

PROCEDURE

1. Ask students to relax and close their eyes. Using guided imagery, take them on a trip through the area to be mapped. "Imagine that you are in *(name of the area)* . . . Put yourself there and tune into the sights of where you are . . . Think about the sounds you hear . . . the smells you smell . . . and how you feel . . . Now imagine that you begin to walk through the area . . . (guide students through different sections of the area) . . . Continue to notice the sights, sounds, and smells around you . . . Pay attention to any major landmarks . . . places you go to often . . . or things you like looking at . . . When you are ready, bring yourself back to the classroom and open your eyes." Students who want to can share their experiences; however, be sensitive to the fact that some people prefer to remain quiet after guided imagery.

2. To get students thinking about the landmarks in the area, have a few students name one landmark they observed. List these on the board.

3. Divide students into groups of four and ask students to sketch from memory a map of the area you have selected. Have students label what they consider key landmarks or major streets. Explain to students that each group's map will be different and that there is no right or wrong way to map the area.

4. Have volunteers share their maps (you might post the maps for all students to see). Discuss the maps and how they differ (see the discussion questions).

5. Ask students what they think the word community means. Accept all answers. Tell them that a community includes all the people who live in the same location and that the people within a community interact with each other and exchange goods, resources, and services so that everyone gets what they need to live there. Tell students that they will be learning more about communities over the next few weeks.

DISCUSSION QUESTIONS

How are the maps the same? Different?
Are the landmarks on the maps the same?
Did other people in your group think of things to put on the map that you hadn't thought of? Can you give an example?
Do the landmarks that a person put on his or her map tell you anything about that person?
What does community mean?
How do communities differ?
How do people's ideas of what a community is differ?

EVALUATION

A discussion of the ways that mental maps differ can serve as evaluation.

EXTENSION IDEA

Have students look at pictures of murals found in different communities in California (see *California*

Murals by Yoko Clark and Chizu Hama and *Street Murals* by Bolker Barthelmeh). Ask, "How are particular murals different? Alike? What types of things are shown in the murals? What do different murals tell you about the community? What do murals tell you about how people view their community? If we were to make a mural of our own community, what might we include?" The class then makes a mural of its community using butcher paper and paints or crayons.

HOME LEARNING SUGGESTION

(Use as follow-up to this activity)

Have students take a parent on a guided imagery trip of the area mapped in the activity. Parents then list what they consider to be important streets or landmarks for the area (instead of mapping). Tell students that parents' lists will be looked at the next day.

RESOURCES

For Students

Barthelmeh, Bolker. *Street Murals.* New York: Alfred A. Knopf, Inc., 1982. Color plates in this book show street murals from the United States and Western Europe.

Clark, Yoko, and Chizu Hama. *California Murals.* Berkeley, Calif.: Lancaster Miller Publishers, 1979. This book provides color plates of street murals found throughout the state.

SOURCE OF ACTIVITY

Strategies and Activities for Using Local Communities as Environmental Education Sites. Selected and developed by Linda G. Lockwood and Charles E. Roth. Columbus, Ohio: ERIC Clearinghouse for Science, Mathematics and Environmental Education, Ohio State University, 1979.

WHAT'S IN A HUMAN COMMUNITY?

SUMMARY OF ACTIVITY

Students design communities that provide all the necessary goods and services. Older students simulate a city council that chooses the best design.

Time: One 30-minute period and one or two 45-minute periods

Setting: Classroom

Materials:
- Butcher paper for each group of four students
- Crayons or markers for each group of four students

Subjects: Social studies, art, language arts

Key Words: Community, living places, working places, schools, playing places, health and safety services, food, beauty, art, categories

RELATED CALIFORNIA FRAMEWORK CONCEPTS

People, their cultures, and the environments in which they live vary from place to place. (Adapted from *History-Social Science Framework*)

As citizens we can participate in our community, state, and nation. (Adapted from *History-Social Science Framework*)

Visual art media can be used to translate ideas, feelings, and values. (Adapted from *Visual and Performing Arts Framework*)

Talking and listening are important ways by which people communicate with and learn from each other. (Adapted from *English-Language Arts Framework*)

OBJECTIVE

Through art, students identify the necessary components of a community.

BACKGROUND INFORMATION

A self-sufficient community has all of the elements that people living there need—residential areas, commercial areas, industrial areas, schools and other public services, recreational areas, areas for food production, and areas that meet the aesthetic needs of residents. Few communities are able to meet all of these needs, however, so people depend on goods produced elsewhere or on transportation to find these necessities.

In this activity students list all of the things they can think of that are included in a community and then, in groups, plan a community that meets the needs of everyone living there. These needs include living places, working places, schools, playing places, health and safety services, food, and places of beauty.

Two options are presented in the activity. The discussion option allows students to share their plans and discuss how the plans meet the needs of the community. If you feel your students are capable, you can choose instead the city council option in which students simulate a city council that must decide on the best plan for the community. Usually the best plan will be the one that provides a balance of needs. Simulations like this one are operating models of real life and provide students an opportunity to role-play or act out a real situation. In a simulation, students evaluate the consequences of decisions before the decisions are actually carried out. In this simulation students interact with each other in the decision-making process, which helps them develop the skills they will need for citizen action and participation in community management.

PREPARATION AND LEAD-UP

Gather the materials. Then for each group of four, draw on butcher paper the physical layout of the

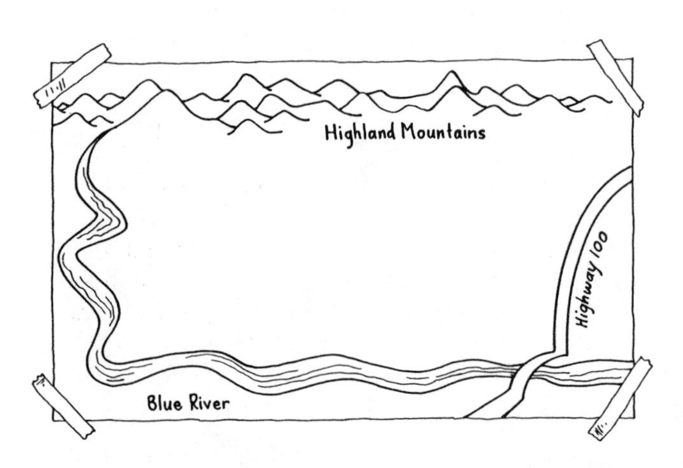

land where the community will be. Working in the same groups as the day before, students share the lists of landmarks and streets their parents made in the home learning suggestion of the previous activity. Students then compare the lists with the maps they made. Have the class discuss how the parents' lists and students' maps are the same, how they are different, and what mental maps tell us about what is important to people and what people's needs are.

PROCEDURE

Day One

1. Review what a community is. Ask students, "What kinds of things are found in a community?" List students' ideas on butcher paper.

2. Explain to students that a community provides all of the things that people living there need, including living places, working places, schools, playing places, health and safety services, food, and beauty and art. List these categories on another piece of butcher paper. Discuss with students how their ideas fit into these categories. Ask, "What other kinds of things might be included in each category? Do any of your ideas not fit into one of these categories? Which of these categories are included on the maps? Did parents include more of these things than you? Why?" Add to the list any new categories that students suggest and save the lists for the next day.

Day Two

3. Tell students that they are now going to be community planners. Each group of four students will design a small community that meets the needs of everyone living there (for the city council option, tell students that a city council will be formed to decide on the best community plan).

4. Divide students into groups of four (you may wish to use different groups than in the previous activity). Tell students that they will have 30 minutes to design a community (for the city council option, tell students they will need to plan a two-minute presentation that will be made to the city council and that more than one person must help make the presentation). Distribute to each group markers or crayons and the butcher paper onto which you drew the community layout.

5. If you choose the city council option, 20 minutes into the task go around and select one person from each group to meet together as the city council. Take them to another part of the room and tell them it will be their responsibility to hear the presentations and vote which proposal is best. Have them develop a strategy for judging the plans (you might assign each council member one or two of the community components discussed above to focus on).

6. Twenty-five minutes after the groups started planning, remind them that they have only five minutes left. When time is up, if you choose the discussion option, post the community plans and discuss with students how the various plans meet the needs of the community (see the discussion questions). If you choose the city council option, collect the plans and tell students that the city council will meet the following day.

Day Three (City Council Option Only)

7. Have city council members sit in front of the room. Appoint a timekeeper to cut off presentations after two minutes. After all presentations have been made, the city council can ask questions (allow only five to ten minutes for questions).

8. Have the council retire for five to ten minutes to select the best proposal. While the council is meeting, each group can develop a list of things it thinks the decision should be based on. The council then returns, announces its decision, and gives reasons why it thinks the proposal it chose is best.

9. Debrief the simulation by asking, "What happened in your groups? How did your group work together—did you work as a team or individually? How did you feel about the city council's decision? If your plan wasn't chosen, how did you feel about it? Did you feel the selection process was fair? Why or why not? Did people in the city council find it difficult to select a plan? Why? What did you learn from this activity?"

DISCUSSION QUESTIONS

Does your community have everything it needs? If not, what should it have?

Is there any important thing found in communities that we left off our category list?

Is any area of your community more important than any other? Why or why not?

How do other living things (animals, trees, other plants) fit into a community?

EVALUATION

Ask students to list five things that are necessary in a community and give an example of each from their own community. Have students pick one of the things and describe what a community would be like without it.

EXTENSION IDEAS

- Take a walking tour of your community. Let students observe firsthand the different features and their layouts.
- Have students write or visit the appropriate city or county offices or invite a community planner to class to find out how land-use decisions are made in your community. Ask, "What happens when new parks, schools, houses, or freeways are planned?"

HOME LEARNING SUGGESTION

(Use as follow-up to this activity)

Have students make a class "Yellow Pages" of places, goods, and services important to them. Give each student two or three file cards. Have students discuss with their families places or services in the community they have used that they would recommend to other students. Students make up a separate card for each place or service and include the name of the place or provider of the service; the address, location, and telephone number; and a short description of what is available there. In class discuss the types of places students recommended. Decide as a class on a system for organizing the cards (for example, a card file arranged by the categories used in the activity). Have cards and the file available to students so they can add to the file or use other students' ideas. Let parents know the file is available for their use, too.

DWELLINGS IN A COMMUNITY

SUMMARY OF ACTIVITY

Students research different areas of California (or different cultures) and create a mural depicting traditional Native American dwellings or dwellings of other cultures.

Time: 20 minutes in class, one or two research periods, 30 to 45 minutes drawing mural

Setting: Classroom, school library

Materials:

- Reference materials for student research (see the resources section)
- Butcher paper or poster board
- Marking pens, crayons, or paint

Subjects: Social studies, art, language arts

Key Words: Community, dwellings, surroundings, natural materials, resources

RELATED CALIFORNIA FRAMEWORK CONCEPTS

People, their cultures, and the environments in which they live vary from place to place. (Adapted from *History-Social Science Framework*)

California's land and environment have changed from prehistoric times to the present. (Adapted from *History-Social Science Framework*)

Visual art media can be used to translate ideas, feelings, and values. (Adapted from *Visual and Performing Arts Framework*)

OBJECTIVE

After researching different geographic regions, students describe ways that dwellings suit their environment.

BACKGROUND INFORMATION

In the past, communities' needs were met entirely by the immediate environment. All food, water, and resources were gathered from the natural surroundings. Although this is still true to some extent in a few cultures of the world, most communities no longer depend solely on the immediate environment. Goods and resources from all over the world are now available in our communities.

At one time dwellings that people lived in varied greatly according to local conditions. The design of homes was determined by the natural building materials available and was suited to the climate in which the people lived. Native Americans living in different regions of California built houses that were particular to their region.

In the California Northwest, Native American houses were built from planks of cedar, pine, or fir trees logged from nearby forests. A pit was dug and the plank house was built over it. The strong, thick walls and roofs kept inhabitants cool in summer and warm in winter.

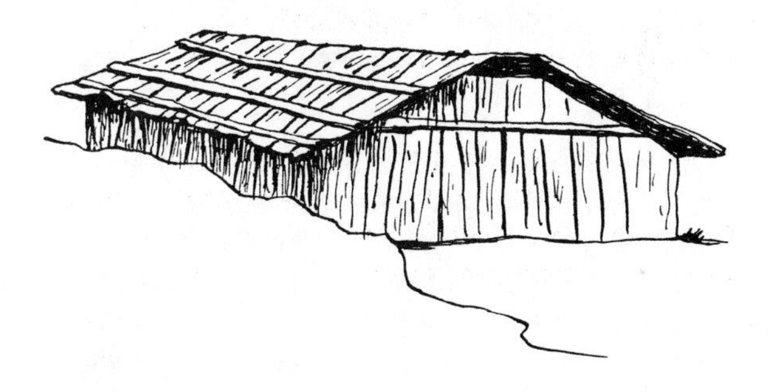

In mountain areas of California, thick slabs of bark from nearby redwood and cedar trees were piled against a central pole until no holes remained except a smoke hole in the top and a small doorway down below. During cold weather a door of tule or animal skin was used.

Most homes built along the California coast were made of tule or brush. A pit about two feet deep was dug, then a frame of willow poles was made to curve over the pit. The frame was covered with brush or tules that were tied with cord made of nettles, milkweed, or hemp fiber.

Some Native American dwellings in the California Central Valley were earth-covered brush shelters. A pit was dug and lined with poles for the framework. The tips of the poles were tied together and brush and tule were laid on top of the framework. A layer of mud several inches thick covered the entire house. This design helped keep out summer's heat and winter's cold. Grasses and plants often grew on the earth-covered roofs so that the dwellings blended into the landscape.

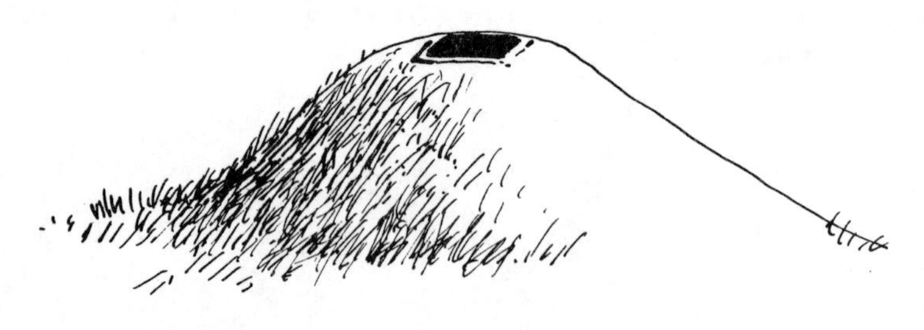

In this activity students look at Native American dwellings in regions of California and find out how they relate to the environment. The activity can also be done by focusing on other cultures around the world. The term "culture" refers to the beliefs, social structure, and material traits of a group or community. The culture as well as the physical characteristics of a community are influenced by the natural environment.

PREPARATION AND LEAD-UP

Have reference materials available for student research or schedule library time for the research. Determine what areas of California students will study or whether they will study dwellings of other cultures around the world.

PROCEDURE

Day One

1. Ask students to relax and close their eyes. Take them on an excursion using guided imagery: "Imagine yourself where you were when you first woke up this morning . . . Put yourself in that place and tune into the sights, sounds, smells, feelings of where you were . . . Get up and begin your day, getting ready for school . . . Notice what running water, electricity, or other conveniences you use . . . Notice the different rooms you walk into and what those rooms are like . . . Pay attention to all your sensations . . . Imagine yourself starting off for school, traveling the way you usually do . . . Before you leave, take a good look at the outside of your home . . . Notice what it looks like, what the shape of the building is like, and what the building is made of . . . As you go to school, pay attention to smells, sounds, feelings, and sights . . . At some point along the way, where you feel comfortable, stop . . . Turn all the way around once, slowly . . . Now let the scene around you change . . . Let the buildings, the road, or sidewalk, the whole community seem to melt away to the way it may have been a long time ago . . . Imagine the day is just beginning once again . . . Imagine yourself now as a member of a Native American tribe (or other culture) who lived in the area at least 200 years ago . . . You are just waking up . . . Notice your surroundings, the sounds, smells, sights, and feelings that greet you . . . Get up and begin your morning activities, paying attention to where you are and what you use to do each thing . . . Notice what your home is like . . . When you are ready, bring yourself back to the present and open your eyes."

2. Invite students to share their experiences, being sensitive to the fact that many students prefer to keep quiet after a guided imagery journey. Tell students that they are going to find out more about

Native American communities (or those of other cultures) and how they were affected by their natural surroundings.

3. Divide students into groups. Each group will research a different area of California like the California Northwest, California Mountain Region, California Coast, or the Central Valley (alternatively, have groups research different cultures around the world). Students will find out about the traditional Native American houses that were found in each area (or traditional houses in other cultures), answering questions like, "What natural materials were used to build the houses? Where did the materials come from? What happened to the houses when they were no longer lived in?" (See the discussion questions as well.) Allow students a couple of days to conduct their research.

Day Two

4. Have students use coloring pens, paints, or crayons to create a mural depicting traditional houses they have found out about. Each house should be placed in its appropriate terrain.

5. Discuss the appropriateness of materials used in the construction of the houses. Ask, "What was the climate in each area like? What materials were used to build the houses? Were these materials easy to find? How did the materials used for building the houses meet the shelter needs of the inhabitants?" Also discuss the communities students researched (see the discussion questions).

DISCUSSION QUESTIONS

How big were the communities?
How did the people in the communities have their needs met? Did they hunt? Grow their own food?
How might the natural surroundings have affected the communities?
How did the surroundings affect the houses you studied?
How do the surroundings affect our community?
Does the weather have any effect? Does the terrain (mountains, ocean, river, bay)?

EVALUATION

Repeat the guided imagery exercise. Ask students to write about how their mental picture changed after studying more about the dwellings of Native Americans (or other culture they researched).

EXTENSION IDEAS

- Have students write a story on "A Day in the Life of a Kid from *(the researched culture)*." Alternatively, have students write a story that compares their own community with a community from the culture they researched.
- Have students draw pictures of houses they would like to live in that use some of the design features of Native American dwellings. Students can write or tell why they would like to live in the houses.

HOME LEARNING SUGGESTION

(Use as follow-up to this activity)

Challenge students to find ways that surroundings affect the design of their home or of buildings in the neighborhood. Give students a data sheet (see sample) and suggest they look for things like

Data Sheet for Home Learning

Features of my home that help keep it cool in summer:

Features of my home that help keep it warm in winter:

Other ways that the environment affects the design of my home:

air conditioning, heating, covered patios, a swimming pool, trees for shade, and porches on the south (sunny) side of buildings.

RESOURCES

For Students

Faber, Gail, and Michele Lasagna. *Whispers from the First Californians.* Alamo, Calif.: Magpie Publications, 1980. This book contains activities and information about Native Americans of California, including comparisons of various regions.

Sauer, Carl. *Man in Nature.* Berkeley, Calif.: Turtle Island Foundation, 1975. This textbook is loaded with information about native people of North America and their ways of life.

Siberell, Anne. *Houses: Shelters from Prehistoric Times to Today.* New York: Holt, Rinehart, and Winston, 1979. Siberell tells about how houses evolved through the ages, showing the development of more and more sophisticated houses and how need, lifestyle, and available materials dictate the kinds of houses we live in.

Dunrea, Olivier. *Skara Brae: The Story of a Prehistoric Village.* New York: Holiday House, 1985. A village in the Orkney Islands (north of Scotland) is the setting for this story that tells how dwellings were built, furnished, and insulated, and how social and physical patterns of the community changed over generations.

SOURCE OF ACTIVITY

Project Learning Tree, "Another Way of Seeing." Washington, D.C.: The American Forest Council, 1977.

Illustrations adapted from:

Elsasser, Albert B., and Robert F. Heizer. *The Natural World of the California Indians.* Berkeley: University of California Press, 1980.

Faber, Gail, and Michele Lasagna. *Whispers from the First Californians.* Alamo, Calif.: Magpie Publications, 1980.

TOOLING AROUND

SUMMARY OF ACTIVITY

Students devise tools to solve different problems, then compare tools from another culture with contemporary tools.

Time: Three 30- to 45-minute periods plus research time

Setting: Classroom

Materials:
- Two or three tools or objects that might be used for tools (see the preparation and lead-up section)
- Drawing paper
- Drawing pens or crayons
- An assortment of contemporary tools

Subjects: Social studies, science, art, language arts

Key Words: Tools, culture

RELATED CALIFORNIA FRAMEWORK CONCEPTS

People, their cultures, and the environments in which they live vary from place to place. (Adapted from *History-Social Science Framework*)

The nature of society is strongly influenced by science and technology. (*Science Framework Addendum*)

Visual art media can be used to translate ideas, feelings, and values. (Adapted from *Visual and Performing Arts Framework*)

Writing enables us to communicate our ideas and can lead to a better understanding of ourselves and the human condition. (Adapted from *English-Language Arts Framework*)

OBJECTIVE

After creating tools to solve different problems, students compare another culture's tools with contemporary tools.

BACKGROUND INFORMATION

Human beings have a tremendous impact on the environment. Everywhere we look we can see things made or arranged by humans. In cities, buildings and streets have been constructed, trees have been planted, and parks and open spaces have been landscaped to create effects we find pleasing. In the countryside, much of the land has been altered by generations of humans so that it looks much different than when people first ventured there.

It is only with the help of tools that we have been able to arrange the world to fit our needs. For thousands of years, people have been using tools to help them solve problems of daily living and to help make their lives easier. All cultures around the world have found ways of using tools. Traditionally, most of these tools came from the immediate environment, using materials like rocks, plants, and animal parts.

Tools from different cultures can look dissimilar even though they might perform the same tasks. For example, a nail that we use is much different from "nails" used by Northwest Coast Native Americans—they used strips of bark laced through holes drilled into the wood—but both types hold together two pieces of wood.

In this activity students are introduced to the idea that oftentimes there is more than one tool that can help solve a single problem. Although different tools may look strange to us at first, when studying them closely we can learn to appreciate that other cultures' tools often serve the same functions as our own. Usually the differences occur because people have learned to meet their needs using the resources available to them.

PREPARATION AND LEAD-UP

Gather two or three tools that students may not recognize like a cherry pitter, stud finder, or telephone cord retractor. Alternatively, find objects such as a stone, shells, or feathers that might be used as tools.

PROCEDURE

Day One

1. Show students the objects you have gathered (if you brought in unusual tools, don't tell students what they are). Divide students into groups of four and have them brainstorm a list of ways that each object could be used. Encourage students to be creative; for example, a stone might be used to pound nails, to keep a car from rolling away, to stop up the bathtub, to sharpen a pencil, to help warm up the bed (if the stone is heated), as a door stop, or as a step ladder.

2. Discuss with students the uses they have thought of for each object. If some of the objects are tools, demonstrate how they are used and what their purpose is.

3. Explain to students that a tool is something that helps you complete a job. Ask, "Can you think of tools you or people you know use?" List student suggestions on the board. Talk about how people who have different jobs must use different kinds of tools (for example, discuss the kinds of tools a carpenter and a plumber might use). Ask students how the tools are different and how they are alike (a carpenter might use a hammer, tape measure, saw, screwdriver, and a drill, while a plumber might use a pipe wrench, pliers, plunger, and a snake).

Day Two

4. Tell students that they are going to design tools for specific jobs. Give them a choice of several challenges such as the following:

- Design a tool that would make heavy objects easier to lift.
- Design a tool that would let you squeeze a slice of lemon without squirting the lemon juice in your eye or on your shirt.
- Design a tool that would enable you to put out candles without spattering wax and without making the wick smoke.
- Design a tool that would keep skeins of yarn or rope from getting tangled.
- Design a tool that would make pictures hang straight.
- Design a tool that would keep your shoes together in the closet.

Pass out paper and colored pens or crayons and have students work individually on the problem of their choice. Students are to draw a picture of the design they have created and write a paragraph explaining how the tool they have designed would be used. Encourage students not to stop at one solution but to think of as many solutions as possible. When students have finished, have volunteers share their designs.

5. Discuss the fact that every culture throughout time has found ways of using tools to solve problems of daily living. Traditionally, most of these tools came from the community's immediate surroundings, and were made from materials like rocks, plants, and animal parts. The needs of people and the materials available to them vary around the world, so the ways people do things and the tools they have created also vary. With fourth grade students you might discuss the materials necessary for the tools they designed. Ask, "Are they materials that are available to our present culture? Were they available to Native American cultures of 200 years ago?"

6. Have students begin research of tools that Native Americans in your area used for building, preparing food, cooking, or making crafts. Have them draw pictures of tools. Alternatively, you might have students research and draw pictures of tools that were used by people of another culture you have studied.

Day Three

7. After the research has been done, bring in an assortment of contemporary tools and have students observe differences and similarities between these tools and tools used by Native Americans (or by people in another culture students have studied). Observations might include the function of tools (how jobs done by the tools are similar or different), the materials used, and how life would be different without the use of these tools.

8. Have students draw pictures of contemporary tools that perform tasks similar to tools used by Native Americans (or by people in another culture that students have studied). Discuss the uses.

DISCUSSION QUESTIONS

What materials were the tools made of?
How were the tools made?
How were they used?

How might the tools available to a community affect the community over time?
Was there a special person in the community who made the tool?
Was there a special person who used the tool?

EVALUATION

Have each student choose one tool from our culture and one tool from a Native American culture or another culture. For each tool, have students describe what the tool looks like, what the tool is made of, how to use the tool (step-by-step directions), and what problem or problems the tool solves.

EXTENSION IDEAS

- Have students re-examine their challenge problem and solution from the point of view of a Native American. Alternatively, design a challenge problem that is appropriate to the Native American lifestyle.
- Have students use "junk" materials to make models of the tools they designed. Stress to students that the tools must benefit society in some way.

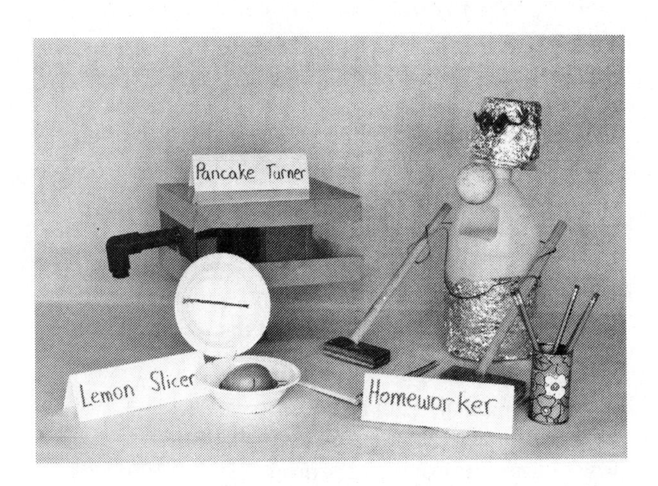

- Have students study baskets made by Native American tribes in your area (check with historical societies, museums, or craft centers to see about borrowing baskets). The class might study how the baskets were made, what tools were used to make them, if there were any people whose specific job was to make the baskets, and how the baskets were used (you might find a resource person in your area who could instruct students in making baskets). Discuss how the baskets compare to contemporary objects used for similar purposes.
- Have students study the different kinds of boats that Native Americans in California designed. Find out what materials were used, what tools were used, whose job it was to make the tools, and how the boats suited the lifestyle of the people that built them. Students might build models using materials similar to those used by Native Americans.
- Have students find out how animals use tools. *Animals That Use Tools*, by Barbara Ford, is a good source of information.

HOME LEARNING SUGGESTION

(Use as follow-up to this activity)

Have students ask parents to identify tools they use at work or home, and how they use them. Students can ask parents if the tool has changed over the years and, if so, how. Students then write a paragraph describing the tool and its uses.

RESOURCES

For Students

Faber, Gail, and Michele Lasagna. *Whispers from the First Californians.* Alamo, Calif.: Magpie Publications, 1980. This book contains activities and information about Native Americans of California, including comparisons of various regions.

Ford, Barbara. *Animals That Use Tools.* New York: Julian Messner Publishers, 1978. This children's book shows ways different animals use tools.

Sauer, Carl. *Man in Nature.* Berkeley, Calif.: Turtle Island Foundation, 1975. This textbook is loaded with information about native people of North America and their ways of life.

INTERVIEWING PEOPLE WHO KNOW

SUMMARY OF ACTIVITY

Students interview an older person from the community to learn how the community has changed.

Time: Two 60-minute periods
Setting: Classroom
Materials: Tape recorder
Subjects: Social studies, science, language arts
Key Words: History, culture

RELATED CALIFORNIA FRAMEWORK CONCEPTS

The nature of society is strongly influenced by science and technology. (*Science Framework Addendum*)

California's land and environment have changed from prehistoric times to the present. (Adapted from *History-Social Science Framework*)

Talking and listening are important ways by which people communicate with and learn from each other. (Adapted from *English-Language Arts Framework*)

OBJECTIVE

After interviewing an older member of the community, students describe ways that the community or culture has changed over time.

BACKGROUND INFORMATION

Older people are tremendous resources for learning how people and their environments have changed. You might invite the grandparent of one of your students to class. If you do not know someone to invite, contact local churches, senior centers, retirement communities, or a local chapter of the Gray Panthers. This activity can also be done by interviewing a person from another culture to find out how that culture differs from your culture.

PREPARATION AND LEAD-UP

Invite an older person to class for an interview and discussion. Let the person know in advance that the goal of the activity is to compare past and present environments and people. Ask the visitor what part of his or her life—schooling, profession, or family, for example—is especially interesting and should be discussed (you may want to tie this in to the previous activity by having the visitor talk about tools he or she has used). If the person grew up in another state or country, find out some background information on that place.

PROCEDURE

Day One

1. Discuss with students what they found out from the previous day's home learning suggestion. Ask, "What tools do your parents use? What tools did they tell you about that have changed over time? How have the tools changed? Why do you think they have changed? What other things do you think might have changed since the time your grandparents were your age?"

2. Explain to the class that it will have the opportunity to interview an older person to find out how the community or the surroundings have changed. Have the class brainstorm a list of questions for the visitor (you may want to give the visitor the questions in advance).

Day Two

3. Announce your visitor: "Today we have a special guest. We have some questions to ask our guest so that we can better understand how people's lives have changed since our guest was your age. After we finish interviewing our guest, we will interview each other, using the same questions. Then we can see how life is different now than when our guest was younger."

4. Interview the guest and tape record questions and answers. At the same time, immediately following, or later on have students interview each other.

5. Review the tape recorded answers of students and the guest. Try to make some conclusions about past and present life.

6. Have the class as a whole write a thank-you letter to the guest or have students write individual letters. Students might want to enclose drawings that depict things the guest said.

DISCUSSION QUESTIONS

Comparing answers of students and our guest, what things are the same?
What things have changed?
How do students' answers differ?
How might our guest's mental map of our community be different from our own mental maps?
In what ways do communities change over time? Stay the same?

EVALUATION

Have students give an example of something that has changed in the community in the last 50 years and explain why they think this change came about.

EXTENSION IDEAS

- Have students interview members of their family and people in the community using the same questions. Students then share the answers they got and make a graph or a timeline of how the community evolved.
- Have students make a booklet about their community with stories written from their interviews. *The Foxfire Book*, edited by Eliot Wiggington, may inspire ideas.

HOME LEARNING SUGGESTION

(Use as follow-up to this activity)

Have students interview their parents about how their family observes a particular holiday. Students might brainstorm questions to ask like, "What special foods do we eat? What games do we play? What songs do we sing? Were these traditions followed when you were young?" Students write down what they found out from the interviews , then compare their findings with the findings of other students.

RESOURCE

The Foxfire Book. Edited by Eliot Wiggington. Garden City, N.J.: Anchor Press/Doubleday, 1968. This book is full of articles from *Foxfire*, a student-produced magazine that examines local folklore.

ESTABLISHING AN ANT COMMUNITY

SUMMARY OF ACTIVITY

Students observe an ant farm and note changes and activities.

Time: 45-minute introduction; observations over one to two weeks done in conjunction with the rest of the unit

Setting: Classroom

Materials:

- Ant farm kit (or one small baking pan, one large baking pan, and one pane of glass large enough to cover the small pan)
- Soil
- Ants (including queen)
- Magnifying lenses
- Small sponge
- Dark cloth
- Plastic containers for ant exploration, one per student
- Cotton swabs
- Bits of food like honey, bread crumbs, meat, or fruit
- "Ant Farm Observations" copycat page for each pair of students

Subjects: Science, math, performing arts, language arts

Key Words: Colony, behavior, observations

RELATED CALIFORNIA FRAMEWORK CONCEPTS

Each species needs a particular physical environment. All living things that share a particular environment are called a community. (*Science Framework Addendum*)

An ecosystem consists of a community of living things interacting with each other and with the physical environment. Major types of ecosystems include aquatic (pond, creek, ocean, or estuary) and terrestrial (grassland, chaparral, forest, or desert). (*Science Framework Addendum*)

Data can be collected, organized, represented, and interpreted using lists, tables, and graphs. (Adapted from *Mathematics Framework*)

OBJECTIVE

Through observations of a classroom experiment, students express ways that members of an ant community cooperate to survive.

BACKGROUND INFORMATION

In the previous activities students learned about human communities—what they are, how they are affected by the environment, and how they have changed over time. The next four activities will build on the students' understanding of "community" by taking a look at biotic (animal and plant) communities. Ants are a wonderful starting point for learning about animals that work together in a community to satisfy needs. They are small, simple to care for, and easy to observe.

There are about 10,000 different species of ants, but all of them live in colonies in which the adults cooperate for the survival of the whole community. Members of the colony are often assigned to different jobs and when an individual is separated from the community it usually dies. A colony consists mainly of sterile female ants, or workers, that are ruled by one or more queens. Ants communicate by touching their antennae and by releasing chemicals onto the surface where they walk.

Most ants build nests under the ground; these nests consist of a maze of tunnels and chambers. Some chambers are used as "nurseries" where the eggs are laid; others are used as storehouses for food. Some chambers may even be used as cemeteries.

Some ant species are hunters and others are farmers that actually grow their own crops. Most ant species, though, are food-gatherers and collect a wide variety of edible materials.

If you purchase a commercially available ant farm, most likely it will include information about how to order ants from a distributor. It may take six weeks to receive ants, so allow plenty of time. You can also collect your own ants, although they are difficult to find during winter. Look for lines of ants marching along sidewalks or paths and follow the lines back to the nest. Carefully dig up the nest and collect as many ants as you can in a container. Be sure to take the queen (she is much larger than the others) or the colony will soon die out.

Feed ants a drop of honey mixed with water, one or two bread crumbs, an ant-sized piece of meat, a dead fly (look for these on window sills), or one or two bird seeds. Don't overfeed ants or the food will rot (if this happens, remove the food with tweezers). Keep a tiny damp sponge in the farm as a source of water.

PREPARATION AND LEAD-UP

Set up the commercial ant farm kit or make a "homemade" ant farm. To make an ant farm, place a small, shallow baking pan inside a larger one. Fill the larger pan with water to prevent the ants from escaping. Place a pane of glass over the inner pan (the glass must not extend beyond or touch the outer pan), and fill the inner pan with soil and ants (if possible, include the queen). Keep a dark covering over the ant colony at all times, except when observing ants. Ants will become inactive or will burrow down where they are difficult to see if the colony is uncovered.

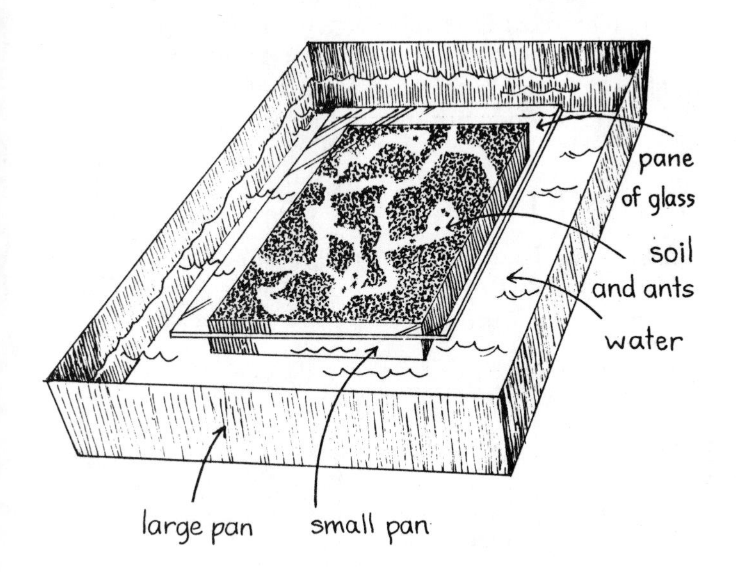

PROCEDURE

1. Explain to students that they will be observing an actual animal community over time. This community is an ant colony. Tell students what you know about ants (see the background information).

2. Caution students to handle ants carefully. This means letting an ant crawl onto your hand rather than trying to pick it up and risk squashing it, and being gentle while handling an ant and putting an ant back in its container when you don't want to hold the ant any longer.

3. Divide students into pairs. Give each student an ant in a container and have students find out what they can about their ant. For example, tell students to hold their ants between thumb and finger and sniff (the smell is formic acid). Ask, "What does your ant do when it is alone? How would you describe its behavior? How does it entertain itself? Is it lonely? Give your ant a grain of sugar. What does it do? Put your ant with your partner's. What do two ants do when they meet each other? Pour water on a small sponge and place it by the ants. What happens? Using a cotton swab, dab drops of honey, flour, crumbs, or other food materials near the ants. What food did the ants like and dislike? Put your ant back with the other ants. How does it behave in its community?"

4. Have each pair of students make up a dramatization showing one thing they found out about their ants. Pair up the pairs (so that there are four students in a group) and have each pair act out their dramatization for the other pair. Bring the class back together and select a few students to act out their dramatizations for the entire class. Discuss with the students what they found out. Ask, "How is your ant like you? How is it different?"

5. Place all ants in the ant farm. Keep hand lenses nearby. Assign students a partner and provide each pair of students an "Ant Farm Observations" copycat page. Over the next week or two have students observe the ant farm for about five minutes every day and record any changes. After the second day of observations you may wish to begin the next activity.

DISCUSSION QUESTIONS

(Use at the end of the observation period)

How do ants cooperate to survive?
How is the queen different from the other ants? What is her role?
What are the tunnels and chambers of the ant farm for?
How do ants help plants and soil?
What could you do to keep your home free of ants without using poisons? (Possible answers include provide food outside, keep the inside clean, and block ants' entrances to house.)
In what ways are the ants in our ant farm a community?
In what ways is an ant community like a human community?
In what ways is an ant community different than a human community?

EVALUATION

Students describe three ant behaviors they have observed. For one of the behaviors students describe why the ants behaved this way and how the behavior might help the ant survive.

EXTENSION IDEAS

- Have students make a map of the space used by the ant colony. Ask, "How are the maps similar? Different?"
- Have students study wasps, bees, termites, or other insects that live in colonies. Ask, "What jobs do the different insect classes perform within the colony?"
- Have students find out more about the ant's life cycle. Ask, "How long do ants live?"

HOME LEARNING SUGGESTION

(Use as follow-up to this activity)

Ask students to look for ants moving in a line outside their homes. Have students drop a small piece of food near the line, measure and record the distance of the food from the line, and note whether the ants moved off the line to get the food (see the sample data sheet that follows). Students can repeat this process several times, varying the distance from the ant line and the food that is dropped. In class discuss students' findings. Ask, "Which foods did the ants seem to prefer? What was the closest you dropped the food without the ant line moving? What was the furthest you dropped the food with the ant line moving?"

SOURCE OF ACTIVITY

Nickelsburg, Janet. *Nature Activities for Early Childhood.* Menlo Park, Calif.: Addison-Wesley Publishing Co., 1976.

Sample Data Sheet

Food Item	Distance Food Placed from Line	Did the ants move off the line to get the food?

Name ______________________________

ANT FARM OBSERVATIONS

Date	New Life	Dead Ants	Other Changes	One ant for two minutes. How did it spend its time?	The queen for two minutes. How did she spend her time?
	Look for:			Watch:	

A TALE OF TWO COMMUNITIES

SUMMARY OF ACTIVITY

Students investigate two different biotic communities and describe similarities and differences between them.

Time: 45 to 60 minutes

Setting: Outdoors

Materials:
- String or other boundary markers
- "Two Biotic Communities" copycat page for each group of four students
- Thermometer for each group of four students
- Trowel or ruler for each group of four students
- Magnifying lens for each group of four students
- Clipboard for each group of four students
- Chart paper and marking pens or chalkboard

Subjects: Science, math, social studies

Key Words: Biotic community, dependent

RELATED CALIFORNIA FRAMEWORK CONCEPTS

Each species needs a particular physical environment. All living things that share a particular environment are called a community. (*Science Framework Addendum*)

An ecosystem consists of a community of living things interacting with each other and with the physical environment. Major types of ecosystems include aquatic (pond, creek, ocean, or estuary) and terrestrial (grassland, chaparral, forest, or desert). (*Science Framework Addendum*)

Data can be collected, organized, represented, and interpreted using lists, tables, and graphs. (Adapted from *Mathematics Framework*)

OBJECTIVE

After investigating two different study sites, students describe similarities and differences between them.

BACKGROUND INFORMATION

A biotic community consists of all the plants and animals that live in an area and are interdependent upon each other. Although plants and animals living in a biotic community may not work together as ants do, they do depend on each other to survive. Plants may depend on animals to pollinate their flowers, disperse their seeds, and fertilize the soil they live in. Animals in turn depend on plants for food and shelter. Animals may also depend on other kinds of animals for food and protection.

Just as physical factors—temperature, moisture, sunlight, and wind—affect human communities, so do physical factors affect biotic communities. These physical factors influence the suitability of an area for particular organisms and determine the kinds of plants and animals that live there.

Both on land and in water, many kinds of communities exist. Naturalists often name a community for the largest or most abundant plant found there. Along with climate, the dominant kind of plant helps determine the conditions of moisture, temperature, and other physical factors that distinguish one community from another. Tide pools, cattail marshes, and redwood forests are examples of community types.

In this activity students broaden their understanding of communities by comparing the soil moisture, air temperature, and types of animals and plants in two different biotic communities. In the next two activities students learn about some of the interrelationships between members of a biotic community.

PREPARATION AND LEAD-UP

Determine two study sites that are different from each other in terms of the soil moisture, air temperature, and types of animals and plants living there. A well-maintained lawn, an asphalt area, a flower or vegetable garden, a vacant lot, a park with lots of trees, the edge of a pond, stream, or lake, an open field, and a forest are examples of possible study sites.

Use string or another indicator to mark enough mini-areas [about five meters (five yards) square] within each study site so that each group of four has its own area to investigate.

Have students practice reading thermometers. Students can place thermometers under running water, on the floor, near the ceiling, or outside the classroom to measure different temperatures.

PROCEDURE

1. Review with students that a human community includes all the people that live in an area. Introduce the term "biotic community" and explain to students that biotic communities include all the plants and animals that live in an area. Tell students that today they will be observing two different biotic communities. Ask, "What might we find in a biotic community?" Remind students that they have learned how human communities are affected by the environment in which they are located. Ask, "How might biotic communities be affected by the environment?"

2. Ask students for suggestions about how to study living things without harming them. Use these suggestions to emphasize that care must be taken when studying plants or animals. Make sure that students understand that plants and animals can be held only temporarily for observing, then should be returned unhurt to the spot they came from. If you are going to be near the school building, remind students that they will need to work without making a lot of noise so that they do not disturb other students.

3. Divide the class into groups of four and hand out the copycat pages. Within each group assign one person to record the group's observations of plant life, one to observe and record observations of animal life, one to observe and record the soil conditions, and one to measure and record the temperature in each study area. Each student is also responsible for taking one tool (clipboard, magnifying lens, thermometer, and trowel or ruler) to the area and for making sure the tool is returned.

4. In describing plant life, each group can record what it observes to be the most common plants found in each location. It is not important that students know names; students can draw a picture of the plant or make up a name that seems to fit such as "huge green tree" or "yellow flower bush."

In describing animal life, each group should note the various kinds of animals present in each location like insects, birds, reptiles, fish, frogs, tadpoles, and mammals, or evidence of animals like nests, webs, feathers, scat, tracks, and burrows (again specific names are not important, students can draw pictures or use generic names).

In examining soil conditions at the two locations, students can use a trowel or ruler to scrape the surface of the ground and obtain a small sample of soil. By feeling the soil students should be able to tell whether it is wet, moist, or dry.

To measure the air temperature at both locations, each group will use a thermometer. If the location includes a pond, stream, or lake students can also record the water temperature.

5. After each group has had sufficient time to conduct investigations and record its findings, ask students to regroup and share their findings. This can be done in a central location outside or back in the classroom (make sure that nothing was left in the study area).

6. Make a large chart listing each of the communities investigated and consolidate and record the data gathered. If the temperature readings for each community are different, help students average them.

7. Discuss differences between the two communities (see the discussion questions). Review factors that make biotic communities different from each other (they have different plants and animals, different moistures, and different temperatures). Tell students that in the next two days they will learn more about biotic communities and about how the members of a biotic community depend on each other.

DISCUSSION QUESTIONS

Which community has the greatest number of plants? Animals? Which has the least of each?
Which community has the wettest soil? The driest?
Which community has the highest air temperature? The lowest?
How are the plants and animals in the two communities the same? Different?

How might soil moisture and air temperature affect members of the community?
Did the amount of plant cover seem to affect the soil moisture?
How might plants affect the animals in a community?
How might animals affect the plants in a community?

EVALUATION

Students describe the differences between the two communities they studied.

EXTENSION IDEA

Revisit each of the communities to determine how humans have affected them. Students might look for things like litter, cut tree stumps, paths, mowed areas, and polluted air or water. Discuss students' observations. "Which human actions have harmful effects on these communities? What might we do to keep further damage from occurring? Which human actions have a positive effect on the community? What might we do to encourage more of these kinds of actions?"

HOME LEARNING SUGGESTION

(Use as follow-up to this activity)

Ask students to observe the plants and animals that live around their homes. Have students draw pictures and write the names of several plants and animals that seem to be the most common (students can make up descriptive names if they don't know the real names). In class, compare the plants and animals students found to those they observed in the activity.

RESOURCE

For Students

Mabey, Richard. *Oak and Company.* New York: Greenwillow Books, 1983. This illustrated book is about a community in an oak tree.

SOURCE OF ACTIVITY

Project Learning Tree, "A Field, a Forest, and a Stream." Washington, D.C.: The American Forest Council, 1977.

Names of group members ______________________

____

____

____

TWO BIOTIC COMMUNITIES

Characteristic	*First Community*	*Second Community*
Plants What are the most common plants? (Draw pictures or write names)		
Animals What are the most common animals? (Draw pictures or write names)		
Air Temperature		
Soil Moisture Wet, moist, or dry?		

FOOD CHAIN SIMULATION

SUMMARY OF ACTIVITY

Students simulate a food chain.

Time: 45 to 60 minutes

Setting: Outdoor area with about 15 meters (50 feet) on a side

Materials:
- Nametags or armbands (see the preparation and lead-up section)
- Four to five liters (four to five quarts) of popped popcorn (or beans or acorns)
- Marking pen
- Timer
- Masking tape
- Graph paper
- One sandwich bag stomach for each student (see the preparation and lead-up section)

Subjects: Science, physical education, math

Key Words: Biotic community, food chain, predators, prey

RELATED CALIFORNIA FRAMEWORK CONCEPTS

Food chains and food webs indicate the eating patterns of the members of an ecosystem. Predators are animals (and a few plants) that kill and eat other animals (prey). (*Science Framework Addendum*)

Data can be collected, organized, represented, and interpreted using lists, tables, and graphs. (Adapted from *Mathematics Framework*)

OBJECTIVE

After a simulation activity, students explain the eating patterns of members of a simple food chain.

BACKGROUND INFORMATION

A human community meets all the needs of its members, including food needs. In a biotic community all the needs of plants and animals living there are met by the various elements of the community. For example, the animals in a particular biotic community must have their food needs met by other members of the community. This means that plant-eating animals depend on suitable plants for food, and animal-eaters, or predators, depend on prey for survival.

A food chain is a simplified way of showing food relationships between plants and animals in a community. The food chain grass → mouse → hawk shows that grass is eaten by a mouse and the mouse in turn is eaten by a hawk (the arrow points in the direction that the food energy is flowing; in this example food energy in the grass goes to the mouse and the food energy in the mouse passes on to the hawk). Placing animals into a visible food chain like this can help us understand what happens to members of a community.

Rarely does an animal eat only one type of food, however, as a food chain might imply. To get a clearer picture of how animals in a community are related to one another, it is often helpful to look at food webs rather than food chains. A food web is the interconnection of the food chains in a community. It shows how members of the community are connected to other members by what they eat.

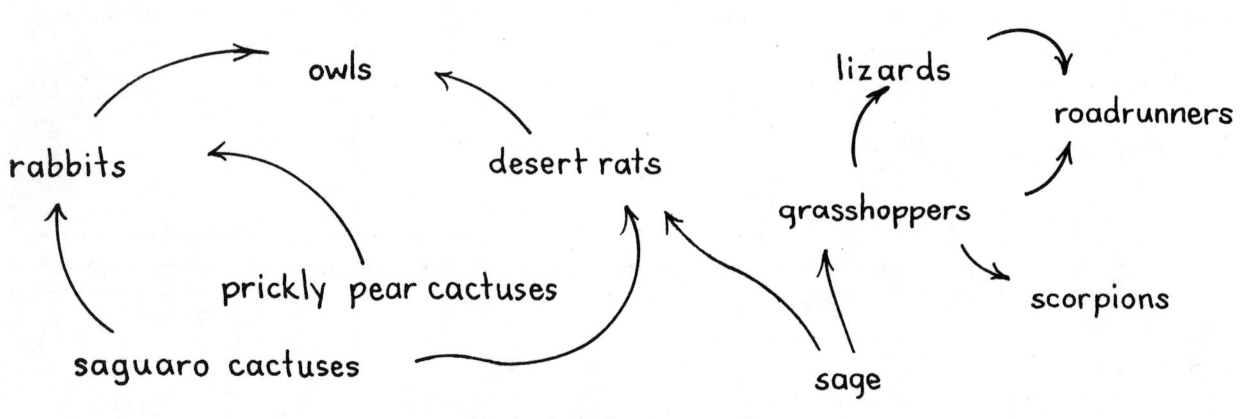

Food web of a desert community

This activity introduces students to the concept that members of a biotic community depend on one another for survival. Feeding relationships of community members are often difficult to observe, but by assuming roles of animals and simulating feeding relationships students can begin to understand that plants and animals in a community are closely tied to each other.

In nature, populations are usually large enough to ensure continuation of a species even though some of the individuals die. In this simulation populations are so small that survival of even one or two of each kind indicates a balanced, ongoing community.

PREPARATION AND LEAD-UP

Prepare one sandwich bag stomach for each student by placing a piece of masking tape on a sandwich bag so that the bottom of the tape is four centimeters (one and a half inches) from the bottom of the bag.

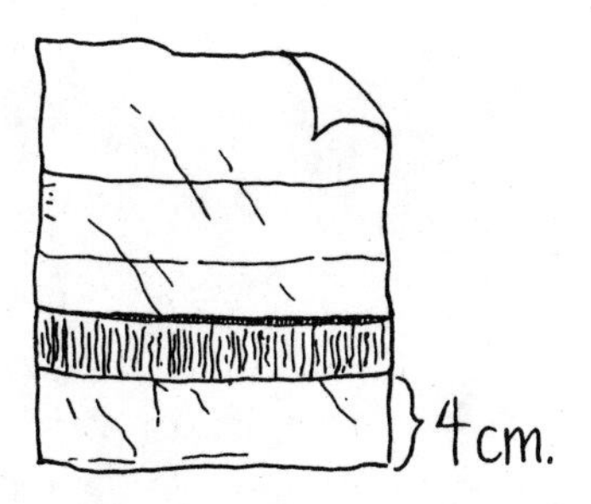

Make nametags out of index cards and yarn, writing one animal name on each, or make armbands in three colors from strips of cloth about 50 centimeters long and 10 centimeters wide (20 inches long by 4 inches wide). Make enough nametags so that up to three-fourths of the class can be grasshoppers while one-third can be frogs and one-third hawks (the extra grasshopper nametags or armbands allow students to change population numbers during the simulation).

Select a site and mark its boundaries. In the simulation popcorn kernels represent the food source for a plant eater. Distribute popcorn around the site, saving some so that students can eat it after the activity.

Write the rules (see step three in the procedure) on graph paper or on the chalkboard. On another piece of graph paper, prepare the chart below.

PROCEDURE

1. Discuss with students how members of a human community must have their needs met by the community. Explain that in a biotic community all the plants and animals living there must have their needs met by the community too. Ask, "How do people in a human community get the food they need? Where does the food come from? Where do animals in a biotic community get their food?"

Discuss with students how plants and animals get their food needs met by other plants and animals. Introduce the concept of food chains and explain that a food chain shows us the relationship between plants and animals and what they eat. As a class, draw a food chain for the ants in the ant farm (seed → ant). Draw a food chain ending with a student in the class (for example, grass → cow → student). Tell students that they will be acting out a food chain to see how food chains work.

2. Write on the board the food chain plants → grasshopper → frog → hawk. Explain that for this activity each student will be either a grasshopper, a frog, or a hawk. To distinguish one animal from another, students will have nametags or colored armbands. The kernels of popcorn represent plants that the grasshopper eats. When the simulation starts, frogs will try to capture (tag) grasshoppers, and hawks will pursue frogs.

Round	# of Grasshoppers	# of Frogs	# of Hawks	Action Taken

3. Explain the rules:
   - Grasshoppers eat only plants (be sure students understand that they don't really eat the plants but put them in their stomach bags).
   - Frogs eat (tag gently) only grasshoppers (they cannot eat popcorn from the ground).
   - Hawks eat (tag gently) only frogs (they cannot eat grasshoppers or popcorn from the ground).
   - If eaten, the student must give up the contents of his or her stomach (bag) to the predator and leave the simulation (the predator puts the stomach contents into his or her stomach).
   - Animals that have been eaten wait on the sideline for the next round of the simulation.
   - A round lasts two minutes or until all of one kind of animal is eaten.
   - You must tag *gently*; no shoving, pushing, or hitting.

4. For the first round, divide the class equally into three groups and assign each group a part so that there are equal numbers of grasshoppers, frogs, and hawks. Distribute the nametags or armbands and the stomachs.

5. Show students the simulation site and boundaries. Explain that only grasshoppers will eat the plants (popcorn) that have been distributed throughout the site. You might have a mock round to be sure that students understand the rules.

6. Play a round of the simulation (the first round often lasts only a few seconds). Count the number of survivors and record them on your chart. To survive, a grasshopper's stomach must be filled to the bottom of the tape on the sandwich bag; a frog's stomach must be filled to the top of the tape; and a hawk's stomach must be completely filled. Animals with less than the required amount "starve."

7. Explain that in order for there to be a balanced food chain, two grasshoppers, two frogs, and one hawk need to be alive at the end of the simulation. Ask for suggestions from students on how they might produce a balanced food chain on the next round (students may suggest things like adding more plants, changing the number of frogs, adding "safety" zones, or giving frogs and grasshoppers a head start).

8. Conduct the simulation again, incorporating one of the students' suggestions (return popcorn to the activity area after each round). Count and record the number of survivors again and indicate the action taken on the chart.

9. Allow students to continue changing components of the simulation until they produce a balanced food chain.

10. Explain to students that tomorrow they will be learning more about ways that animals and plants in a biotic community depend on each other.

DISCUSSION QUESTIONS

What numbers of each type of animal created a balanced food chain?

What would happen if there were only one-half the number of available plants?

If there were no frogs, what would happen to the plants? To the grasshoppers? To the hawks?

Plants, grasshoppers, frogs, and hawks are all members of a community. How are they important to each other?

How might hawks help the frogs survive?

EVALUATION

Students write about or discuss how a food chain helps them understand the connections between plants and animals living in a community.

EXTENSION IDEAS

- Repeat the simulation adding one or more new organisms (for example, lizards or birds that eat the grasshoppers, or rabbits that eat the plants). As a class, diagram the food web used in the new simulation.
- Have students make their own food chain diagrams, tracing foods they eat back to the food's origins. Alternatively, as a class diagram the food chains of various foods.
- Have students explore an outdoor area to discover some of the food relationships among plants and animals living there. Students might look for evidence that animals have eaten plants or other animals (a spider web or a pile of bird feathers would indicate the latter). Groups of four students can diagram food chains and food webs derived from their observations.

HOME LEARNING SUGGESTION

(Use as lead-up to the next activity)

Write a letter to parents asking them to help students think of 15 jobs in the human community that are necessary for the community to survive. See Sample Letter on next page. Tell parents that students are expected to write a story or draw a picture showing what the community would be like if no one performed one of these jobs. This information will be used the following day.

SOURCE OF ACTIVITY

Adapted from *Outdoor Biology Instructional Strategies* (OBIS), "Food Chain Game." Developed by Lawrence Hall of Science, University of California. Nashua, N.H.: Delta Education, 1982.

Sample Letter

Dear Parent:

This week we are learning about human and natural communities. Would you please help your child list about 15 jobs in the human community that are necessary for the community to survive? I would also like your child to choose one of the jobs and write a story or draw a picture showing what the community would be like if no one did that job.

JOBS IN A BIOTIC COMMUNITY

SUMMARY OF ACTIVITY

Students take a census of an outdoor site and write "job descriptions" for the organisms observed.

Time: 15 to 30 minutes in classroom, 30 minutes at outdoor site

Setting: Classroom; outdoor area with a variety of vegetation

Materials:

- Markers to mark boundaries
- "Community Census" copycat page
- "Community Services" copycat page
- Trowel or ruler for each group of four students
- Magnifying lens for each group of four students

Subjects: Science, social studies, math

Key Words Community, role, jobs, residents, census, soil looseners, garbage collectors, food makers, movers, population controllers, fertilizers, data

RELATED CALIFORNIA FRAMEWORK CONCEPTS

All living things that share a particular environment are called a community. (*Science Framework Addendum*)

An ecosystem consists of a community of living things interacting with each other and with the physical environment. Major types of ecosystems include aquatic (pond, creek, ocean, or estuary) and terrestrial (grassland, chaparral, forest, or desert). (*Science Framework Addendum*)

Data can be collected, organized, represented, and interpreted using lists, tables, and graphs. (Adapted from *Mathematics Framework*)

There is a great diversity within communities. (Adapted from *History-Social Science Framework*)

OBJECTIVE

After observing a biotic community, students describe the roles of organisms in the community.

BACKGROUND INFORMATION

Every living thing is interdependent with the other living things in its community. Each species fills a role, which is called its ecological niche. An organism's niche is determined by the space it inhabits and by its relationship to other members of its species and the community.

In human communities, people have different jobs that help the community as a whole survive. In biotic communities organisms have different roles, or niches, that enable each species and the community as a whole to survive. For example, lichens and fungi act as soil producers by breaking down rock and organic material to form soil. Sow bugs and earthworms act as recyclers by breaking down organic material (dead plants and animals) and returning it to the soil for reuse. Some animals act as transporters by transporting seeds and other objects from place to place in their fur or in their bellies.

In human communities, people live in different parts of the community. In biotic communities plants and animals dwell in different parts also. Some animals, like earthworms, live and work in the underground. Animals like lizards live and work at ground level. Squirrels and birds live and work above the ground (in bushes, trees, or in the air).

This activity builds on the concept that animals and plants in a biotic community are interdependent. It helps students understand the concept of "jobs" in a biotic community by having students observe plants and animals and decide what job or role they have. The "Community Census" copycat page lists sample jobs of animals and plants that students may observe.

PREPARATION AND LEAD-UP

Select an outdoor study area with a variety of vegetation and mark the boundaries. A small area similar to brushland, desert, or forest may be found on the school grounds, in a nearby park, or in a vacant lot. Suburban or rural schools may have access to fields, woods, ponds, streams, or seashores.

PROCEDURE

1. Review the human jobs that students found out about in the home learning suggestion of the previous activity and have students share their stories or pictures. Introduce the idea that other organisms also have roles or jobs (see the background information).

2. Describe the different parts of a biotic community. Tell students that in nature some organisms live and work underneath the ground, some live and work at ground level, and others live and work above the ground, like in a shrub, tree, or in the air.

3. Explain to students that they will be census takers. Their job will be to locate the members of a community and to decide what jobs the members might have. Students should understand that it is okay if they do not know some of the members' jobs. Within their group, students can try to figure out one way that the animal or plant in question affects other members of its community and can make up a name for that "job."

4. Divide the class into teams of four students and pass out the "Community Census" copycat page. Each team will fill out one page. Review the data sheet and the definitions. Introduce new words and help students read and understand the different jobs listed. Ask students if they can think of other jobs that animals or plants in a community might perform.

5. Remind students that plants and animals can be held only temporarily for observing, then must be returned unhurt to the spot they came from. If you are going to be near the school building, students also need to be reminded to work quietly. Take students outside to the pre-selected site.

6. Have students make an inventory of the site and complete the copycat page. Discuss students' findings (see the discussion questions).

7. Review the concept that members of a community are connected to each other by who or what they eat and by the different jobs they perform. Tell students that over the past couple of weeks they have learned about the things that make up and affect human communities and the things that make up and affect biotic communities. Explain that over the next few days students will have the chance to put together all the things they have learned about human and biotic communities.

DISCUSSION QUESTIONS

What are some of the community members and their jobs?
Who lives and works underground? At ground level? Above the ground?
Do any community members live or work in other places?
Are there any organisms that "moonlight," that is, have more than one job?
Are there any organisms that seem to have no jobs?
What did you discover that surprised you the most?
How does this community compare with your own community?
What would happen to this community if all the population controllers were removed? If all the fertilizers were removed?

EVALUATION

Ask each student to make a list of three things that are happening at the site. Have each student share his or her list with another student. Students can modify their lists as they discuss them. Direct each student to write a paragraph on "What Is Happening Here" using his or her list.

EXTENSION IDEAS

- Have students research some of the animals and plants they observed to find out more about how these organisms affect the biotic community. Students can focus on one organism and write about it.
- Have the class make a food web by using as examples the organisms observed in the activity. The food web could be in a mural, on the chalkboard, or part of a simulation with students portraying organisms.
- Have students draw a web of the people within the school community (the principal, teachers, students, gardeners, cafeteria workers, and custodial staff) to show how they support each other. Ask what would happen if part of the

web, like the principal or custodial staff, wasn't there.

HOME LEARNING SUGGESTION

(Use as follow-up to this activity)

Have students complete the "Community Services" copycat page. For younger students, write a note to parents asking them to help students read and understand any new words. In class, discuss how the services in nature compare with the services in their community. Ask, "How are they alike? How are they different?"

RESOURCE

For Students

Hughey, Pat. *Scavengers and Decomposers: The Clean-up Crew.* New York: Atheneum, 1984.

This story is about the mammals, birds, fish, and other creatures that keep the earth free from organic trash and provide necessary chemicals for the cycle of life.

SOURCE OF ACTIVITY

"Community Services" copycat page adapted from: Hernbrode, William R. *Multi-Disciplinary Wildlife Teaching Activities.* Columbus, Ohio: ERIC Clearinghouse for Science, Mathematics and Environmental Education, Ohio State University, 1978.

Name ____________________________

COMMUNITY CENSUS

Community Member	*Address (underground, on the ground, above the ground)*	*Job*

Examples of Jobs

Soil Looseners: Animals that turn and loosen the soil so that plants can grow more easily. Examples: earthworm, gopher, mole.

Garbage Collectors: Animals that eat dead plants and animals. Examples: ant, sow bug, termite, turkey vulture, pigeon, gull, crow.

Food Makers: Plants that use the sun's energy to make food. Examples: all green plants.

Movers: Animals that move things (like seeds) from one part of the community to another part. Examples: bird, squirrel, dog, cat.

Population Controllers: Animals that eat other animals and keep the community from getting too crowded. Examples: cat, snake, spider, lizard, frog, hawk, robin.

Fertilizers: Animals and plants that fertilize the soil by adding wastes, fallen leaves, or dead plant parts. Examples: all animals and plants.

Name ______________________________

COMMUNITY SERVICES

Can you match the services found in nature with services found in your community?

Services in Nature

1. A river cleans itself by flushing water through its system.
2. The sun gives plants energy that helps them grow.
3. A bear protects its territory.
4. The wind spreads seeds.
5. Monkeys groom each other.
6. Vultures eat dead animals.
7. Squirrels store nuts.
8. Wasps gather mud and make nests.

Community Services

A. Farmer
B. Power Company
C. Garbage collection
D. Police protection
E. Home building
F. Beauty parlor
G. Bank
H. Sewage treatment plant

THE IDEAL COMMUNITY

When we see the land as a community to which we belong, we may begin to use it with love and respect.
—ALDO LEOPOLD

SUMMARY OF ACTIVITY

Students design a community where people and other living things could live harmoniously, then resolve how to deal with problems that affect their community.

Time: Two to four 45-minute periods (or more)

Setting: Classroom

Materials: Anything that can be used to make a model like heavy cardboard or masonite for bases, glue, berry baskets, toothpicks, toilet paper tubes, margarine tubs, popsicle sticks, styrofoam balls, pipe cleaners, dried grass or twigs, construction paper, tempera paint, brushes, plastecene, or playdough; or anything that can be used to make a map like large pieces of paper, colored construction paper, tape, marking pens.

Subjects: Social studies, art, science, language arts

Key Words: Harmony, community, land-use planning

RELATED CALIFORNIA FRAMEWORK CONCEPTS

The effect on other populations needs to be considered when human activities that affect the environment are evaluated. (*Science Framework Addendum*)

As citizens we can participate in our community, state, and nation. (Adapted from *History-Social Science Framework*)

Visual art media can be used to translate ideas, feelings, and values. (Adapted from *Visual and Performing Arts Framework*)

Talking and listening are important ways by which people communicate with and learn from each other. (Adapted from *English-Language Arts Framework*)

OBJECTIVE

Students design and construct model communities where people, other animals, and plants could live together.

BACKGROUND INFORMATION

Throughout this unit students have been learning about factors that make up and affect communities, how human and biotic communities are similar, and how the environment influences communities and culture. In this activity students synthesize what they have learned by designing a community where people, plants, and animals could live together. Students then determine how they would solve problems that affect their ideal communities.

PREPARATION AND LEAD-UP

Gather the materials to make models or maps. You may want to ask students to help you with this.

PROCEDURE

1. Explain that over the next few days students are going to have the opportunity to build ideal communities where people, other animals, and plants could live in harmony. Ask the class to name things the community might include for humans (see the maps created in the activity "What's in a Human Community?"). Ask, "What kinds of things should the community include for other animals? What should it include for plants?" Help students make a list of things they might include in their model or map like houses, farms, stores, parks, office buildings, lakes, rivers, forests, and meadows.

2. Have students relax and close their eyes, then take them on a trip using guided imagery. "Imagine that you are in the community where you would like to live . . . It is the ideal community for you . . . This is a community that has everything in it you need . . . and everything you like . . . In this community, people live safely and happily . . . Other animals also live safely and well . . . Plants live well here, too . . . Think about what the area around the community looks like . . . what the houses look like . . . what the other buildings look like . . . what the streets look like . . . Think about the kinds of things your community needs so that people, plants, and wildlife can live in it together . . . When you are ready, open your eyes." Afterwards, talk about the things students visualized. Ask, "What features made your communities livable to humans, wildlife, and plants?"

3. Divide students into groups of four and distribute the materials. Allow groups two to four 45-minute periods to make a model or map of a community where they would like to live, where animals, plants, and people could live together.

4. When all of the teams are finished, have each team share its design and compare the results. Ask, "What design features make the communities livable for plants? For animals? For humans? How is your own community similar to and different from the ones you have designed?"

5. Give each team a different challenge problem and have students discuss within their teams how they would change their design to solve the problem. You might ask teams to write up their resolutions. The challenge problems are:

- A jeans manufacturing plant has just moved into your community, bringing with it 1,000 new people. How would you change your design to fit this increased number of people?

- A drought hits your community. How would you change your design to deal with it? Are there any special things you would do to help the wildlife living in the community?

- The number of squirrels that live in your community is increasing rapidly and squirrels are eating the walnuts off the trees in everyone's yard. How would your community deal with a great increase in the number of wildlife living there? Is there any design change you could make to fit an increase in wildlife?

- The government is planning to build a major freeway that would go right through your community. Where would you want the freeway placed so that it would have the smallest effect on your community? How would a freeway affect the plants, animals, and people in your community?

- This year has brought unusually high rainfall to your community. How would you change your design to minimize the effect of so much rain?

- Your community has become a "trendy" place for people in your area to shop and eat. Because so many people come into the community, you are having parking, litter, and traffic problems. How would you change your design to take care of these problems?

- Oceanland Safari is an amusement park that has large exhibits, whale and dolphin shows, and an African safari area. Oceanland Safari has chosen your community as the place for its new park. Where would you put the park? How might the park affect your community?

- Dogs have become a real problem in your community. There are so many dogs that they are making messes all over the streets, sidewalks, and yards. There are also many stray dogs that roam the neighborhoods. How would your community deal with too many dogs?

DISCUSSION QUESTIONS

What changes did you make to your design to solve your challenge problem?
Do you think the problem and your solution were realistic?
In what ways is our own community livable for people, other animals, and plants?
What kinds of things do you think could be done to make our own community more livable?

EVALUATION

Students describe at least three things about the community they designed that make it suitable for people, other animals, and plants.

EXTENSION IDEAS

- Give each design team a different problem than the one they had before. Have students decide how they would change their design to solve the new challenge.
- Contact the local planning department to find out what changes they anticipate making as the community grows. Ask students whether they think the changes will make their communities better or worse places to live.

HOME LEARNING SUGGESTION

(Use as follow-up to this activity)

Ask students to make a new mental map of their community (similar to the mental maps in the first activity of this unit), making sure to include as many things as possible that make it a community. Ask, "How does this mental map compare with the ones you made in the first activity? Did you include more or different things? Did you include things that deal with plants or animals? Do any of the things show how the community is suited to its environment?"

Adaptation and Variation

Fourth and Fifth Grades

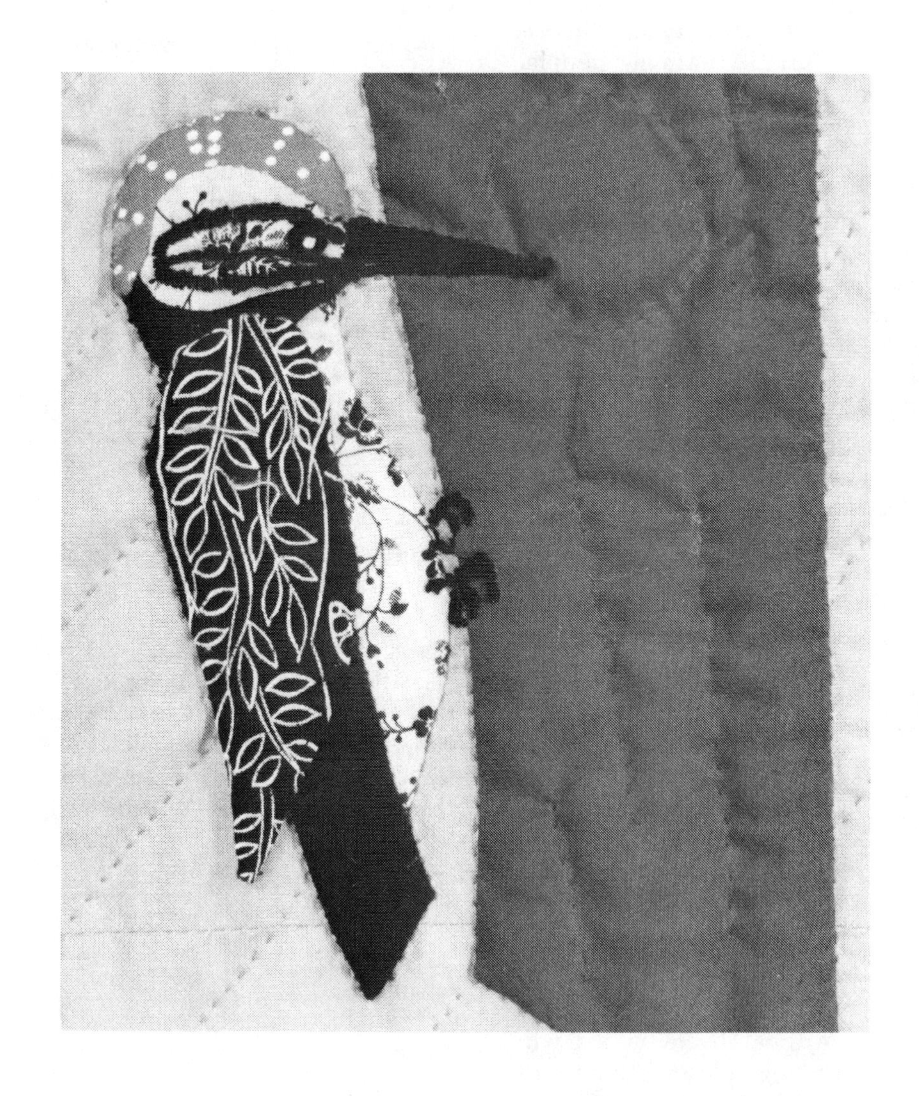

Introduction to the Unit

An incredible diversity of living things shares our earth with us. Inhabiting the sea, the land, and the air are living things of nearly every physical and behavioral type. All living things have evolved specific characteristics that help them survive in their habitat; these characteristics are called *adaptations.* Adaptations enable organisms to obtain and store food, water, and air; to move about; to protect themselves; to survive in various temperatures; and to reproduce their own kind. In this unit students become more aware of the great diversity among living things and learn that living things have a variety of adaptations that enable them to survive.

The unit begins by introducing students to the concept that individuals of a species have *variations.* Students look at variations among people, particularly the people in the class. Students then look for variations among animals and begin to think about how an animal's appearance can affect its ability to survive. The concept of adaptation is introduced in the third activity, when students study camouflage.

The following two activities focus on adaptations of birds. Birds are marvelous animals for studying adaptations because the ways that they are uniquely suited to their particular habitats and lifestyles are obvious even to young students. In the next two activities students are introduced to adaptations of other animals that help the animals obtain food, then to adaptations that help animals survive in their own habitat.

The next three activities focus on adaptations of plants. In the last activity students are given the opportunity to think about human adaptations that help us survive.

NOTE: Many of the activities in this unit will generate lots of discussion and sharing among students as they become excited about and interested in what they are doing. If your class becomes noisy during the activities, it indicates students are thoroughly involved in their learning.

Advance Planning

Several of the activities in this unit require some advance planning. For "Animal Diversity" you will need to gather 10 to 15 photographs or illustrations of various animals for each group of four students (for a class of 30, this means 80 to 120 pictures). Good sources for animal pictures include old calendars and magazines or nature journals such as *Ranger Rick, Sierra, Audubon,* or *Natural History.* You might ask parents to help gather these pictures.

Some of the materials required for "Bird Bills" may take time to track down, so start now. You might ask students to bring in marbles as you will need about 300.

"Food-Getting Devices," "Seed Dispersal," and "Invent-A-Plant" require a variety of materials that students can use to construct invented organisms exhibiting various adaptations. You might write the following note to parents asking for their donations.

Sorting Activities

Throughout the unit students are given opportunities to sort humans, other animals, and plants according to various characteristics. Sorting helps students look for differences and similarities between things in order to classify them. Classifying or arranging objects into sets having common properties gives students a basis for making new observations. It is important that students come up with their own categories for sorting; resist the urge to suggest categories.

Sequencing a set of objects, such as from smallest to largest or lightest to darkest, allows students to focus on the ordered relationship among objects. While some children in fourth and fifth grades are able to order a set of objects with a finely graduated sequence in mind, others sort by trial and error. In any case, it is worthwhile for students to explore ordered relationships as another way of gathering comparative data about the world around them.

Two-way classification (or multiple membership classification) is a more complex form of classifying that requires the ability to recognize that an object can belong to more than one class or set. A pile of leaves can be sorted from lightest to darkest and from smallest to largest, resulting in a matrix:

LEAVES	Light	Dark
Small		
Large		

This ability to recognize two or more attributes simultaneously frees children from viewing their

Sample Letter

Dear Parent:

Over the next few weeks we will be constructing plants and animals that exhibit various adaptations. We will need a multitude of "junk" materials like toothpicks, empty toilet paper or paper towel rolls, margarine tubs, empty cereal boxes or other boxes, rubber bands, string, pins, paper fasteners, cardboard, buttons, small metal springs, thread spools, cotton, corks, bottle caps, straws, styrofoam packing beads, wire, popsicle sticks, egg cartons, styrofoam balls, pipe cleaners, styrofoam or paper cups, clean styrofoam meat trays, and clothespins.

I will place a big box in our classroom labeled "Donations" in which we will store the materials until we need them. Please send "junk" materials to school with your child by

______*date*______.

world through one-at-a-time observations. It marks a new understanding of the complexities of objects and of the kinds of generalizations that can be made about them.

Inclusive classifying is an even more complex form of classifying that requires the ability to recognize that one set of objects is included within a superordinate set of objects and that all the objects in the smaller set are part of the larger set. Students with this ability understand relationships among two or more sets that share characteristics and recognize that there is a logical relationship between the superordinate and subordinate sets. For example, all dogs are mammals but not all mammals are dogs.

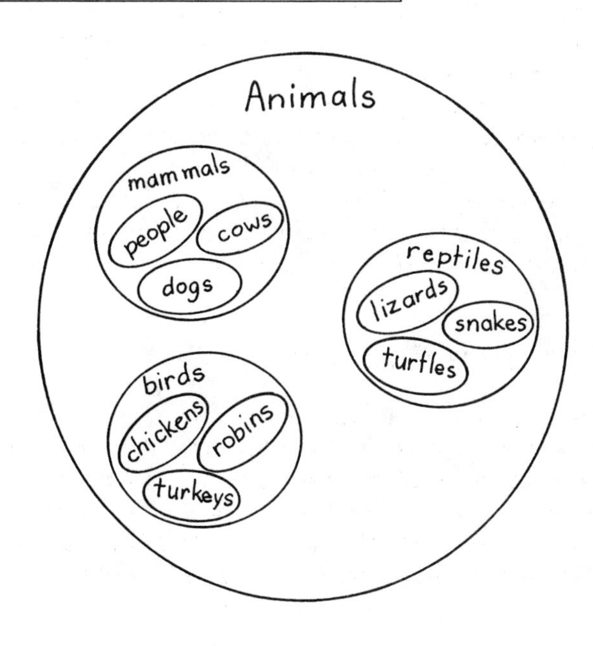

Resources

Gould, Stephen Jay. *The Panda's Thumb.* New York: W. W. Norton and Company, 1980. This easy-to-read book is full of essays about evolutionary theory and natural history.

Lowery, Lawrence F. *Learning About Learning: Classification Abilities.* Berkeley, Calif.: University of California, 1981. Described by the author as a "personal workshop," the book focuses on classification abilities related to learning.

Ornduff, Robert. *Introduction to California Plant Life.* Berkeley, Calif.: University of California, 1974. Ornduff describes the diversity of wildflowers, shrubs, and trees found in California and how each plant has adapted to living where it does.

For Students

Berger, Gilda, and Melvin Berger. *Fitting In : Animals in Their Habitats.* New York: Coward, McCann, and Geoghegan, Inc., 1976. The authors describe characteristics of animals living in different habitats and how each animal has adapted to its particular habitat.

Blocksma, Mary. *Amazing Mouths and Menus.* Englewood Cliffs, N.J.: Prentice-Hall, Inc., 1986. This book looks at how and what various animals eat.

Bremmer, Tony. *How Birds Live.* London: Usborne Publishing Ltd., 1978. Bremmer describes interesting and unusual birds and explains their amazing behaviors.

Stein, Sara. *The Evolution Book.* New York: Workman Publishing, 1986. These activities and investigations explore the four billion years of evolving life on earth.

UNIT TIMELINE ■ Participation in Activity

Page	Activity	Week 1					Week 2					Week 3					Week 4				
189	Variations Among Us	■	■																		
194	Animal Diversity			■																	
197	Camouflage Hunt				■																
200	Bird Bills					■	■														
204	Artful Bird Adaptations							■													
207	Food-Getting Devices								■	■											
209	Adaptation Advantages										■										
212	Plant Adaptations											■									
214	Seed Dispersal												■	■							
217	Invent-A-Plant														■						
220	Human Adaptations															■					

VARIATIONS AMONG US

SUMMARY OF ACTIVITY

Students sort themselves according to different characteristics.

Time: Two 45-minute periods, over two days

Setting: Classroom

Materials:
- Copycat page
- Paper with two overlapping circles drawn, one drawing for each pair of students (see preparation and lead-up)

Subjects: Science, math, language arts

Key Words: Characteristic, attribute, variation, species, observable

RELATED CALIFORNIA FRAMEWORK CONCEPTS

Human beings have characteristics by which they can be identified, described, and classified. (*Science Framework Addendum*)

Variations exist among individuals of a species. (*Science Framework Addendum*)

Using one or more attributes, objects can be classified and sorted by observing similarities and differences, describing and recording relationships, and making generalizations. (Adapted from *Mathematics Framework*)

OBJECTIVE

Students sort and sequence themselves as a method of observing individual differences.

BACKGROUND INFORMATION

Throughout this unit students will be learning how organisms are adapted to the particular environment in which they live. Adaptations vary from species to species; for example, the ways that animals obtain and conserve water, protect themselves against predators or parasites, minimize the effects of extreme temperature, and reproduce vary enormously. Small differences among species can make one species more suited to a particular environment than another species.

Although a species is a group of living things that has common attributes and can reproduce its own kind, small differences occur among individuals of one species. These differences are called variations. Variations exist in physical and behavioral characteristics. Human beings have variations in build and in the color of skin, hair, and eyes. The number of petals on a daisy varies from flower to flower. Giraffes vary in their height. This activity introduces students to the concept that individuals of a species have variations by having students look at variations among people.

A variation can be an advantage, a disadvantage, or neutral to an organism's ability to survive in a particular environment. An extraordinarily tall giraffe has the advantage of being able to eat leaves out of a shorter giraffe's reach. A daisy with too few petals may have a disadvantage because it might not attract the insects necessary for pollination. Small variations in the shape of the human foot may have no effect on a person's ability to survive. Most variations within a species are neutral to the organism's survival.

PREPARATION AND LEAD-UP

Draw two large overlapping circles (for Venn diagrams in step four) on pieces of paper, one drawing for each pair of students. Students may help do this.

PROCEDURE

Day One

1. Introduce the activity by playing "Guess My Rule" with your students. Without telling the class which characteristic you have in mind, ask one student at a time to come up and stand on either side of you so that students on one side share one characteristic and students on the other side share another characteristic. For example, if you were to select the characteristic brown hair/not brown hair, you would direct one student at a time to line up to the right of you if the student has brown hair and to the left of you if the student does not have brown hair. The challenge is for the class to guess the rule by which you have sorted students. (Other possible "rules" are green eyes/not green eyes, wearing blue jeans/not wearing blue jeans, wearing a T-shirt/not wearing a T-shirt, or wearing shoes that tie/wearing shoes that don't tie.)

2. After students have determined your rule, choose a different characteristic and sort students again. When you feel students are ready, have individual students think of characteristics and sort the class accordingly; the rest of the class then tries to guess the characteristic. Anticipate that students may identify racial differences. Prepare to acknowledge and respond to those differences in a positive way.

3. Choose two students who have healthy egos and have them stand in front of the class. Ask the class to name observable ways that the two students are alike and different. As the class responds, record responses on the chalkboard using a Venn diagram.

4. Divide students into pairs and challenge them to find as many ways as possible that they are

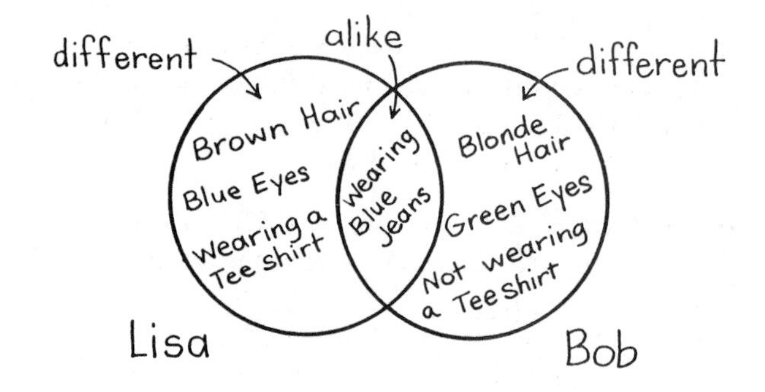

similar to and different from their partners. Partners should record their findings in a Venn diagram, using the paper you have prepared with two overlapping circles. Have volunteers share matching and contrasting characteristics.

5. Write the word "characteristic" on the board and talk about what it means (a quality, property, or feature of something or someone). Discuss the kinds of characteristics that people have; for ex-

ample, hair color, eye color, favorite ice cream, number of people in their family, favorite kind of books, or hobbies. Ask students which of these characteristics are *observable*.

6. Ask the class, "What characteristics are shared by everyone in the room?" Challenge students to come up with as many shared characteristics as possible, such as two arms, two eyes, two ears, two legs, hair on head, or five fingers on each hand.

Day Two

7. Review what a characteristic is. Divide the class into groups of eight to ten students and help each group sequence itself according to height so that students put themselves in a line that goes from the shortest to the tallest student.

8. After students have sequenced themselves, choose a different characteristic and help students sequence themselves again. Examples of characteristics for sequencing include lightness to darkness of hair, length of hair, length of feet, size of hands, and date of birth. After a few times, have students suggest a characteristic to sequence by.

9. Hand out the "Two-Way Classification" copycat page. Explain to students that they are going to write in the names of classmates who have *both* characteristics corresponding to each square.

10. Looking at the first column of the copycat page, ask students if there is anyone in the class who has owned a pet and who has lived in another community. All students should write in the top left square the names of classmates who fit these two characteristics. Ask students if there is anyone who owns a pet and knows a language other than English. Students should write in the next square down the names of classmates who fit these two characteristics. Continue demonstrating how to use the matrix until students seem able to work with it on their own. Allow students a few minutes to circulate and find a student for as many remaining squares as possible. Discuss their findings. "Does any square not have someone who fits in it? Does anyone not fit any of the squares? What characteristics could we add to our matrix to make sure everyone fits?"

11. Introduce the word *variation*. Emphasize that natural differences, both physical and behavioral, exist within any group of living things of one kind, including humans. Remind students of the variations they observed among members of the class. Pick a familiar animal (a dog, cat, or rabbit) and ask students what variations exist in a group of animals of this kind (for example, size, shape of nose, color of fur, length of fur, curly or straight hairs, or behavior).

DISCUSSION QUESTIONS

What "jobs" do dogs do?

What are some ways that variations in dogs make them suited for different jobs? (For example, some dogs, like sheep dogs, are herders by nature; some dogs can be trained to be "seeing eye" dogs because they are loyal and smart; and small dogs are better suited for apartment living than larger dogs.)

Can you think of ways that variations in humans (or other animals) could be helpful or harmful?

EVALUATION

Have each student draw a picture of two people that illustrates at least five characteristics in which the people vary.

EXTENSION IDEAS

- Ask students, "How many different types of hair can you find in our class?" Take a few hairs of each type from willing victims and mount them with tape onto cards. Challenge students to find a way of grouping the hair types; for example, by color, by curliness, or by thickness.
- Have students collect clover leaves with different patterns. Ask, "How many variations can you find?"
- Have students team up to design a new matrix, similar to the copycat page but with different characteristics. Challenge students to complete the matrix either as a class or individually.

HOME LEARNING SUGGESTION

(Use as follow-up to this activity)

Ask students to complete a matrix like the one following by filling in the names of their family members where appropriate. Do a sample matrix using class members first, then have students draw a matrix to take home. Next day in class make a class graph of the results by tallying the numbers of light hair/light eyes, light hair/dark eyes, dark hair/light eyes, and dark hair/dark eyes. Discuss, "Which group had the most people? The least? Are people with dark hair more or less likely to have light eyes? Are people with light hair more or less likely to have dark eyes?"

		EYES	
		Light	Dark
HAIR	Light		
	Dark		

SOURCE OF ACTIVITY

Adapted from *Science 5/13*, "Like and Unlike." London: Macdonald Educational, 1973.

Name ______________________________

TWO-WAY CLASSIFICATION

For each square, find someone in the class who fits it. Write his or her name in the square.

	Owns a pet	Plays an instrument	Oldest child in family	Left-handed	Right-handed
Has lived in another community					
Knows a language other than English					
Born in California					
Loves spinach					
Has brown hair					

ANIMAL DIVERSITY

SUMMARY OF ACTIVITY

Students sort pictures of animals to find out how various animals are alike and how they are different.

Time: 30 to 45 minutes

Setting: Classroom

Materials:
- Butcher paper or newsprint
- 10 to 15 pictures of animals for each group of four students (collected from calendars or magazines)

Subjects: Science, art, math, language arts

Key Words: Characteristics, variation

RELATED CALIFORNIA FRAMEWORK CONCEPTS

There is a great diversity among living things. The many different kinds of living things have characteristics and behaviors by which they can be described, identified, sequenced, and classified. (*Science Framework Addendum*)

A species is a kind of living thing whose individuals have many similarities and can reproduce their own kind. Variations exist among individuals of a species. (*Science Framework Addendum*)

Using one or more attributes, objects can be classified and sorted by observing similarities and differences, describing and recording relationships, and making generalizations. (Adapted from *Mathematics Framework*)

OBJECTIVE

Students sort pictures of animals as a method of identifying similarities and differences.

BACKGROUND INFORMATION

In this activity students begin to look at characteristics of animals and to build an appreciation for the diversity of living things. In the following activities students investigate some of the reasons why living things vary.

PREPARATION AND LEAD-UP

Collect pictures of animals from calendars, magazines, and other sources mentioned in the introduction to this unit. Be sure to save the pictures because they will be used throughout the unit.

PROCEDURE

1. Divide students into groups of four. Give each group a set of 10 to 15 animal pictures.

2. Have groups sort the pictures into two piles so that all of the animals in each pile are the same in some way. Allow groups to share their results. Have students mix up the pictures, then sort them again into two piles based on various characteristics. Pair off groups and have each group try to guess the other's rules after each sorting.

3. As a class, discuss different ways that animals in the pictures could be sequenced. Examples might include by size, by darkness or lightness of color, or by number of legs. Ask each group to sequence its set of pictures by one characteristic. Have groups share which characteristic they used. Direct the groups to sequence the pictures again using different characteristics.

4. Direct groups to again sort their pictures into two piles. This time, however, groups should then sort each pile into two more piles so that they have a total of four piles. Ask, "How are the animals in the smaller piles the same as the animals in the larger piles from which they were sorted? How are they different? How are the animals in all four piles alike?"

5. Discuss the ways that the animals are alike and ways that they differ. Tell students that many animals differ in the ways they look and in the ways they are able to live. Emphasize that natural differences, both physical and behavioral, exist within any group of living things, even among humans. Remind students of the variations they observed among members of the classroom. Explain that over the next few weeks students will be learning how these differences can help animals survive in the places they live.

DISCUSSION QUESTIONS

Show students selected animal pictures. For each picture ask, "How do you think this animal's characteristics might affect its ability to survive?"

EVALUATION

Have students name four different characteristics by which animals could be sorted into different groups.

EXTENSION IDEAS

- Have students create a Venn diagram, based on two animals. Discuss ways that the two animals are different and ways they are similar.
- Have students sort animal pictures by two characteristics simultaneously—number of legs and ability to fly. Copy the following matrix on pieces of butcher paper or newsprint (be sure that the squares are large enough to hold pictures). Instruct students to sort their pictures into the appropriate squares of the matrix.

HOME LEARNING SUGGESTION

(Use as follow-up to this activity)

Give students the "Greeps and Byclops" copycat page. Ask each student to use the clues given to pick out the distinguishing characteristics of each type of creature. Once students have figured out how to identify each creature, they can draw their own variations.

SOURCE OF ACTIVITY

Copycat page from Downie, Diane. *Math for Girls.* Berkeley, Calif.: University of California, 1981.

	NUMBER OF LEGS				
	0	2	4	6	8 or more
Can Fly					
Cannot Fly					

Copycat Page

Name ______________________________

GREEPS AND BYCLOPS

These are GREEPS:

 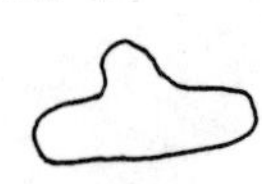 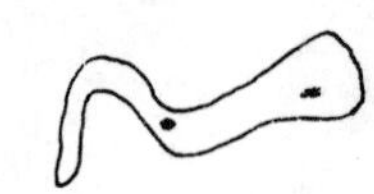 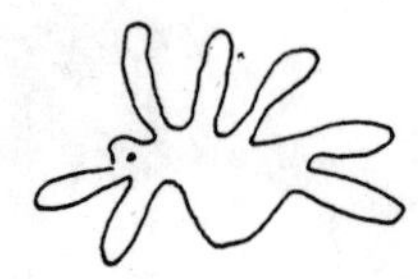

These are not GREEPS:

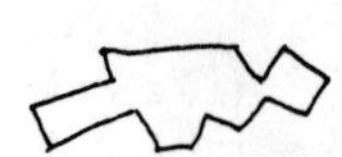   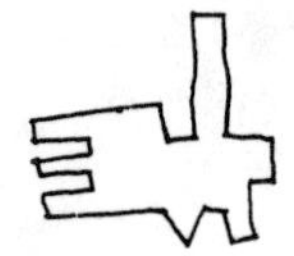

Which of these are GREEPS? (Circle the GREEPS.)

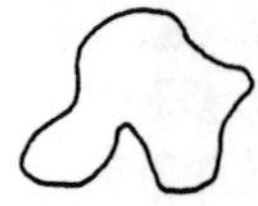  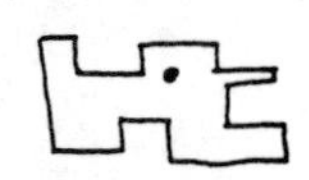  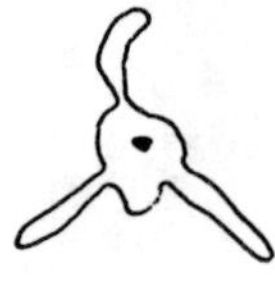

These are BYCLOPS:

These are not BYCLOPS:

 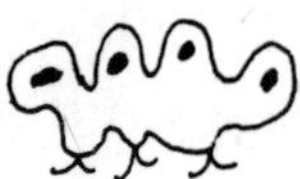  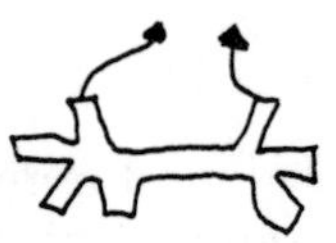

Which of these are BYCLOPS? (Circle the BYCLOPS.)

Draw your own GREEP	Draw your own BYCLOP

CAMOUFLAGE HUNT

SUMMARY OF ACTIVITY

Students hunt for colored "worms" in two habitats and compare results.

Time: 45 minutes

Setting: Two different outdoor sites, such as on lawn and on soil (or two different indoor areas)

Materials:
- Toothpicks (4 colors, about 50 of each color)
- 60-centimeter (24-inch) square piece of cardboard or styrofoam board with holes punched in it
- One pair of scissors
- Small piece of paper
- Tape

Subjects: Science, math, language arts

Key Words: Camouflage, adaptation, habitat, variation, survival, predator, prey

RELATED CALIFORNIA FRAMEWORK CONCEPTS

Living things have adaptations that enable them to live in their particular habitats. (*Science Framework Addendum*)

Data can be collected, organized, represented, and interpreted using lists, tables, and graphs. (Adapted from *Mathematics Framework*)

OBJECTIVE

Through a simulation activity, students compare the abilities of different "worms" to survive based on adaptive coloration.

BACKGROUND INFORMATION

An adaptation is any special feature of an organism that helps improve its chances for survival. Camouflage is one type of animal adaptation. Many animals have colorations and markings on their skin and fur that help them blend into their habitats. These features enable the animals to be camouflaged and hidden from a predator's view.

In this activity students are introduced to the notion of adaptation by looking at how a variation may help an animal survive in a particular area or habitat. Students are also introduced to the idea that an adaptation protecting an animal in one habitat may not protect the animal in another habitat.

PREPARATION AND LEAD-UP

Identify the boundaries for two different outdoor areas each about 10 meters by 10 meters (30 feet by 30 feet), or large enough for the class to move around in. Distribute equal numbers of colored toothpicks ("worms") in each area (you might try having half the class "hide" the worms for the other half). Alternatively, you can choose two indoor areas; make sure they are different in background color (for example, a brown carpet and a red tile floor).

Punch holes in a foam-core board or cardboard to make a graph. Label the graph by indicating the colors of toothpicks. On the top, tape a piece of paper on which to record students' predictions.

PROCEDURE

1. Show students several of the "worms" (toothpicks) and ask them to tell you in what way the worms vary. Explain that today students will be learning about how variations help worms survive. Tell the class, "Today we're going to pretend that we're birds that eat these worms. It's early morning and we're hungry. In our world, morning is very short so when I say 'It's morning!' you'll want to gather food as quickly as possible. But remember, when I say 'Stop,' you must stop eating."

2. Take the class outside to one of the sites. Point out the boundaries. Ask students to predict which colors they will find the most of and which colors the least of. Record their predictions by writing the numbers one through four above the appropriate colors on the graph with one indicating "most found" and four indicating "least found."

3. Say "It's morning!" Allow students to gather toothpicks for about five seconds. After students have finished "eating," have them stick their

toothpicks into the graph according to the color so that toothpicks of the same color are in a row.

4. Discuss the results. "What colors did we find the most of? The least of? The same of? How did our prediction hold up? How can you explain these results?"

5. Repeat the activity in the second site. Afterwards ask, "We found the most of which color in each site? The least of which color in each site? Why did we find more of some colors? Now pretend that you are a worm. If you were a green worm, which area would you want to be in so that you could hide from birds and survive best? If you lived in the dirt area, which color would best hide you from birds? How does a worm's color seem to help it survive?"

6. Introduce students to the word *adaptation*. Ask, "Is camouflage an adaptation?"

DISCUSSION QUESTIONS

Which worms have an adaptation that enables them to live in the grassy area?

Which worms have an adaptation that enables them to live in the dirt area?

Does an adaptation that helps a worm survive in one area always help the worm survive in a different area? Why not?

Can you think of real animals that have adaptations that help them hide?

EVALUATION

Students describe how a worm's coloration might help it survive.

EXTENSION IDEAS

- Have students use marking pens to color natural wood toothpicks so that they blend into a particular habitat like a lawn or carpet. Students may discover that variations in the patterns of different colors provide better camouflage than solid colors alone.
- Paint toilet paper rolls with white latex paint—these will be students' "animals." The next day select an outdoor site with various habitats and divide it into two areas. Divide the class into two groups and assign each group one of the areas. Challenge students to use tempera paint, clay, toothpicks, popsicle sticks, cotton, glue, or other materials to camouflage their animal so that it is hidden in a particular spot within their area. Have each group try to find all of the animals that the other group camouflaged.
- Some animals' adaptations call attention to the animal in order to attract mates or to warn potential enemies that the animal is poisonous or distasteful. Have students fill out a slip of paper with their name, favorite color, a pattern choice (checkered, triangles, stripes, spots, rectangles, or diamonds), and a choice of area (grassy, leafy, or rocky). Put the papers into a hat and have each student pick one. Without telling whose paper they selected, students then make a design that will attract attention in the area listed,

using the color listed and one other color of their own choosing. Challenge students to see whether they can recognize "their" designs. Discuss why it is important that some plants and animals are able to attract others.

HOME LEARNING SUGGESTION

(Use as lead-up to the next activity)

Allow each student to take home a toothpick. Have students find a kitchen tool that can pick up the toothpick effectively. Brainstorm possibilities in class first, then the next day talk about the results.

SOURCE OF ACTIVITY

Project Learning Tree, "Birds 'n' Worms." Washington, D.C.: The American Forest Council, 1986.

BIRD BILLS

SUMMARY OF ACTIVITY

Students simulate different types of bird bills to find out how size and shape of the bill is related to food items gathered.

Time: Two 45-minute periods
Setting: Outdoor or indoor area
Materials:

- Two or more pictures of birds
- Chart paper
- Marking pens
- Paper cups, one per student
- Marbles (about 300)
- Round toothpicks (about 500)
- 3/16-inch washers or pennies (about 300)
- 10 metal or durable plastic spoons
- 10 pairs of chopsticks, tongue depressors, popsicle sticks, or clothespins (spring-type)
- 10 pairs of scissors or tweezers

Subjects: Science, math

Key Words: Adaptation, bird bills, beaks

RELATED CALIFORNIA FRAMEWORK CONCEPTS

Animals have adaptations that enable them to obtain and conserve food, oxygen, and water; excrete waste products; move; protect themselves against predators; minimize effects of extreme temperatures; reproduce; and so forth. (*Science Framework Addendum*)

Data can be collected, organized, represented, and interpreted using lists, tables, and graphs. (Adapted from *Mathematics Framework*)

OBJECTIVE

Through a simulation, students compare and analyze the effectiveness of different bird bills for food gathering.

BACKGROUND INFORMATION

In the previous activity students were introduced to coloration as one animal adaptation. In this activity students are introduced to birds' feeding adaptations.

Bird bills are tools that help birds seize and eat their food. The variety of shapes and sizes of bills enables birds to consume almost every conceivable type of food. Birds that feed on similar types of foods have adapted similar bills that help them get their food.

Insect eaters generally have slender, pincer-like bills of varying length. Examples: swift, swallow, warbler.

Fish eaters have long, sharp bills, often hooked at the tip, with serrated margins to help hold onto slippery fish. Examples: cormorant, merganser.

Predators (of other birds or rodents) have powerful, hooked bills for tearing and cutting flesh and skin. Examples: peregrine falcon, golden eagle.

Seed and nut eaters usually have short, stout bills for cracking seeds open. Examples: finch, sparrow, pigeon.

Nectar feeders are characterized by long, slender bills ideal for reaching into flowers. Example: hummingbird.

In this activity students discover that the success of a particular bill type in acquiring and eating food is related to the food item being gathered. By comparing the outcome when one food item is available to the outcome when three food items are available, students begin to understand that a diverse food supply can support different kinds of birds.

PREPARATION AND LEAD-UP

Find an area to conduct the activity; outside on grass is best so the marbles don't roll. The area should be about 10 meters by 10 meters (30 feet by 30 feet) or large enough for the entire class to move around in.

Using butcher paper, prepare two class data sheets like those in the illustration. Label the data sheets "One Food at a Time" and "All Three Foods at Once."

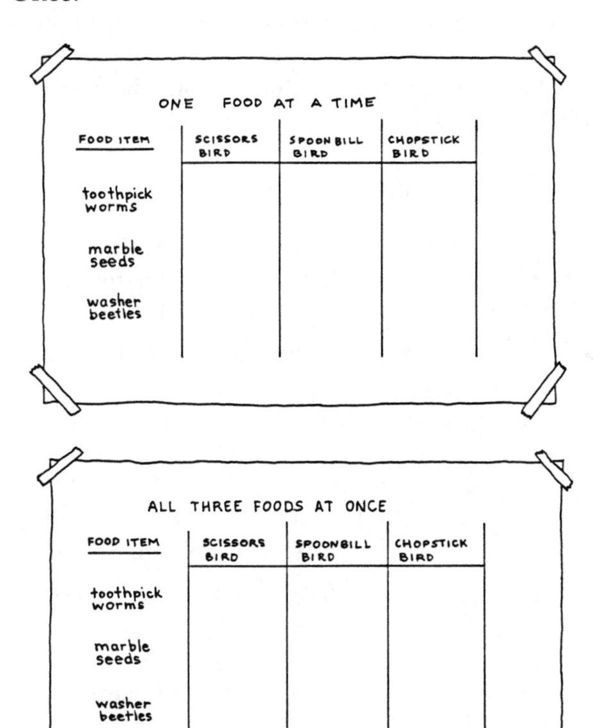

PROCEDURE

NOTE: This activity will probably require two periods and can be broken up at a variety of points. Break it at a place that makes sense for your time constraints and class.

1. If students did the home learning suggestion of the previous activity, introduce this activity with a discussion of what they found out. Otherwise, introduce the activity with step two.

2. Display two or more pictures of birds and discuss ways that the birds vary; for example, the birds may be different colors or different sizes or they may have differently shaped feet or bills. Review the term *adaptation*, then focus on one of the variations that students described and ask how the variation might be an adaptation that helps the bird survive.

3. Tell students that today they will be learning about different bird bills (or beaks) and how these help birds survive. Divide the class into three groups (counting off by threes) and assign a different bird bill—spoons, chopsticks (or tongue depressors, popsicle sticks, or clothespins), and scissors (or tweezers)—to each group. Give each student a paper cup, which will be his or her stomach.

4. Distribute one of the food items (marble "seeds," toothpick "worms," or washer "beetles") around the study area. Be sure to spread the food over a large area to avoid bumping or crowding. Explain that students are to pick up as many of the food items as possible using their beaks, then drop the food items into their stomachs. Food items may not be scooped up or thrown into the stomach and the stomach must be held upright. At the

signal to stop, all birds must stand up at once. Remind students that bumping, shoving, pushing, or taking other birds' food are not allowed.

5. Give the signal to start eating. Stop the round after about three minutes (before the food runs too low).

6. Have students regroup according to the type of bill they have so that everyone in each group has the same kind of bill. Have each group count the total number of food items in all the stomachs and report the group results to the class. Record the data on the class data sheet entitled "One Food at a Time."

7. Test the other two food items, one at a time, and record the results on the data sheet. Analyze and discuss the data after each test. "Which type of bird was able to eat the most of the food item? Which ate the least? How did the type of bill help or not help you eat the food item? Which bill is best at eating toothpick worms? Marble seeds? Washer beetles? With only this one food item available, which type of bird would be most likely to survive? Which bird has the best adaptation for eating this food item?"

8. Conduct the test again but this time distribute all three food items at once. Record the results on the data sheet entitled "All Three Foods at Once."

DISCUSSION QUESTIONS

If only one kind of food is available in a certain area, do you think you would find lots of different kinds of birds there? Why or why not?

What happened when all three food items were available at once?

If many different kinds of food are available in a certain area, how might that affect the types of birds found there?

EVALUATION

Display pictures of foods birds eat like fish, seeds, flower nectar, mice, shrimp, water plants, and insects (or write these words on the board). Give students the "Bird Bill Types" copycat page and ask them to identify which bill type is best for each type of food.

EXTENSION IDEAS

- Repeat the activity using other bills, other foods, or other habitats. Compare the results with the results of this activity.
- Study whether distribution of food is a factor in how birds eat the food. Repeat the activity, distributing food items fairly evenly. Then clump each food item a few yards from each of the other food items and allow the birds to feed where they wish. Look for differences in feeding behavior when food distribution is changed.
- Take students on a walk, with binoculars, to observe birds feeding in the schoolyard or neighborhood. Alternatively, set up a bird seed feeder in the schoolyard. Students can observe how birds use their beaks to crack open seeds.

HOME LEARNING SUGGESTION

(Use as lead-up to next activity)

Ask students to bring in pictures of birds, real or make-believe, that show different kinds of bird bills. Magazines, calendars, and coloring books are good sources. Remind students they should first get permission from their parents to cut out the pictures.

Name ______________________

BIRD BILL TYPES

LONG, SHARP
Good for catching slippery objects.

Food items:
____

VERY LONG, THIN
Good for probing into small areas, like flower petals.

Food items:
____

LONG, SLENDER
Good for probing in mud.

Food items:
____

CHISEL-SHAPED
Good for drilling into the bark of trees.

Food items:
____

SHORT, THICK
Good for crushing hard objects.

Food items:
____

HOOKED
Good for grabbing onto flesh.

Food items:
____

BROAD
Good for scooping and straining water.

Food items:
____

ARTFUL BIRD ADAPTATIONS

SUMMARY OF ACTIVITY

Students design imaginary birds and write reports describing the birds' adaptations.

Time: One or two 45-minute periods

Setting: Classroom

Materials:
- Unlined drawing paper
- Coloring pens or crayons
- Pictures of birds

Subjects: Science, art, language arts

Key Words: Adaptation

RELATED CALIFORNIA FRAMEWORK CONCEPTS

Animals have adaptations that enable them to obtain and conserve food, oxygen, and water; excrete waste products; move; protect themselves against predators; minimize effects of extreme temperatures; reproduce; and so forth. (*Science Framework Addendum*)

Visual art media can be used to translate ideas, feelings, and values. (Adapted from *Visual and Performing Arts Framework*)

OBJECTIVE

Students design imaginary birds and describe their adaptive characteristics.

Adaptation	Bird	Advantage
Beaks		
Pouch-like	Pelican	Can hold fish
Long, thin	Avocet	Can probe shallow water and mud for insects
Chisel-shaped	Woodpecker	Can break and probe tree bark for insects
Hooked	Hawk	Can tear meat
Short, stout	Finch	Can crack seeds and nuts
Slender, long	Hummingbird	Can probe flowers for nectar
Feet		
Webbed	Duck	Aids moving in water
Long toes	Crane	Aids walking on mud
Taloned	Hawk	Can grasp food when hunting prey
Grasping	Robin	Aids sitting on branches
Legs		
Long, powerful	Ostrich	Aids running
Long, slender	Heron	Aids wading
Powerful muscles	Hawk	Aids lifting and carrying prey
Wings		
Large	Eagle	Aids soaring while hunting
Slender	Swallow	Gives speed and ability to maneuver for finding insects
Long, narrow	Albatross	Aids gliding while hunting
Coloration		
Bright feathers	Male birds	Attraction for mating
Duller colors	Female birds	Aids in camouflage while nesting

BACKGROUND INFORMATION

Birds have many different adaptations, including the shape and size of beaks, feet, legs, and wings, as well as coloration. These adaptations have evolved so that each bird is suited to its particular environment and lifestyle.

In this activity students learn that there are advantages for birds to look the way they do. Students learn some of the ways that birds are physically adapted to their environments. Students are also introduced to the concept that organisms are uniquely suited to their habitat, to the place in which they live.

PREPARATION AND LEAD-UP

Gather the materials.

PROCEDURE

1. Introduce the word habitat. Discuss bird adaptations by looking at pictures of birds brought in by students (from the previous activity's home learning suggestion) or pictures you have gathered. Have students point out ways the birds may be adapted.

2. Divide students into groups of three. Tell students that they will design their own birds with help from others in their group.

3. Give each student a piece of drawing paper. Show students how to fold their paper into four equal sections.

4. Have each student begin to create an original bird by drawing the bird's head in the first quarter of the paper. Stress to students to use their imagination when creating birds—their designs do not need to be the same as "real" bird adaptations or parts. When students are done drawing their birds' heads, have them draw two short vertical lines that extend into the next quarter of the paper to indicate where the neck is. Students then fold the head back and pass their papers to the person to their right.

5. In the second quarter of the paper each student draws the body and wings without looking at the head. Again encourage students to use their imagination. When they are through, have students mark lines where the legs should begin. Students then fold back that section and pass the paper to the person to their right.

6. In the third section students draw the legs and feet. When through they should fold that section back and, without opening the paper, pass the birds back to the original person who drew the head. Have students open their pictures.

7. Based on the bird's appearance and using their imagination, each student should decide the bird's name, where the bird lives, and how the bird is adapted to its habitat. Have students write these descriptions in the fourth section of their paper. Students can then complete their drawings by adding a background that depicts the bird's habitat.

DISCUSSION QUESTIONS

In what ways is your bird adapted to the place where it lives?

In what ways are real birds adapted to the places where they live?

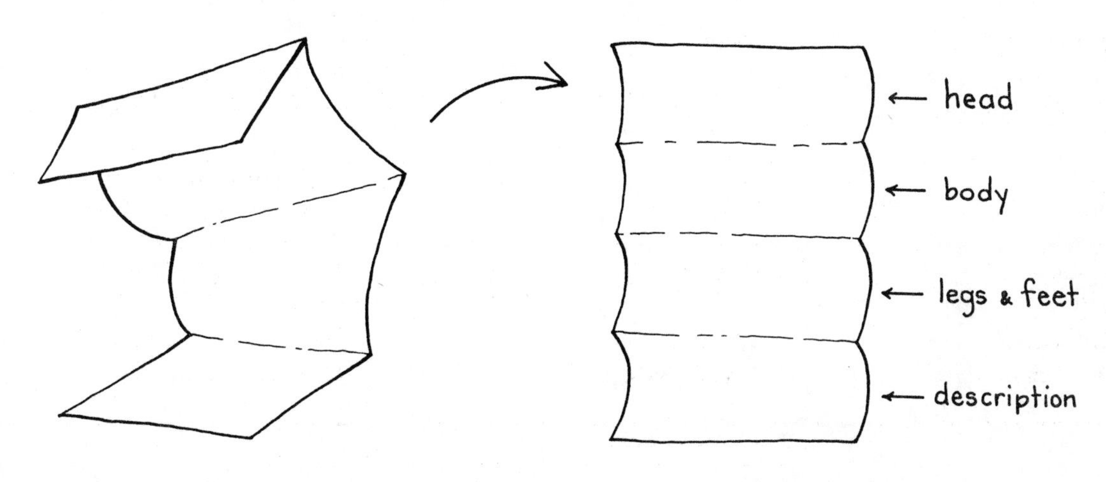

EVALUATION

Students name two bird adaptations for each of the following body parts, listing their advantages: beaks, feet, legs, color.

EXTENSION IDEAS

- Make a class flip book of the imaginary birds. Staple all the birds together with several staples at the left edge, then cut along the fold lines to within half an inch of the left edge. Students can then create their own birds using the various head, body/wing, and leg/feet parts. The flip book can serve to stimulate ideas for creative writing projects.
- Go for a walk to look for and identify adaptations of real birds. Have students write about or draw pictures of these adaptations.
- Have students gather information about specific birds from encyclopedias, pictures, articles, and other materials, then write a report about the adaptations of these birds. You might make an outline to help organize the reports.

HOME LEARNING SUGGESTION

(Use as follow-up to this activity)

Have students write short stories about their bird. Things students should think about when writing the stories include, "What is it like to be a ______________? What do you eat? What might try to eat you? Where do you sleep?"

SOURCE OF ACTIVITY

Adapted from *Project Wild Elementary Activity Guide,* "Adaptation Artistry." Boulder, Colo.: Western Regional Environmental Education Council, 1985.

FOOD-GETTING DEVICES

SUMMARY OF ACTIVITY

Students create food-getting devices that can catch and pick up food.

Time: 30 to 40 minutes to introduce and begin projects; additional time to complete projects

Setting: Classroom

Materials:
- Challenge slips (see preparation and lead-up)
- A variety of "junk" materials like toothpicks, popsicle sticks, cardboard, wire, pipe cleaners, styrofoam or paper cups, egg cartons, boxes, and meat trays
- Materials for fastening like rubber bands, glue, scotch tape, string, pins, paper fasteners

Subjects: Science, art

Key Words: Predator, prey, food-getting device

RELATED CALIFORNIA FRAMEWORK CONCEPTS

Animals have adaptations that enable them to obtain and conserve food, oxygen, and water; excrete waste products; move; protect themselves against predators; minimize effects of extreme temperatures; reproduce; and so forth. (*Science Framework Addendum*)

Visual art media can be use to translate ideas, feelings, and values. (Adapted from *Visual and Performing Arts Framework*)

OBJECTIVE

Students create food-getting devices as a way of demonstrating adaptations that help an animal obtain food.

BACKGROUND INFORMATION

In the previous activities students looked at adaptations of birds. In this activity students are introduced to adaptations of other animals that help the animals survive.

Animals have adaptations that enable them to gather or capture food and to eat it whether the food is roots, vegetation, or other animals. These adaptations are referred to in this activity as food-getting devices. Examples of food-getting adaptations include beaks, claws, teeth, and tongues. Some bird beaks are thick to crack open seeds; other beaks have hooks on them to tear the flesh of prey. Hawk and eagle claws enable these predators to dig into and hold onto prey. Insects, too, often have the equivalent of claws to hold onto prey. Beavers have teeth that enable them to gnaw at wood; dogs have sharp teeth to grab onto and tear at their prey. Frogs and lizards grab flying insects with their quick-moving tongues.

PREPARATION AND LEAD-UP

Write the following challenges—and any you wish to add—on slips of paper, one challenge to each slip.

Make a food-getting device that could pick up an egg.
Make a food-getting device that could catch a flying insect.
Make a food-getting device that could dig up roots.
Make a food-getting device that could pick up leaves.
Make a food-getting device for getting at animals that live underground.
Make a food-getting device that a meat eater would use.
Make a food-getting device for breaking nuts and eating the meat.

PROCEDURE

1. Discuss different food-getting devices, using examples from the activities "Bird Bills" and "Artful Bird Adaptations," as well as other animals familiar to students. You might use the pictures from the "Animal Diversity" activity to illustrate the different devices.

2. Give each student a challenge. Have students design and build a food-getting device to meet the challenge.

3. Ask students to share their devices. Students can demonstrate how the devices work.

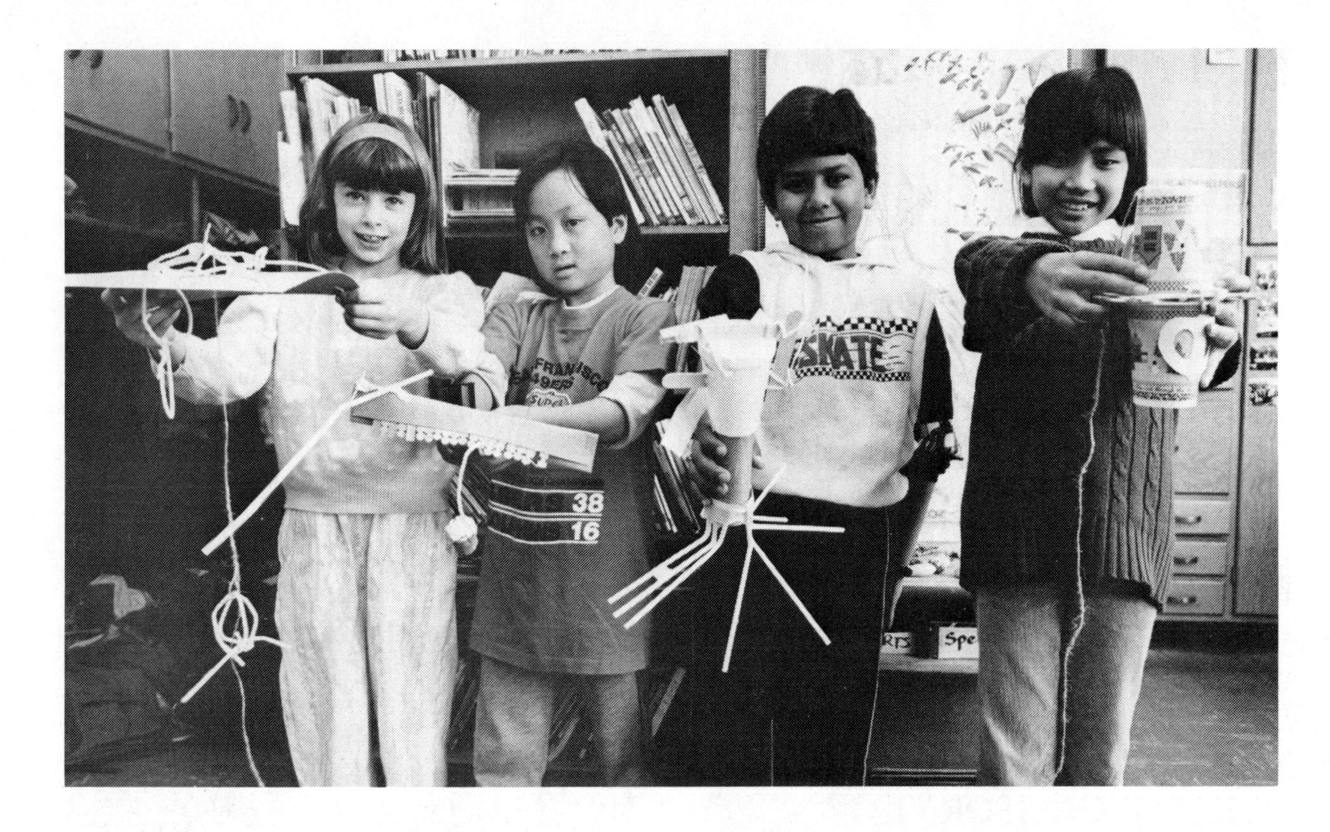

DISCUSSION QUESTIONS

Can you think of a real animal that might use a food-getting device similar to the one you have designed?

How do food-getting device adaptations help animals survive?

Why are there so many different kinds of food-getting devices?

What would happen if every animal had the same food-getting device?

What adaptations do plants and animals have to avoid being eaten by other animals?

EVALUATION

Students look at numbered pictures of real animals with food-getting adaptations identified in the challenges. Students match the number of the picture to statements about the adaptations, such as: This animal has an adaptation that helps it pick up an egg, catch a flying insect, dig up roots, pick up leaves, get at animals that live underground, eat meat, or break nuts and eat the meats.

EXTENSION IDEAS

- Take the class on a walk around the schoolgrounds or in a nearby park (if possible). Have students look for animals and decide what kind of food they eat.
- Challenge students to draw a picture of a plant or animal that is adapted to survive the food-getting device they designed in the activity. Ask students to share their drawings, then as a class discuss them.

HOME LEARNING SUGGESTION

(Use as follow-up to this activity)

Have students take home a different challenge from the one they did in class and make a food-getting device from household objects. Students can share their devices in class.

SOURCE OF ACTIVITY

Outdoor Biology Instructional Strategies (OBIS), "Adaptation-Predator-Prey." Developed by Lawrence Hall of Science, University of California. Nashua, N.H.: Delta Education, 1975.

ADAPTATION ADVANTAGES

SUMMARY OF ACTIVITY

Students look at pictures of animals to identify and categorize adaptations.

Time: 30 to 45 minutes

Setting: Classroom

Materials:
- Pictures used in "Animal Diversity" activity
- Reproduced copycat page
- Books and magazines with pictures of and information about various animals (optional)
- Chart paper and pen (optional)

Subjects: Science

Key Words: Adaptation, obtaining or storing, locomotion, protection, temperature, reproduction

RELATED CALIFORNIA FRAMEWORK CONCEPTS

Animals have adaptations that enable them to obtain and conserve food, oxygen, and water; excrete waste products; move; protect themselves against predators, minimize effects of extreme temperatures; reproduce; and so forth. (*Science Framework Addendum*)

Data can be collected, organized, represented, and interpreted using lists, tables, and graphs. (Adapted from *Mathematics Framework*)

OBJECTIVE

Given a set of pictures, students identify and classify animal adaptations.

BACKGROUND INFORMATION

Students have looked at adaptations of birds and at food-getting adaptations of other animals. In this activity students look for animal adaptations that fall under the categories obtaining and storing food, moving about (locomotion), protection, temperature, and reproduction. Bird adaptations that relate to these categories follow in chart below.

PREPARATION AND LEAD-UP

Gather the materials.

PROCEDURE

1. Divide students into groups of four and have each group work with three or four of the animal pictures used in the second activity of this unit. Have students look for adaptations in the pictures, then list their observations on the board or on chart paper.

2. After all observations are listed, ask students if some adaptations serve the same purpose (for example, bird wings and fish fins are both adaptations that help the animals move about). Help students group the lists into categories similar to

Category	Bird Adaptation
Obtaining and storing food	Beaks (see the activity "Bird Bills")
Moving about	Wings, feathers, and light bones for flying Claws (some birds are able to climb and hang onto trees) Webbed feet (help birds move in water)
Protection	Camouflage coloration Sharp claws Protective behavior (some birds fly in flocks)
Temperature	Feathers (seabirds and birds that live in cold environments have downy feathers to help stay warmer) Oil in feathers (to help keep water birds waterproof) Feathered legs and feet (common to arctic birds)
Reproduction	Coloration (helps attract mates) Eggs

obtaining and storing food, moving about, protection, temperature, and reproduction.

3. Distribute the copycat page and the remaining animal pictures to students (each group should now have 10 to 15 pictures). Have students fill in the chart using information from the pictures and from books and magazines. For each animal they study, students should write a description of adaptations that help the animal obtain and store food, move about, adjust to temperature, protect itself, and reproduce. Students should look for as many adaptations as possible, but they should not be concerned if they don't observe adaptations for each category.

DISCUSSION QUESTIONS

What adaptations do animals have to help them obtain and store food?
What kinds of adaptations do animals have for moving about?
What kinds of adaptations do animals have for protection?
What kinds of adaptations do animals have for different temperatures?
What kinds of adaptations do animals have for reproduction?
Can one animal possess more than one adaptation?
How do adaptations help animals survive?

EVALUATION

The completed copycat pages will help you evaluate students' understanding.

EXTENSION IDEA

Have each student invent an animal (the animal can be drawn or actually constructed). Students then write about their animal, telling how it obtains and stores food, moves about, protects itself, reproduces, and adapts to temperature.

HOME LEARNING SUGGESTION

(Use as follow-up to this activity)

Have students look for pictures in magazines of an animal that has an adaptation that helps it obtain and store food, move about, protect itself from predators and from harsh temperatures, or reproduce. Discuss the adaptation in class.

Copycat Page

Names ______________________

____

____

____

ANIMAL ADAPTATIONS

Adaptations for:

Name of Animal	Obtaining and Storing Food	Moving About	Temperature	Protection	Reproduction

PLANT ADAPTATIONS

SUMMARY OF ACTIVITY

Students look at different plants and discuss how they vary and what types of adaptations they might have.

Time: 30 minutes

Setting: Classroom

Materials: Five or more houseplants (different types)

Subjects: Science, math, language arts

Key Words: Adaptations, variations

RELATED CALIFORNIA FRAMEWORK CONCEPTS

Plants have adaptations that enable them to obtain and store water, produce and store food, protect themselves against predators and parasites, receive sunlight, minimize the effects of extreme temperatures, reproduce, and so forth. (*Science Framework Addendum*)

Using one or more attributes, objects can be classified and sorted by observing similarities and differences, describing and recording relationships, and making generalizations. (Adapted from *Mathematics Framework*)

OBJECTIVE

Students observe a variety of common plants and identify their adaptive characteristics.

BACKGROUND INFORMATION

Students have been learning about adaptations that help animals survive. In this activity students are introduced to the notion of adaptation and variation in plants. Students discuss ways that houseplants can be sorted and sequenced and adaptations that plants have which help them survive.

Plants adapt in many ways. They have chlorophyll in their leaves that enables them to manufacture food using the energy from sunlight. Most plants have roots for obtaining water from the soil. Some plants, like cacti and succulents, have fleshy leaves for storing water.

Some plants are protected by thorns. Some like milkweed have poisons (usually plants are poisonous to some but not all potential predators; for example, monarch butterflies feed on milkweed).

Desert plants often have "hairs" which help shade the plants from hot desert sunlight. Some plants (like deciduous trees) "hibernate" during winter. They protect themselves from cold temperatures by pulling their chlorophyll and other important components into the trunk and branches for storage, then drop their leaves.

Many plants have seeds, flowers, and fruit that are all part of the reproductive system. The flower's prime function is the production of seeds. Within the flower's ovary are eggs that develop into seeds when fertilized (pollinated). The ovary matures into the fruit, which often protects the seed and aids in the seed's dispersal. Flowers often have adaptations to attract insects and birds because these animals move from flower to flower and help pollinate the plant's eggs. Brightly colored petals, sweet smells, and nectar (which is food for pollinators) are flower adaptations that increase chances of reproduction.

Although plants are not able to move about, they have adapted other ways to help them survive. Some of these adaptations will be studied in the "Invent-A-Plant" activity. One important way that plants have compensated for their inability to move is in their adaptations for reproduction. Plants that produce seeds often employ some mechanism whereby the seeds are dispersed so that they will not compete directly with the parent plant. In the next activity students will take a close look at specific seed dispersal mechanisms.

PREPARATION AND LEAD-UP

Gather five or more different houseplants. Your students might like to bring plants from home.

PROCEDURE

1. Review what students have learned about animal adaptations (different animals have different characteristics; many of the differences are adaptations that help animals survive). Tell students that today they will be looking at plants to see what kinds of variations exist between plants.

2. Show students a variety of houseplants. Have the class discuss ways that the plants vary, how they could be sorted, and how they could be sequenced. As a class, sort the plants into two groups and then sort each of those groups into two. Ask, "How are plants alike? In what ways do they differ? Do they differ in ways similar to the ways animals differ?" Help students look for adaptations that enable plants to be protected from predators and harsh temperatures, obtain and store food and water, and reproduce (see the discussion questions).

3. Ask, "Do plants have adaptations that help them move about? Can you think of ways that parts of plants move about?" If students haven't already mentioned it, bring up the idea that plants' seeds need to move in order to grow. Tell students that for the next couple of days they will be learning more about ways that plant seeds move about.

DISCUSSION QUESTIONS

What adaptations do plants have to help them obtain and store food and water?
What adaptations help some plants protect themselves?
What adaptations help plants survive in different temperatures?
What adaptations do plants have for reproduction?

EVALUATION

Students draw a picture of a plant and write a short statement describing at least two adaptations that help the plant survive.

EXTENSION IDEA

Have students research a particular plant to find out more about its adaptations. Cacti, seaweed, redwoods, pine trees, maple trees, and flowering plants are good plants to study.

HOME LEARNING SUGGESTION

(Use as lead-up to the following activity)

Ask students to bring from home samples of different kinds of seeds. Brainstorm with students beforehand the types of seeds they might find (for example, dried beans and peas, grains like rice, fruit seeds, sesame seeds, poppy seeds, dill seeds, sunflower seeds, peanuts, and nuts).

SEED DISPERSAL

SUMMARY OF ACTIVITY

Students sort various seeds and are read a book about how and why seeds differ, then they "adapt" seeds to be dispersed by mechanisms constructed in class.

Time: Two 45-minute periods, plus some time to add to the "Seed Dispersal" chart

Setting: Classroom

Materials:
- The book *Seeds Pop-Stick-Glide*
- Butcher paper
- Marking pens
- Tape, paste, or glue
- Dried lima beans (or other large beans), one pound bag
- Construction materials (construction paper, rubber bands, toothpicks, scissors, pencils, red tempera, balloons, pieces of cord, cotton or feathers, small metal springs, pipe cleaners, egg cartons, cardboard, and any other useful materials)
- One sandwich bag filled with 15 to 20 *different* beans for each pair of students
- Container of water (optional)

Subjects: Science, art, math

Key Words: Seed, flower, fruit, seed dispersal, adaptation, dispersal mechanism

RELATED CALIFORNIA FRAMEWORK CONCEPTS

Plants have adaptations that enable them to obtain and store water, produce and store food, protect themselves against predators and parasites, receive sunlight, minimize the effects of extreme temperatures, reproduce, and so forth. (*Science Framework Addendum*)

Using one or more attributes, objects can be classified and sorted by observing similarities and differences, describing and recording relationships, and making generalizations. (Adapted from *Mathematics Framework*)

Visual art media can be used to translate ideas, feelings, and values. (Adapted from *Visual and Performing Arts Framework*)

OBJECTIVE

Students design seed dispersal mechanisms as a way of examining the adaptive characteristics of seeds.

BACKGROUND INFORMATION

Most plants produce seeds as a means of reproduction; if conditions are right, the seeds grow into new plants. In order for the new plants to survive, they need minerals, air, and water, as well as sunlight, which provides the necessary energy for transforming these raw materials into nutrients. If a seed is dropped underneath a plant, it may have difficulty growing because the older plant could deprive the new plant of sunlight or of one or more of the raw materials.

One type of plant adaptation that helps ensure species survival is a seed dispersal mechanism in which seeds are distributed to other growing sites that are more favorable. Some plants have developed seeds with hooks on them, such as burrs and foxtails, so that the seeds can "hitchhike" on an animal or person to different locations. Some plants, like pyracanthas, have developed seeds that are surrounded by tasty fruit; these seeds are eaten by animals, go unharmed through the animals' digestive system, then are dispersed to a different location through the animals' scat. Other plants, like dandelions, have developed seeds that are shaped so that they are dispersed by wind. Still other plants have seeds that disperse themselves; violet seeds, for example, develop within a fruit that squeezes the seeds as it dries. The seeds finally "pop out" and can travel several feet.

In this activity students study some of the ways that seeds are dispersed. Students are given the opportunity to use what they have learned to "invent" a seed that has a specific dispersal mechanism.

PREPARATION AND LEAD-UP

Using butcher paper and marking pens, prepare a "Seed Dispersal" chart as shown in the illustration. Find a place to post it where it can stay for several days.

The seed dispersal chart requires some practice using matrices where students sort by two differ-

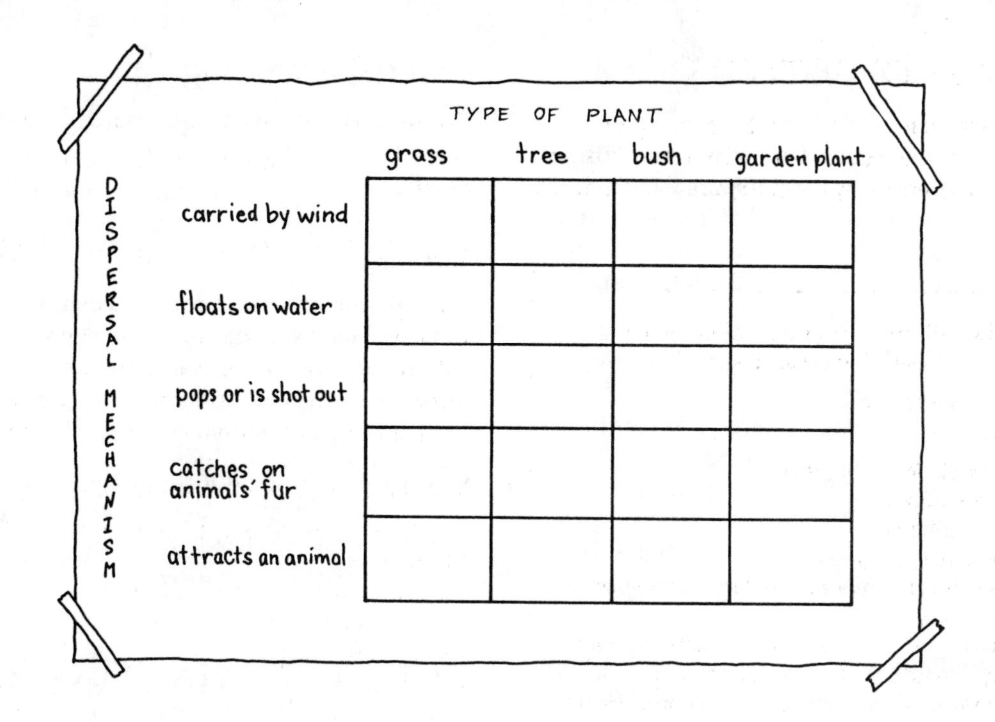

ent characteristics at once. The "Variations Among Us" and "Adaptation Advantages" activities will have given students practice using this type of matrix.

PROCEDURE

Day One

1. Divide students into pairs and give each pair a sandwich bag filled with different beans. Have pairs divide their beans into two piles so that beans in each pile are alike in some way. Direct students to then divide their two piles into two more piles. Ask, "Looking at the two small piles that came from a larger pile, how are the beans alike? Different? Are there any characteristics that all the beans share? In what ways are the beans different from one another?"

2. Discuss the purpose of seeds. Ask what types of things a seed needs in order to grow into a plant. Explain that not all seeds can grow where they fall and that some seeds are dispersed (that is carried, blown, or pushed away).

3. Review the concept of adaptation, which is any special feature an organism has that helps improve its chances for survival and reproduction. Discuss with students how seed adaptations might help plants survive and reproduce.

4. Read Patricia Lauber's book *Seeds Pop-Stick-Glide* to the class. This book has marvelous photographs and clearly written information about various types of plants and their seed dispersal mechanisms.

5. Introduce the seed dispersal chart to students. Explain that over the next few days or week the class will try to fill in all of the squares of the matrix with as many seeds as possible (use the home learning suggestion in conjunction with this activity). When students bring in a seed for the chart, they should decide how that seed is dispersed, then glue or tape a sample of the seed in the proper box (remind students that some seeds may be dispersed in more than one way). Leave the chart up so that students can add to it (if appropriate, you might allow students time to look for seeds in the schoolgrounds or in a nearby vacant lot, park, or other open space).

Day Two

6. Allow students time to glue or tape the seeds they have found to the seed dispersal chart. Ask,

"What types of seeds seem easiest to find? Hardest?"

7. Explain to students that they will be applying what they have learned about dispersal mechanisms to adapt a plain seed so that it uses a particular mechanism. Give each student a lima bean seed to be dispersed and one of the following challenges:

Modify your seed to float on water at least five minutes.
Modify your seed to attract a bird or other animal.
Modify your seed to fly at least three feet.
Modify your seed to hitchhike on an animal or person for 20 feet.
Modify your seed with a mechanism that will throw the seed two feet away from the parent plant.

8. Provide students with materials for modifying their seeds. Allow 15 to 20 minutes for construction of the adaptations.

9. Have volunteers share their dispersal invention. You might provide a container of water for testing floating seeds.

DISCUSSION QUESTIONS

Can you think of plants that actually have features like the seed dispersal mechanisms you constructed?
What might happen if plants did not have seed dispersal mechanisms?

EVALUATION

Display real seeds that are examples of dispersal types like seeds that float, seeds that attract birds or other animals, seeds that are carried by the wind, "hitchhikers," and seeds that are dispersed by mechanical means. Number the seeds and ask students to identify how the seeds are adapted for dispersal.

EXTENSION IDEAS

- Give each student another lima bean to take home. Have each student try to modify the bean to meet a challenge different from the challenge he or she tried before, using objects found at home.
- Have students make mosaics using seeds and yarn glued to cardboard. Ask, "Are some seeds easier to work with than other seeds? Why?" (Seeds with hooks may prick fingers, for example.)
- As a class, study more about how plants reproduce. Each student might study one kind of plant, then the class can discuss how plant reproductive systems differ.

HOME LEARNING SUGGESTION

(Use as part of this activity)

Give students the opportunity to look for seeds for the seed dispersal chart as a home learning activity. Challenge students to see how many different types of seeds they can find at home. Remind students to try to think of how the seeds are dispersed.

RESOURCE

Lauber, Patricia. *Seeds Pop-Stick-Glide.* New York: Crown Publishers, Inc., 1981. This book describes in pictures and words the variety of ways plants disperse seeds.

SOURCE OF ACTIVITY

Outdoor Biology Instructional Strategies (OBIS), "Seed Dispersal." Developed by Lawrence Hall of Science, University of California. Nashua, N.H.: Delta Education, 1979.

INVENT-A-PLANT

SUMMARY OF ACTIVITY

Students construct models of imaginary plants that are "adapted" to survive under specified environmental conditions.

Time: 60 minutes or more

Setting: Classroom, schoolyard, or neighborhood

Materials:

- Materials to make models of plants (toothpicks, construction paper or other paper, buttons, thread spools, glue, tempera paint, cotton, corks, bottle caps, straws, clay, and styrofoam packing beads)

Subjects: Science, art

Key Words: Adaptation, habitat

RELATED CALIFORNIA FRAMEWORK CONCEPTS

Plants have adaptations that enable them to obtain and store water, produce and store food, protect themselves against predators and parasites, receive sunlight, minimize the effects of extreme temperatures, reproduce, and so forth. (*Science Framework Addendum*)

Living things have adaptations that enable them to live in their particular environments. (*Science Framework Addendum*)

Visual art media can be used to translate ideas, feelings, and values. (Adapted from *Visual and Performing Arts Framework*)

OBJECTIVE

Students create imaginary plants that illustrate ways in which plants are adapted to their environment.

BACKGROUND INFORMATION

Unlike animals, plants are not able to move when wind, water, heat, cold, sunlight, dryness, or animals become a problem. Plants can compensate, however, for their immobility, allowing them to live and reproduce in particular environments. The special characters that allow plants to survive in specific environments are examples of adaptations.

PREPARATION AND LEAD-UP

Prepare slips of paper with the following challenges written on them (one challenge per student).

Invent a plant that is lawnmower-proof.
Invent a plant that can live on the surface of a pond.
Invent a plant that can withstand high winds.
Invent a plant that grazing animals would not eat.
Invent a plant that can hold on to a rock in swift rivers and streams.
Invent a plant to catch insects.
Invent a plant adapted to store water.
Invent a plant that can compete with other plants for sunlight.

Take students for a short walk to look for adaptations of plants (see the background information in the activity "Plant Adaptations" for more specific information). Ask, "What adaptations do plants have that help them obtain and store food and water? What adaptations do some plants have that help protect them? What adaptations help plants survive in different temperatures? What adaptations do plants have for reproduction?"

PROCEDURE

1. Back in the classroom, challenge students to invent plants to survive under certain conditions. Distribute a challenge slip to each student.

2. Have students make their plant using the "junk" materials you have collected.

3. Ask students to write a paragraph describing their plant's adaptations and the type of place where the plant would live best. Have volunteers share their plants and describe the features that help the plants survive.

4. Review the word habitat, which is the place where a plant or animal lives (its "home") that includes everything the organism needs to survive. Discuss the probable habitat and unique features of each plant.

DISCUSSION QUESTIONS

Where would each plant be best suited to survive?
How would each plant be unsuited for different habitats?
How are plants adapted to seasonal changes?

EVALUATION

Show students real plants (or pictures of plants) that are adapted in ways similar to the plants they invented. Have students write down how the plants are adapted and ways the adaptations might help them survive.

EXTENSION IDEAS

- Give students additional challenges. Alternatively, have students create more challenges for each other.
- Make plant sun prints showing different plant adaptations. Have the class discuss the purposes of the adaptations.

HOME LEARNING SUGGESTION

(Use as lead-up to the next activity)

Send home with students the "Human Adaptations" copycat page. Ask parents to discuss with their child ways that humans obtain and store food, move about, protect themselves, and adjust to temperatures. This information will be used in the next activity.

SOURCE OF ACTIVITY

Outdoor Biology Instructional Strategies (OBIS), "Invent A Plant—Adaptation." Developed by Lawrence Hall of Science, University of California. Nashua, N.H.: Delta Education, 1975.

Sample Letter

Dear Parent:

In our class we have been studying adaptations of animals and plants. An adaptation is any special feature of a living thing that helps improve its chances for survival. Camouflage is an example of an adaptation many animals possess that protects them from natural enemies. Thorns on a rose bush are an example of a plant adaptation that also protects.

Please spend a few minutes with your child to discuss ways that people do the things on the accompanying page, and have your child write down the things you discussed.

Name ______________________________

HUMAN ADAPTATIONS

HOW DO PEOPLE:

Obtain and store food and water?

Move about?

Protect themselves?

Adjust to temperatures?

Which ways do you think are adaptations? Put an "A" next to each adaptation.

HUMAN ADAPTATIONS

SUMMARY OF ACTIVITY

Students discuss how humans are adapted, then experiment with one human adaptation—the opposable thumb.

Time: 30 to 45 minutes

Setting: Classroom

Materials:
- Masking tape
- Unshelled peanuts

Subjects: Science, language arts

Key Words: Adaptation, opposable thumb

RELATED CALIFORNIA FRAMEWORK CONCEPT

Human beings have characteristics by which they can be identified, described, and classified. (*Science Framework Addendum*)

OBJECTIVE

Students identify human adaptations and conduct an experiment demonstrating the importance of the opposable thumb.

BACKGROUND INFORMATION

Throughout this unit students have looked at ways that animals and plants are adapted to the place they live and to their lifestyles. In this activity students are given the opportunity to think about adaptations that humans have that enable us to survive.

The most profound adaptation that we possess is our well-developed brain, which enables us to manipulate the environment around us and make it livable. We are able to live in extremely diverse habitats because of our ability to invent solutions to survival problems. We no longer depend solely on our bodies for obtaining and storing food and water, moving about, protecting ourselves, or adapting to various temperatures. Instead, we depend greatly on the complex systems we have developed to satisfy these needs. Listed below are some of the systems we have developed to meet our needs.

While these methods for satisfying our survival needs are ways that we have actively adapted to our environment, they are not evolutionary adaptations. Evolutionary adaptations are genetic rather than characteristics we consciously affect. Our advanced brain is an example of an evolutionary adaptation.

Another example is our opposable thumb. Because our thumbs oppose the rest of our fingers, we are able to manipulate objects with our hands —an adaptation that has enabled us to develop tools and technologies to enhance survival. In this activity students experiment with their thumbs to learn how this adaptation greatly affects their lives.

PREPARATION AND LEAD-UP

Gather the materials.

PROCEDURE

1. Use the previous activity's home learning suggestion as a starting point for discussion about how we meet our needs for obtaining and storing food and water, moving about, protecting our-

Category	Adaptation
Obtaining and storing food	Agriculture, food processing, freezers, refrigerators, silos
Obtaining and storing water	Water pipelines and systems, reservoirs
Moving about	Cars, bicycles, trains, trucks, buses, transportation systems, airplanes, boats, space shuttles, shoes
Protection	Police, fire fighters, armies, knives, guns, homes, pesticides and other chemicals
Temperature	Clothing, shelter, fire, heaters, air conditioners

selves, and adjusting to temperatures. Ask, "Which of these are adaptations? How do these human adaptations vary from animals' adaptations? How are they alike?"

2. Introduce students to an adaptation that humans have to help them survive—the opposable thumb. Ask, "How important do you think your thumb is to you? How do you think your life would be different if you didn't have a thumb? What experiment might we try to find out?"

3. Using masking tape, tape students' thumbs to their index fingers (students can help tape each other). Make sure when taping that the top of the thumb is taped securely so that students cannot "cheat" by using their thumbs a little. Have students attempt to button or unbutton a shirt, hold and write with a pencil, or fold a piece of paper. Give each student a peanut, and with their thumbs still taped, ask students to shell and eat the nut.

DISCUSSION QUESTIONS

Could you do all the things? Which was hardest? Easiest?
How do we use our opposable thumb?
How does your thumb help you survive?
Can you think of other animals that have this adaptation?
What other ways are people adapted for survival?

EVALUATION

The discussion can help evaluate students' understanding.

EXTENSION IDEAS

- Have students research and compare human opposable thumbs to those of monkeys, apes, and pandas. How are they similar? How are they different?
- Demonstrate the advantage of having both eyes in front of the head instead of on the side. Have students cover one eye with an eye patch and try playing "catch" with a ping-pong ball. Students can also design and make masks that only let them see to the side, using materials such as construction paper, manila folders, index cards, mirrored plastic, and string or elastic. Discuss the advantages and disadvantages of eyes in front and eyes on the side of the head.
- Borrow from a dentist a plaster cast of a human mouth and have students look for different kinds of human teeth (incisors, the wedge-shaped teeth in front, rip out bites of food; cuspids or canines, the pointed teeth next to the incisors, tear food; bicuspids, having two points, are behind the cuspids and crush food; and molars, the nearly flat teeth in the back of the mouth, grind food). Students can investigate how different teeth are used by chewing various foods (celery, cheese, carrots, apples, nuts, bananas, peanut brittle, and beef jerky are good to try) and comparing how their teeth treat each food.

Energy

Fifth and Sixth Grades

Introduction to the Unit

Energy is the capacity to do work or the ability to make things move. Energy comes in several forms—sound, light, heat, active (kinetic energy), and stored (potential energy)—and can be converted from one form to another. When we speak of energy as a resource we are usually talking about potential energy that can be converted to other, more useful types of energy like heat, light, motion, or sound. Examples of potential energy resources are food, water held behind a dam, coal, oil, and gasoline.

Energy is a vital part of our everyday lives. Food provides us with the energy to live and grow, we depend on electrical energy for our refrigerators and lights, energy provides us with hot water in our homes, and our cars and buses require energy from gasoline. We depend on energy in various forms for everything we do.

As a nation we have become economically dependent on large amounts of energy. This dependence has caused problems like air pollution and acid rain (caused by burning fossil fuels like petroleum, oil, natural gas), the possibility of damaging oil spills (caused by drilling rigs or tankers), political and military tensions (caused by dependence on foreign oil), the dwindling supply of oil and other fossil fuels, and safety questions about nuclear power plants and the wastes produced there.

Because energy is a broad, complex, and controversial topic that affects the quality of our lives and the environment, it is important that it be addressed in the classroom. In the first two activities students conduct hands-on experiments with solar energy. In the following activity students learn through observation and discussion ways to tell when energy is being used. The following two activities help students gain an understanding of more commonly used energy sources. In the final two activities students look at energy use at home and try some energy conservation measures.

Throughout this unit the teacher might encourage students to bring in energy articles they find in newspapers and magazines. Have students read or summarize their articles for the class and keep a bulletin board available for posting current energy news. Help students see the relationship between the activities of this unit and the news articles they collect. Make explicit the tie between what students are learning in the classroom and what is happening in the rest of the world.

Advance Planning

For the first two activities, "Let the Sun Shine In" and "Testing a Hypothesis," you will need one thermometer for each pair of students and one styrofoam cup or other standard container for each student. For "Researching Energy Sources" you will need to make sure that students have access to reference materials about energy. Several titles are suggested in the activity. Additionally, you may wish to check out books from the public library or ask if local utility companies and ecology centers distribute free literature on energy.

Resources

See the California State Resource Agencies section for energy materials available from energy agencies.

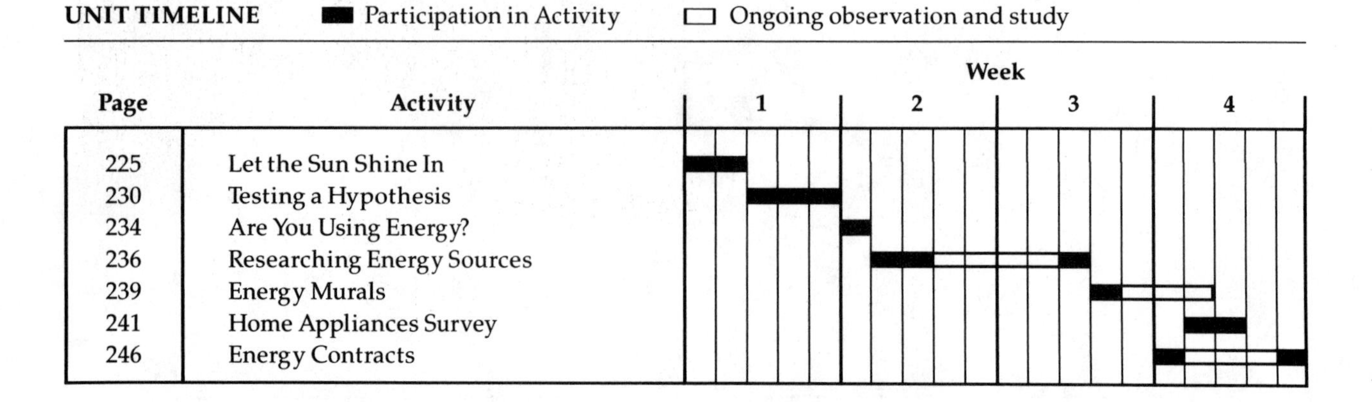

UNIT TIMELINE ■ Participation in Activity □ Ongoing observation and study

Page	Activity
225	Let the Sun Shine In
230	Testing a Hypothesis
234	Are You Using Energy?
236	Researching Energy Sources
239	Energy Murals
241	Home Appliances Survey
246	Energy Contracts

LET THE SUN SHINE IN

SUMMARY OF ACTIVITY

Students construct a model solar home and compare their models to see which trap heat most effectively.

Time: Two 45-minute periods

Setting: Classroom, outdoors

Materials:
- Styrofoam cups, one for each student
- Scissors
- Tape
- Construction paper
- White paper
- Plastic bags
- Thermometers
- Copycat page, one per student
- Two pieces of butcher paper (optional)

Subjects: Science, math, language arts, art

Key Words: Design, temperature, solar energy, experiment, variable, constant

RELATED CALIFORNIA FRAMEWORK CONCEPTS

Sources of useful energy include sunlight, earth's heat (geothermal), wind, water flow, nuclear reactions, and fossil fuels. (*Science Framework Addendum*)

Energy takes many forms: e.g., heat, light, electricity, sound, and motion of objects. (*Science Framework Addendum*)

OBJECTIVE

Students design and construct a one-room model home, observe and record the air temperature inside the model while it is exposed to direct sunlight, and list variables that affect the temperature.

BACKGROUND INFORMATION

The sun is our most important energy source. It is constantly radiating light energy that plants convert into chemical energy and store through photosynthesis. This is the process green plants use to produce their food, which allows them to grow and to provide food for people and other animals. Solar energy is also important because when it is absorbed by objects the energy is converted into heat.

When we think of "solar homes" usually we think of homes that have special equipment to heat water or living space. Even without investing in expensive remodeling or equipment, however, most people can take advantage of some solar energy for heating their homes. Curtains left open during the day let in the sun's rays; south-facing windows let in the most sunlight and warmth. Closing curtains at night will trap heat inside and

keep a house warmer. On hot sunny days, houses can be kept cooler if curtains remain closed, thus reducing sunlight entering the home.

In this activity students construct a model home that allows the air inside to heat up when the model is placed in sunlight. Students should be encouraged to make creative and experimental use of the available materials. You may wish to call the models "homes," although students do not need to spend time making them look like houses. Appearance is unimportant; how the models work to capture and retain heat is vital. Students will use their models to experiment with ways of using the sun's energy for heating.

This activity is open-ended. Open-ended experimentation allows students the opportunity to make discoveries based on what they do and observe. Students investigate at their own pace and along their own lines of interest. The discussion following the activity can be directed to help students make sense of the experimental results and introduce them to the concepts of variable, constant, and solar energy, which will be investigated further in the next activity.

In an experiment a variable is a factor being tested. A constant is a factor not being tested. For example, if students were conducting an experiment to see whether the orientation of the window in their models affected how hot the air got inside, the orientation of the windows would vary. Some models would be placed with the windows facing the sun; others would be placed with the windows facing away from the sun. In this experiment, all other things about the models except ability to catch heat should be constant or identical—all models should be the same size, color, etc. By testing one variable at a time, the effects of that one variable can be assessed. Testing two variables together usually produces more complex results; it may be difficult to assess how each variable affected the outcome of the experiment.

For best results, collect the temperature data on a sunny day when the temperature is at least 14° C (57° F). Even if the sky is overcast, however, students should get significant results.

To make their models, students may use a large inverted styrofoam cup or any other identical cardboard or styrofoam container (like small boxes or styrofoam hamburger boxes). Whatever you provide, all containers must be identical, in order for students to accurately compare their experimental results. Make sure you have enough containers so that each pair of students can have two (one for this activity and one for the next activity).

PREPARATION AND LEAD-UP

Decide how to make the materials available to the class. You may find it convenient to place materials on a table and have each pair of students select one person to get and return materials. Choose a place for students to safely store their houses between work sessions. Copy the rules in step three onto a sheet of butcher paper or the chalkboard.

Make two copies of the copycat page per student. Students will need one copy for this activity and one for the next activity.

Be sure students know how to read a thermometer. Students can practice by taking temperature readings around the classroom or school grounds if necessary.

PROCEDURE

Day One

1. Ask, "Have any of you noticed that some places in your home are warmer than other places? Why are some of the warmest spots near windows?" (Some of the coldest spots are also near windows.) "How do you think the heat from the sun gets inside the house? What are some things about a house that might let in more heat from the sun?"

2. Divide the class into pairs. Challenge students to make a one-room model home that will capture and hold heat from the sun. Let students know that they will test their homes to see how hot the air inside each will get after 10 minutes.

3. Explain that each team may use the materials provided in any way as long as the following rules are followed. Post the rules where they will be visible to students while students work on their models.

RULES FOR BUILDING HOMES

- Each team will build a model of a one-room home.

- Each home must be made of one styrofoam cup (or whatever standard container has been provided).
- Each home must include a point of entry for the thermometer.
- Each house must be designed so that when the house is in the sun, the bulb of the thermometer will be shaded from direct sunlight. (If the bulb of the thermometer is in direct sunlight, it will not record the air temperature accurately but keep rising as the sun continues to heat the thermometer itself.)

4. Let students know how much time they have to design and build their models. While teams work, circulate to be sure all team members are participating. Ask, "How do you think this design will help your model capture heat from the sun?" You may need to remind students about the rules. When students are finished, collect and store the models for the next day.

Day Two

5. Have students predict which houses will reach the highest temperature. Tell students that while they are outside, they will need to complete certain tasks. They will read their thermometers at the designated times, record the temperature readings on their copycat page, and complete the questions on the page. Remind students of appropriate behavior outside.

6. Distribute the copycat pages. Explain that students will read the temperature on their thermometer four times (when you tell them) and record it in the appropriate place on their page. Point out where to record the temperature. Ask, "What is the purpose for recording the first temperature in the shade?" (This gives the air temperature in the house before it is heated by the sun and can be used to compare with the final temperature.) Explain that in between recording each temperature students will work on the other sections of their copycat pages.

7. Outside, have all students place their models in the shade. After about three minutes (you may have students explain their model designs during this time), give students a 10-second warning, then tell them to read their thermometers and record the temperature. Have students move their models to the sun. Give a 10-second warning and call time for the next temperature reading. Call time again after five minutes and after 10 minutes. Students should work on their copycat pages in between each temperature reading. (Note: if the solar homes are larger than a large styrofoam cup, you may want to have students take another reading at 15 minutes. The larger the volume of air inside the house, the longer the house will take to heat.)

8. Back inside the classroom, discuss students' results. Ask, " How high did the air temperature in your model get?" Find out what groups got the highest temperatures and ask, "What is different about these models than the others? What might explain the temperature differences?" (Different designs and errors in reading thermometer are two possibilities.) How are the houses the same? How are they different? What kinds of designs seemed to allow in or keep heat? What kinds of designs seemed to keep heat out or let it escape easily? How could you alter the design of your model given the results of this experiment?" Explain to students that their models made use of solar energy (heat from the sun) to heat the air inside.

9. Introduce the terms variable and constant. Ask, "What variables might affect how hot your model would get in the sun?" List on a piece of butcher paper or on the chalkboard variables students suggest. The list may include things like direction of window, size of window, covering on window, or color of model. Tell students that during the next activity they will choose one of these variables, devise an experiment to test it, and conduct the experiment. Save the list for the next activity.

DISCUSSION QUESTIONS

How much hotter was the air in your house after it had been heated by the sun? (Have students compare the first- and last-recorded temperatures on their copycat pages.)

How do the results compare with your predictions?

How do your results compare to results that other teams got?

Did you encounter any problems? How did you solve them?

What does this experiment show about using solar energy to heat a house or other building?

What are some drawbacks to a home that uses solar energy for heating? (One drawback is that it may get too hot in summer.)

Why do some people put folding cardboard shades in the front windows of their parked cars?

EVALUATION

Each student draws a design for a model home that will heat up in the sun. Students should consider variables listed by the class in step nine. (This evaluation also acts as a lead-up to the next activity.)

EXTENSION IDEA

The sun has played important social, spiritual, and artistic roles throughout history. Have students find depictions of the sun in the art of ancient Egypt, India, Central America, or elsewhere. The sun also appears in current advertisements and modern art. Students can make their own sun art, inspired by the art of the past or present.

HOME LEARNING SUGGESTION

(Use as follow-up to this activity)

Have students investigate their own homes. Which rooms get the warmest on sunny days? Which way are the windows facing in these rooms? Have students draw a diagram of their homes, including rooms, windows, and the orientation of their homes.

RESOURCE

Great Explorations in Math and Science (GEMS), "Hot Water and Warm Homes from Sunlight." Berkeley, Calif.: Lawrence Hall of Science, University of California, 1986. This guide provides detailed instructions for several structured experiments in solar energy.

Name ________________________

LET THE SUN SHINE IN

Record your temperatures here.

Time and place	*Temperature*
Shade	
0 minutes, sun	
5 minutes, sun	
10 minutes, sun	

Draw a picture of your model and the sun, showing which part of the model is facing the direction of the sun. Label all the parts of the model.

Describe how your model home is specially designed to capture heat from the sun.

TESTING A HYPOTHESIS

SUMMARY OF ACTIVITY

Students continue to experiment with solar heating by formulating and testing a hypothesis about the most effective way to trap heat.

Time: Three 45-minute periods

Setting: Classroom, outdoors

Materials:
- List of variables from the previous activity
- Styrofoam cups (or other containers identical to the ones used in the previous activity), one for each student
- Scissors
- Tape
- Construction paper
- White paper
- Plastic bags
- Thermometers
- "Let the Sun Shine In" copycat page from the previous activity, one for each student
- "Testing a Hypothesis" copycat page, one for each student

Subjects: Science, math

Key Words: Solar energy, variable, constant, experiment, hypothesis, prediction

RELATED CALIFORNIA FRAMEWORK CONCEPTS

Sources of useful energy include sunlight, earth's heat (geothermal), wind, water flow, nuclear reactions, and fossil fuels. (*Science Framework Addendum*)

Energy takes many forms: e.g., heat, light, electricity, sound, and motion of objects. (*Science Framework Addendum*)

Data can be collected, organized, represented, and interpreted using lists, tables, and graphs. (Adapted from *Mathematics Framework*)

OBJECTIVE

Students compose a hypothesis to test one variable, conduct an experiment to test their hypothesis, and evaluate the outcome of the experiment.

BACKGROUND INFORMATION

Solar home heating systems are more common in California and the Southwest than in the rest of the United States. Other countries that have lots of sunshine and few other energy sources, like Israel, depend on solar energy for a significant portion of their energy.

Solar home heating takes advantage of the energy emitted daily by the sun. Glass windows in solar homes trap the heat energy, a black or dark surface is used to absorb the energy, and special materials store the energy until night, when it is cool and heat is most needed. Water, stones, or bricks—thermal mass—are capable of storing heat and then releasing it at night.

Although the equipment needed to actively capture solar energy is expensive, the energy itself is free and renewable. Solar energy does not create pollution or other environmental effects when used to heat water or to produce electricity (pollution or other environmental damage may be caused during the manufacture and transportation of materials need for solar collectors, however).

In this activity the class chooses one variable from the list developed in the last activity, develops a hypothesis based on a prediction about the variable, and designs an experiment to test the hypothesis. During the design of the experiment, students may come to see the need to test only one variable while keeping other factors of the models constant. You may need to ask leading questions, however, to help make this clear for some students.

A hypothesis is a statement that can be tested experimentally. Designing a hypothesis can involve making a prediction about a variable. One or more experiments may be able to show whether a hypothesis is correct.

This activity is designed for the whole class to test one hypothesis. However, it may be adapted easily so that each team chooses a variable to test and writes its own hypothesis. In this case students should be grouped in teams of four so that the team can work in pairs to design and compare two model homes.

PREPARATION AND LEAD-UP

Decide how to make the materials available to the class. Choose a place for students to safely store their model homes in between work sessions. Use one copy of the "Let the Sun Shine In" copycat page from the previous activity for each student.

PROCEDURE

Day One

1. Review the results from the previous activity. Ask, "What did you learn from testing your model home in the sun?" Discuss the list of variables. Ask, "How might these variables affect how hot a model would get inside?"

2. Have students choose one of the variables on the list to test in an experiment. Help students develop a hypothesis based on the variable they chose. Unless students are already familiar with what a hypothesis is, they will need some guidance. You might begin by asking, "What did you observe about this variable? How did this variable affect how hot the models got inside?" Help students word their hypothesis; for example, "Models that have a window facing the direction of the sun heat up more than models whose window faces away from the direction of the sun." Remember, the hypothesis must be testable.

3. Once the wording of the hypothesis has been chosen, have students help design an experiment. Ask, "How could we test our hypothesis?" Discuss plausible suggestions and choose one method. Ask, "How should the models be designed? Do they need to be identical? What should be constant about all the models? What is the variable we are going to test and how should it be different in different models?"

4. Record the major steps in the experiment so that students can refer back to them. You may want to record the steps on the board, on butcher paper, or transcribe them onto paper so that you can make a copy for each student.

Day Two

5. Provide materials, as in the previous activity. Have students work in teams of two to build models according to the requirements of their experiment. Collect and store the models for the next part of the activity. Have students make predictions about the results of the experiment.

Day Three

6. Distribute copies of the "Let the Sun Shine In" copycat page. Review the procedure for collecting data outdoors. Take the houses outside. As in the previous activity, have students read and record the temperature inside their model in the shade and after zero minutes, five minutes, and ten minutes in the sun (unless, of course, the experiment dictates that some houses must be in the shade).

7. Prepare a chart on the chalkboard (or on butcher paper if you want to save it) so that students can list their data. Have each team choose one person to post the team's final temperature on the chart.

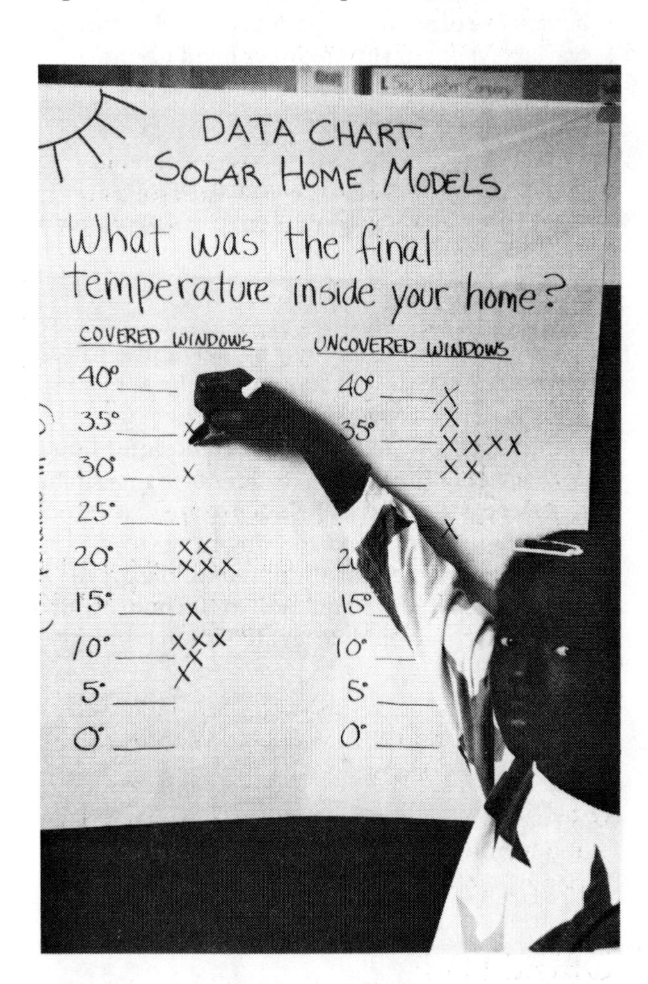

8. Discuss the results of the experiment (see the discussion questions). Introduce students to ways people capture and use solar energy; for example, hot water heaters, space heating, thermal mass, glass, and black backing (see the background information).

DISCUSSION QUESTIONS

How do the results compare to the predictions you made?

Do the results of the experiment agree with the hypothesis?

What does this experiment tell you about using solar energy for heating?

What other experiments could you do to find out more about using solar energy?

When an engineer is designing a house to take advantage of solar energy for heat, what things (variables) might the engineer need to consider?

EVALUATION

After finishing the experiment, have students complete the "Testing a Hypothesis" copycat page.

EXTENSION IDEAS

- Have students modify their model homes to make a home that will stay cool in the sun (students may need to begin with another cup or container). Ask, "How would you design a home to stay cool in the desert?" Students may wish to experiment with variables such as insulation, overhanging roofs, and shading from trees. They might make models of trees and experiment to see where, in relation to the house and the sun, trees should be located for maximum shading effect.
- Have students design and draw an actual solar home, incorporating what they learned about solar heating. You may want to post the list of variables students should consider while designing their solar home.
- Some solar housing developments provide tours or access for school groups. Students can see housing designed to take advantage of the sun's energy. They may see that some of the variables they tested or discussed in the classroom are important in real-life solar energy design.

HOME LEARNING SUGGESTION

(Use as follow-up to this activity)

Have students investigate how much the sun heats up the inside of a car. Students can use a thermometer (perhaps with the help of a parent) to record the temperature inside a car before and after the car has been in full sun for an hour. If students do not have a thermometer, have them describe in writing what the temperature felt like before and after. Ask, "Why does the air in the car get hotter than the air outside? What does this tell you about using the sun's energy for heating? What could you do to prevent the air inside the car from getting so hot?"

RESOURCE

Great Explorations in Math and Science (GEMS), "Hot Water and Warm Homes from Sunlight." Berkeley, Calif.: Lawrence Hall of Science, University of California, 1986. This guide provides detailed instructions for several structured experiments in solar energy.

Name ____________________

TESTING A HYPOTHESIS

What was the hypothesis you tested?

What variable did you test?

What things were constant in the models used in the experiment?

Explain the experiment.

What were the results of the experiment?

What did you learn from this experiment?

ARE YOU USING ENERGY?

SUMMARY OF ACTIVITY

Students run to see what effects using energy has on their own bodies, search out other ways to determine when energy is being used, and explain in writing how they can tell whether energy is being used.

Time: One 30- to 45-minute period

Setting: Classroom, outdoors

Materials:
- Butcher paper
- Marking pens
- Writing paper

Subjects: Science, physical education, language arts

Key Words: Energy, heat, light, motion

RELATED CALIFORNIA FRAMEWORK CONCEPTS

Energy takes many forms; e.g., heat, light, electricity, sound, and motion of objects. (*Science Framework Addendum*)

Every energy conversion involves some loss of useful energy to the surroundings, usually as heat. (*Science Framework Addendum*)

OBJECTIVE

Based on observations they make about their own bodies after running, students develop and write general statements about how to tell when energy is being used.

BACKGROUND INFORMATION

Solar energy probably is not a direct source of the energy your students use. In this activity students look at the ways they use energy every day, a focus that will continue throughout the remainder of the unit.

There are several things to look for when trying to determine if energy is being used. One way is to check to see if heat is being produced. Almost all common uses of energy give off some heat as a by-product. For example, a light bulb in use becomes hot to touch, a refrigerator motor gives off heat, and a TV or radio gets warm if left on for a while. Many uses of energy also make something move or produce light. A washer spins, a TV lights up, and an alarm clock rings. (Other means of detecting when energy is being used, such as cooling and plant growth, are not covered in this activity.)

PREPARATION AND LEAD-UP

Write the headings "Produces Heat," "Produces Light," "Produces Sound," and "Causes Motion" separately on four pieces of butcher paper.

PROCEDURE

1. Ask, "What work did the sun do in the solar home experiments?" (It heated the air in the house.) Tell students that as part of their study of energy, you want them to use some of their body's energy to run around the track (or another appro-

priate area). Take the class outside and have them run as fast as they can for about three minutes. Return to the classroom.

2. Ask, "How did you feel after you ran? What changes did you notice in your body?" Most likely students will mention that they got hot. Explain that one of the signs that energy is being used is that heat is produced. Introduce three other methods of determining that energy is being used —motion, production of light, and production of sound. Post the four labeled sheets of butcher paper. Ask, "Which of these happened when you used energy by running? Which apply to the solar home experiments you did?" Have students record each of these uses of energy on the appropriate pieces of butcher paper (for example, running could be listed under "produces heat," "produces sound," and "causes motion").

3. Give students writing paper and have them write complete sentences that begin "I can tell energy is being used when . . . " Volunteers can share their writing.

4. Tell students that they will expand their study of energy by investigating ways they use energy every day (see the home learning suggestion).

DISCUSSION QUESTIONS

Where does your energy come from?
In what other ways besides running do you use energy?
Can you move something without using energy?
Is it possible for you to use absolutely no energy at all? Try it.

EVALUATION

Students' writings from step three can be used to evaluate their understanding.

EXTENSION IDEAS

- Have students demonstrate something that uses energy and explain how they know energy is being used. You may want to allow students to bring props from home or require students to use materials (if needed) from the classroom.
- Have students record how their bodies get energy (foods and beverages) for one day. As a class, trace the direct energy transfers involved from the sun to a student's stomach. (For example, the sun provided energy for corn to grow, the corn provided energy for the chicken to live and grow, and the chicken provided energy for a student to live and grow. These energy transfers can be indicated with arrows: sun → corn → chicken → student.) Have students trace one of the foods they ate from the sun to themselves. Students can write and illustrate a short paper called "The Sun Gives Me Energy."

HOME LEARNING SUGGESTION

(Use as lead-up to the next activity)

Before beginning the next activity, students should go on an energy hunt of their homes. Have students list 10 or more ways they and their families use energy at home. Students should also list the sources of energy (such as electricity or natural gas) if possible. Students may wish to ask their parents about energy sources if they are unsure.

RESEARCHING ENERGY SOURCES

SUMMARY OF ACTIVITY

Students generate a list of questions about fuels they use each day, work in groups to research answers to some of the questions, then present their information to the class.

Time: Three 30- to 45-minute periods, plus other time for the whole class or individual groups to work on their presentations

Setting: Classroom, library visit (optional)

Materials:
- Books on energy sources and encyclopedias
- Butcher paper
- Drawing materials

Subjects: Science, language arts

Key Words: Electricity, gasoline, natural gas, nuclear power, hydroelectric power, fossil fuels, solar power, wind power, renewable, non-renewable

RELATED CALIFORNIA FRAMEWORK CONCEPTS

Sources of useful energy include sunlight, earth's heat (geothermal), wind, water flow, nuclear reactions, and fossil fuels. (*Science Framework Addendum*)

We depend heavily on fossil fuels for our current energy needs, especially for power generation, transportation, and space heating. Fossil fuels were formed long ago from buried plants and animals. Since we are using these fuels up faster than they are being formed, other energy sources will need to be developed. (*Science Framework Addendum*)

Talking and listening are important ways by which people communicate with and learn from each other. (Adapted from the *English-Language Arts Framework*)

OBJECTIVE

Students synthesize information they gather from books and other sources and communicate through oral and visual means something they have learned about energy.

BACKGROUND INFORMATION

Until a hundred years ago oil from petroleum was an insignificant energy source. Today over half of our energy needs are supplied by oil, and our dependence on other fossil fuels, like natural gas and coal, has increased. The following charts show sources of energy used in California and how that energy is put to use.

California's Energy Sources (1985)	
Petroleum	54.0%
Natural Gas	31.0%
Hydroelectric	4.9%
Nuclear	4.7%
Coal	3.3%
Geothermal, solar, wind, and other	2.3%

California's Energy Usage (1985)	
Industrial and Commercial	38%
Transportation	34%
Energy Losses from Electricity Generation and Transmission*	15%
Residential	13%

* Much energy is lost in the generation of electricity. If coal is burned to generate electricity, for example, three units of coal are consumed for each unit of electricity generated.

When comparing energy sources it is important to consider which are renewable and which are non-renewable. *Renewable energy sources,* like solar, hydroelectric power, wind, wood, geothermal, and tidal energy, can replace themselves within our lifetime. *Non-renewable energy sources,* like fossil fuels (oil, coal, and natural gas), and uranium do not readily replace themselves and are likely to run out someday.

Many energy planners are encouraging greater reliance on a variety of renewable energy sources. In addition to replacing themselves, these sources do not pollute the environment as burning fossil fuels in cars and other vehicles does or as nuclear power plants do. Moreover, using renewable energy increases the number and variety of energy sources available to us, which leads to a stable supply of energy (in other words, by using a wide variety of energy sources we aren't putting all our eggs in one basket).

In this activity students investigate their own energy use, most of which probably depends on non-renewable energy sources. If students do not have much prior knowledge about energy sources and the way they use energy, they will probably need to rely on you during the activity to help them generate questions.

As students conduct their research, they may turn up contradictory information and differences of opinion. This is to be expected; energy is a controversial issue and well-informed experts have differing views.

Encourage students to find and share news articles about energy. Help students relate what they learn to important issues, events, and inventions.

PREPARATION AND LEAD-UP

Arrange to have books on energy and one or more encyclopedia sets available either in your classroom or in the library. If students will be working in the classroom, you may also want to check out books from the local public library in order to have a good selection available (a children's librarian should be able to suggest some titles).

Write the headings "Ways We Use Energy," "Energy Sources We Use," and "Energy Questions" separately on three pieces of butcher paper.

PROCEDURE

Day One

1. Post the labeled pieces of butcher paper. Ask students what they found out from the previous activity's home learning assignment and record their comments on the butcher paper labeled "Ways We Use Energy." Ask students what kinds or sources of energy they can think of and record their comments on the sheet of butcher paper labeled "Energy Sources We Use."

2. Introduce the terms renewable energy and non-renewable energy. Ask, "Which of the energy sources on our list do you think are renewable? Which do you think are non-renewable? Why do you think it is important to know whether or not an energy source is renewable?"

3. Divide students into teams of four. Have each team brainstorm questions about energy uses and sources. One team member should record all questions on paper. After several minutes, stop the brainstorming and have each team choose its two or three best questions to report to the class. Record these questions on the butcher paper labeled "Energy Questions." (If students need help getting started, you may want to suggest some questions like "What is electricity? How is it made? How does it make things work?")

4. Have each team choose a question to investigate and tell the question to the class. You can eliminate duplicate questions if you want and help teams revise their questions as needed.

Day Two

5. Display the available resources and discuss how to use them. Direct students to read and take notes, which they will then share with their team members while the team prepares a presentation for the class.

6. After students do the research, have the teams reconvene. Explain that each student is to have a role in his or her team's presentation. Each team should design and make a poster or chart to be used during its presentation. Distribute drawing materials and a piece of butcher paper to each team.

Day Three

7. Have each team make its presentation. After each presentation, discuss and summarize the information presented (see the discussion questions).

8. Encourage students to take notes while other groups are making presentations (see the evaluation section). Students may add to their notes during the discussion.

DISCUSSION QUESTIONS

What kinds of energy do we seem to use most?
Which energy sources are renewable?
Which energy sources are non-renewable?
Why is it important to think about which energy sources are renewable and which are non-renewable?
What environmental problems result from using some kinds of energy? (Cars and industry produce air pollution, mining for coal and uranium causes vegetation to be stripped from hillsides, and damming rivers to produce hydroelectric power means surrounding areas are flooded.)

Which energy sources seem to be less harmful to the environment?
Did you find any contradictory information (two books that gave different information)?
Does anyone here use any solar or wind energy? How are these two sources similar and different to other kinds of energy we use?
Which sources would you like to see as the main sources of energy when you are an adult?

EVALUATION

Give students a worksheet that lists the energy sources addressed by team presentations. Have students summarize what they learned about each source, referring to their notes.

EXTENSION IDEAS

- Ask students to save all sections of newspapers for several days until you have enough newspapers for each student to have one. Brainstorm a list of energy-related words and record them on butcher paper. Distribute one newspaper to each student and have students circle and record on a separate sheet all energy words they find. Add any new energy words to the list and continue adding to it throughout the unit. The list can be used for writing lessons.
- "Toast" is a brief and excellent film that shows step by step the energy used to produce a piece of toast, beginning with the sun that supplies growing grain with its energy. This film is distributed by Bullfrog Films in Oley, Penn. 19547, and can be rented from the University of California Extension Media Center, 2176 Shattuck Avenue, Berkeley, Calif. 94704, (415) 642-0460.

HOME LEARNING SUGGESTION

(Use as follow-up to this activity)

Ask, "Is energy used for transportation? How do you know? What kinds of energy are used?" Ask students to safely observe traffic on a busy street or highway and make a list of what is being transported. Have students bring their lists to school, then combine the lists to make a class list of all the things being transported. Don't forget to include people. Discuss some of the problems with using gasoline-powered vehicles for transportation (oil is a non-renewable energy source; cars cause traffic jams, air pollution, and accidents). Have students suggest other means of transportation that would use less energy. Ask what forms of transportation other than cars students use. (These include students' own two feet, bikes, buses, roller skates, and skateboards.)

RESOURCE

For Students

Ardley, Neil, and others. *How Things Work*. New York: Simon and Schuster, Inc., 1984. This reference book answers many questions about energy and how we use it.

ENERGY MURALS

SUMMARY OF ACTIVITY

Students design and make murals illustrating some of the things they have learned about energy.

Time: One 45-minute period to start, plus additional time to complete the murals

Setting: Classroom

Materials:
- Butcher paper
- Drawing materials
- Old magazines, scissors, and glue (optional)

Subjects: Art, science, social studies

Key Words: Renewable, non-renewable, energy sources

RELATED CALIFORNIA FRAMEWORK CONCEPTS

Sources of useful energy include sunlight, earth's heat (geothermal), wind, water flow, nuclear reactions, and fossil fuels. (*Science Framework Addendum*)

We depend heavily on fossil fuels for our current energy needs, especially for power generation, transportation, and space heating. Fossil fuels were formed long ago from buried plants and animals. Since we are using these fuels up faster than they are being formed, other energy sources will need to be developed. (*Science Framework Addendum*)

Visual art media can be used to translate ideas, feelings, and values. (Adapted from the *Visual and Performing Arts Framework*)

OBJECTIVE

Students draw murals to illustrate relationships between how people use energy and the sources of that energy.

BACKGROUND INFORMATION

The large scale of a mural encourages freedom of expression. A mural may be realistic or fanciful and is meant to communicate thoughts, feelings, and ideas in an aesthetic way.

PREPARATION AND LEAD-UP

If possible, have books on murals available for students to look at (see the resources listed at the end of the activity). Discuss things to think about when designing and making a mural; for example, murals are most effective if there are sharp contrasts between colors, if drawings are large, if lettering is large and clear, and if elements of the mural fit together or are connected in some way.

PROCEDURE

1. Tell students they will work in teams to design and draw murals using their knowledge about energy. Discuss and list on the board some of the things students should consider when designing their murals: content, orientation on paper, connections between drawings, background, titles or written explanations, and design elements such as bold colors and strong lines. If books about murals or pictures of murals are available, share them with the class.

2. Present topics for murals to students or allow students to think of their own topics. Teams may illustrate an energy source and how it is used, something they learned doing the research for the previous activity, ways we use energy every day, renewable energy sources, non-renewable energy sources, or another energy topic of their choice.

3. Divide students to work in teams of four to eight (you may want to combine two of the research groups from the previous activity to make a mural team). Allow time for discussion and planning before the drawing begins. Make sure each student is responsible for some portion of his or her team's mural.

4. After the murals are completed, have one or two representatives from each team explain their mural to the class. You may wish to arrange for the murals to be displayed in the library, hallways, or school office.

DISCUSSION QUESTIONS

How can murals and other art be used to communicate with other people?

What do you think these murals tell other people?

Can you think of any times outside of school when you have learned about energy? How and what did you learn? Was art used?

EVALUATION

Murals can serve as an evaluation of student understanding or students can write a paragraph about what a mural other than their own tells them about energy.

EXTENSION IDEA

Have students use other means to convey information about energy. Students can work in teams of four to develop a skit, write a song, or create a poster that teaches about energy (students may need to do additional research to be sure their facts are correct). Teams can perform or display their educational project for the class.

HOME LEARNING SUGGESTION

(Use as follow-up to this activity)

Ask students to look for a picture that depicts energy being used in some way and to bring the picture to class. Students can share and discuss their pictures in teams of four or with the whole class.

RESOURCES

For Students

Barthelmeh, Volker. *Street Murals.* New York: Alfred A. Knopf, 1982. Murals from the United States and Western Europe are presented in color.

Clark, Yoko, and Chizu Hama. *California Murals.* Berkeley, Calif.: Lancaster-Miller Publishers, 1979. This book has color photos of murals from around the state.

HOME APPLIANCES SURVEY

SUMMARY OF ACTIVITY

Students survey and tally energy-using aids and appliances they have at home, contribute their information to a class graph, and discuss the advantages and disadvantages of some common appliances.

Time: Two 30- to 45-minute periods

Setting: Classroom, home

Materials:
- Several small electric appliances such as a toaster, hair dryer, electric knife sharpener, or electric clock
- Copycat page, one for each student
- Butcher paper
- Felt markers or crayons

Subjects: Science, math, language arts

Key Words: Energy, appliance, waste, conserve, alternative, benefit, consequence

RELATED CALIFORNIA FRAMEWORK CONCEPT

We depend heavily on fossil fuels for our current energy needs, especially for power generation, transportation, and space heating. Fossil fuels were formed long ago from buried plants and animals. Since we are using these fuels up faster than they are being formed, other energy sources will need to be developed. (*Science Framework Addendum*)

OBJECTIVE

After conducting a survey of the appliances in their homes and graphing the results, students analyze the positive and negative effects of using some common appliances.

BACKGROUND INFORMATION

As the following per capita energy use chart shows, the United States uses more energy per

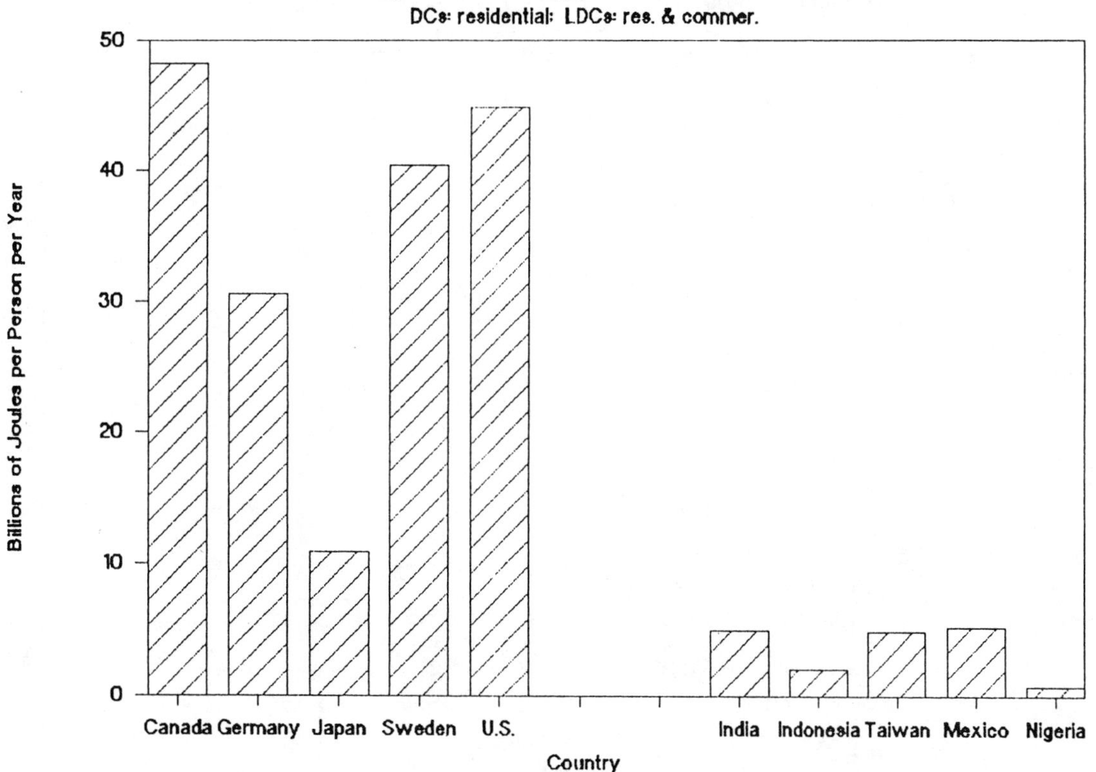

person than most other countries. Americans use 12 percent more energy than Swedes, 48 percent more energy than Germans, 300 percent more energy than Japanese, and 760 percent more energy than Mexicans.

Using more energy-efficient equipment (cars, appliances, factory machines, and the like), eliminating unnecessary energy uses, and conserving energy could greatly reduce the United States' high per capita energy use. Conservation is often called the cheapest source of new energy because implementing conservation measures is much cheaper than building and installing any type of energy producer.

In the previous three activities students looked at some of the ways they use energy and sources of that energy. This activity focuses students' attention on the appliances they have at home.

Students' survey results will indicate how many appliances students have but not which appliances use the most energy. The total energy use chart gives average residential use for some common appliances. These are average figures so if you live in a warm area, for instance, heating use will be less than indicated by the chart while air conditioning use may be more.

PREPARATION AND LEAD-UP

On butcher paper, draw a bar graph like the graph that is illustrated. The graph will need to be tall enough and wide enough to accommodate many kinds of appliances as well as a large number of each kind (think how many lamps you have in your home and multiply that number by the number of students in your class).

PROCEDURE

Day One

1. Display a few common household appliances that use energy. Discuss the advantages and disadvantages of each appliance.

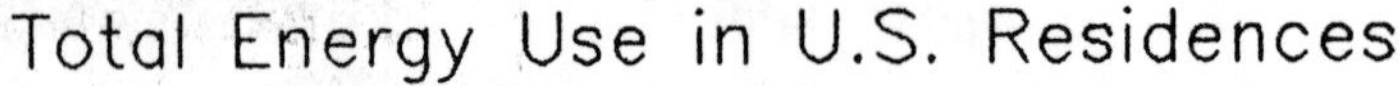

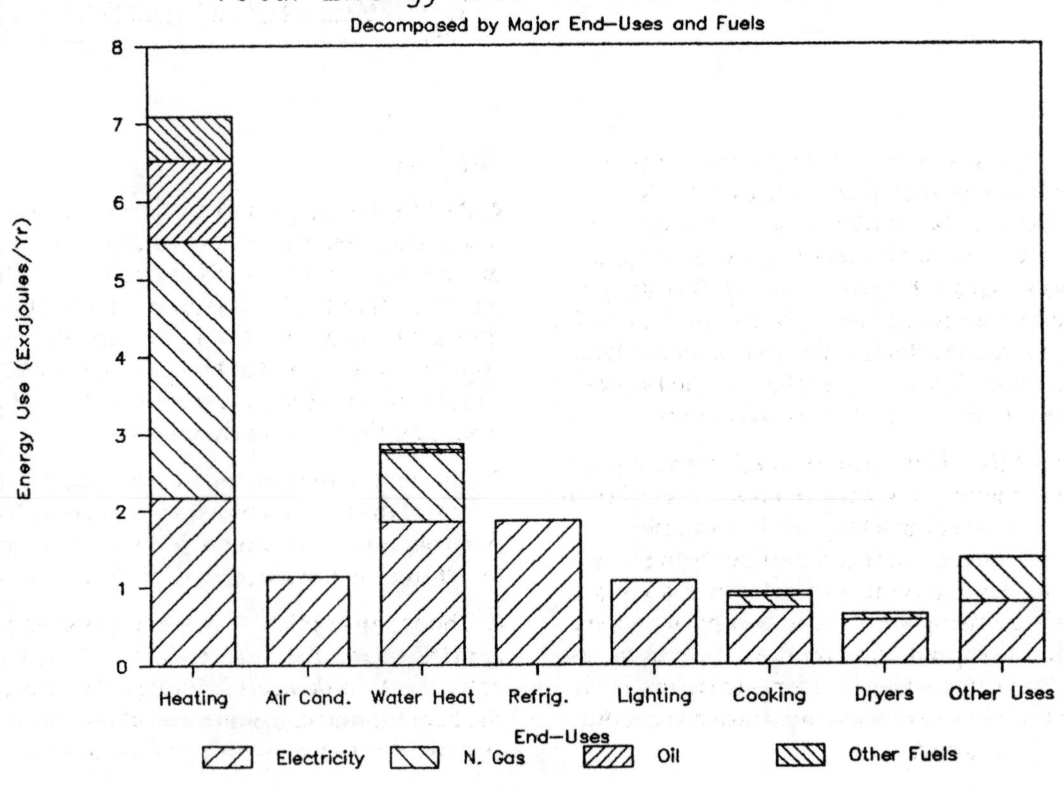

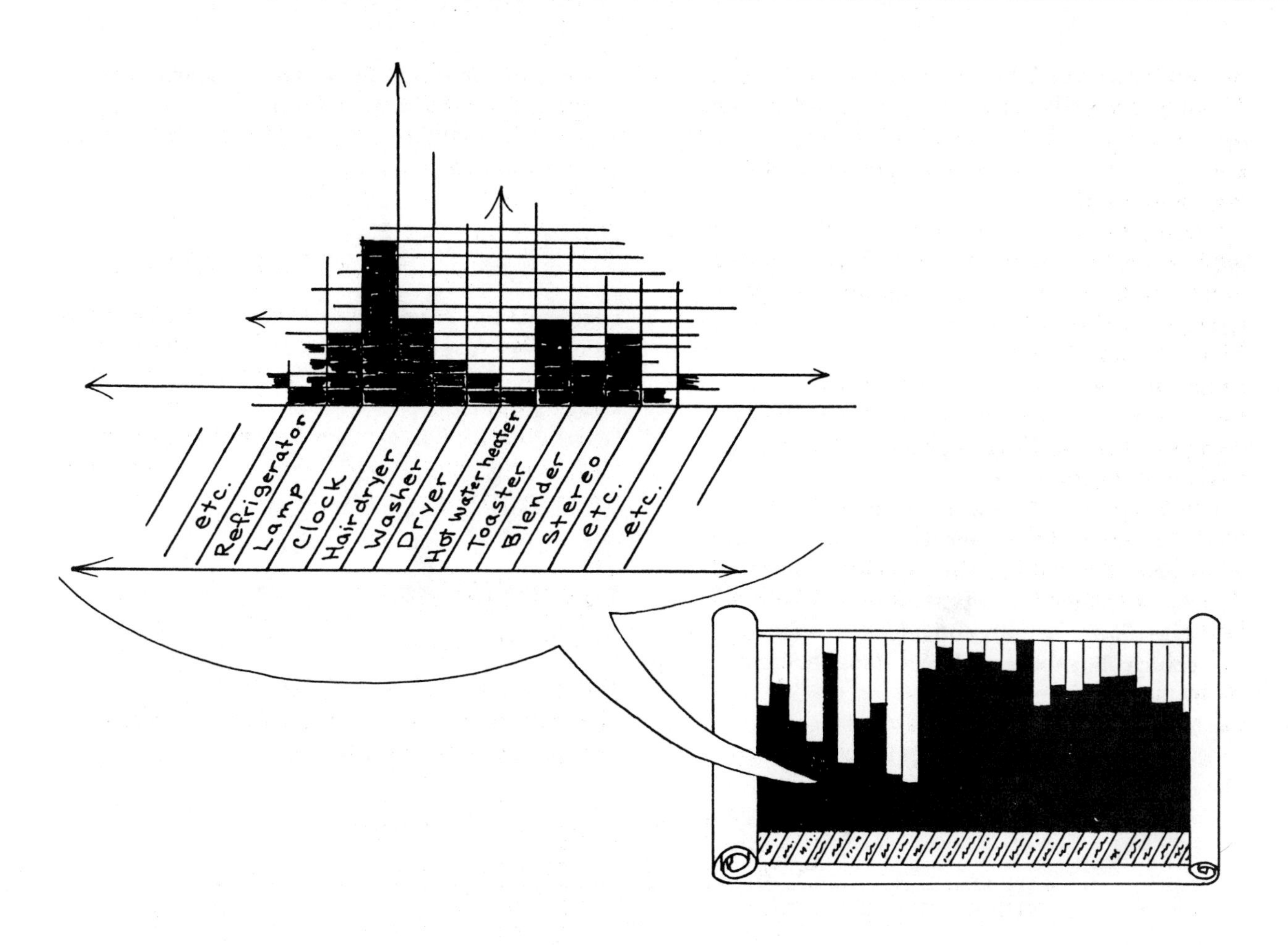

2. Tell students that they will tally the kinds and number of energy-using appliances in their homes. Explain that students are to look for and record only those appliances that use energy, not appliances that are human-powered. Ask students to suggest some energy-using home appliances. If they do not name refrigerators and water heaters, mention them. These two appliances are big energy consumers in most California homes.

3. Hand out the "Home Appliances" copycat page and explain how you want students to record their information. Keeping a tally, as the example shows, is a convenient way for students to record their data. Have students estimate the total number of energy-using appliances they have at home and record this prediction on their copycat pages. Emphasize that you want students to survey each room in their house if possible in order to get the most accurate count.

Day Two

4. Post the bar graph and allow time for students to add their results (students may need to add data during recess or the lunch period in order to record it all). Make sure students understand that they are to record the kind and number of each appliance they found at home; for example, they should color in three squares in the TV column if they have three TVs in their house.

5. Discuss the information on the graph. Ask, "What is the most common appliance? Which appliances are least common? Which appliances do you think use the most energy? How can you tell?"

6. Choose an appliance from the graph and write it on the board. Ask students to think of an alternative that would use less energy. As a class, list the benefits and consequences of the appliance and the alternative. Repeat the exercise with one or more appliances. Tell students that in the next activity they will choose a way to save energy for one week.

DISCUSSION QUESTIONS

Which of the appliances on the list do you really need?
Are there appliances on the list that you think you do not need?
Is there a difference between an energy "need" and an energy "convenience"?
Do we use more energy than we need?
How do we waste energy?
Why is energy conservation important?
How can we conserve energy?
What changes could you make in your home right now to conserve energy?
What do people usually consider when they make a choice about something that uses energy?

EVALUATION

Have students list four common appliances used in their homes or school and at least one alternative for each appliance that uses less energy. Students can list the advantages and disadvantages of each alternative.

EXTENSION IDEA

Have students conduct a survey of school appliances that use energy. Students can then recommend ways to reduce energy consumption at school (see the "Establishing an Energy Task Force" action project).

HOME LEARNING SUGGESTION

(Use as follow-up to this activity)

Have students ask parents, grandparents, or older members of the community what appliances they had as children. Have students list the appliances and the energy sources each appliance used (remember that the body is an energy source).

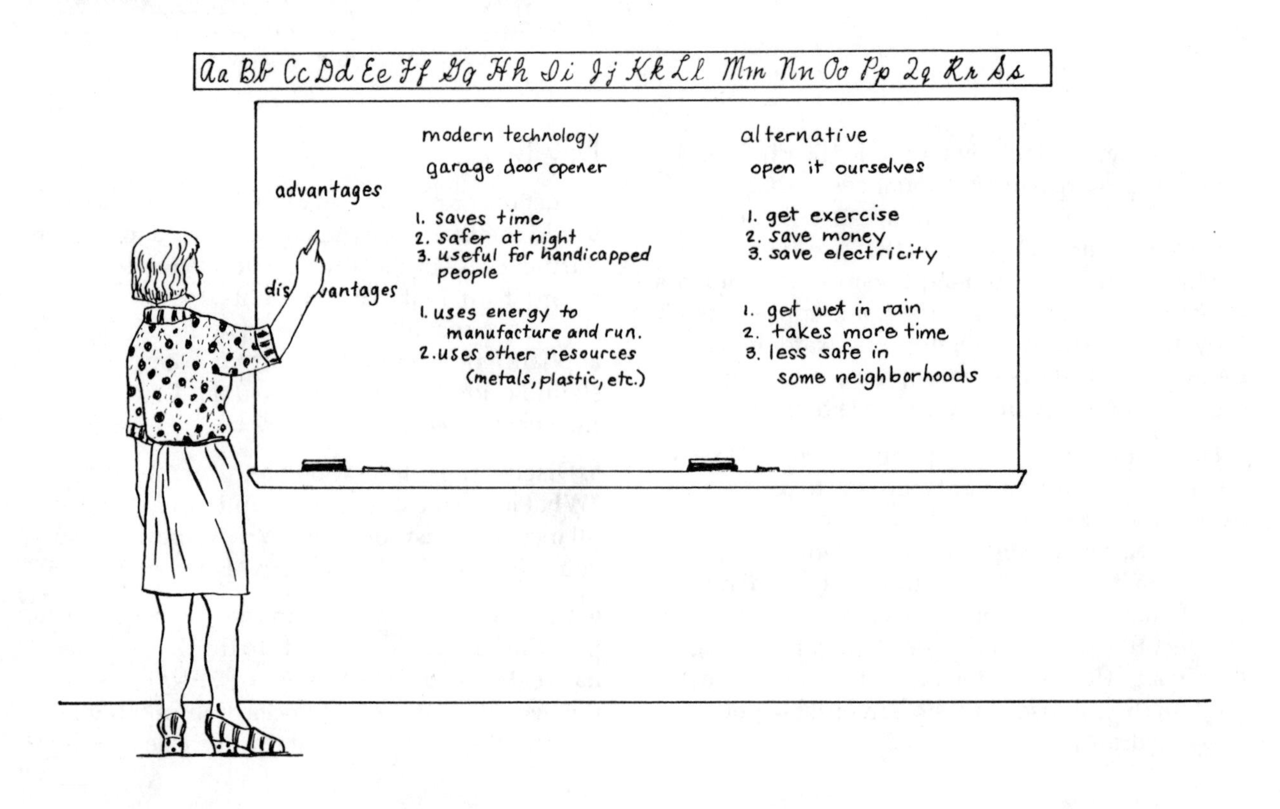

Name ____________________

HOME APPLIANCES

List all the appliances you have at home. Be sure to record the number of each kind that you find.

Example: electric clock ~~||||~~ |

ENERGY CONTRACTS

SUMMARY OF ACTIVITY

Students decide what actions they would be willing to take for one week to save energy, write a contract stating their intentions, then discuss the results after a week.

Time: Two 30- to 45-minute periods, one week apart

Setting: Classroom, home

Materials:
- One piece of butcher paper
- Writing paper

Subjects: Science, language arts

Key Words: Energy usage, conservation, alternative, choice, action

RELATED CALIFORNIA FRAMEWORK CONCEPTS

Conservation of resources is an ethical concern of individuals and societies. (*Science Framework Addendum*)

Care and conservation in the use of energy and in the choice of energy sources involve personal behaviors as well as public policy. (*Science Framework Addendum*)

OBJECTIVE

Students choose alternative actions to conserve energy, carry out the actions for a week, and evaluate the results.

BACKGROUND INFORMATION

Americans use more energy per person than people in almost any other country, including countries with similar lifestyles. There are many ways we can conserve energy. Conservation can be as simple as acquiring the habit of turning off lights when we aren't using them or as complex as developing cars that use renewable energy sources. Conservation can also mean changing behaviors; for instance, taking shorter showers or walking instead of driving for short trips.

A 1986 study sponsored by a major California utility found that if Californians used more efficient lights and appliances, energy consumption would be cut by 25 percent. The initial cost for these energy-saving appliances would be greater than appliances used today, but the appliances would pay for themselves over time.

This activity gives students the opportunity to decide how they can conserve energy. Obviously, the actions students undertake will not affect global or national energy consumption; however, the world is shaped as much by the seemingly minor actions of many people as it is by the significant actions of a few people. It is important for students to know they can make choices that make a difference.

PREPARATION AND LEAD-UP

On butcher paper write an energy contract like the contract illustrated for step three.

PROCEDURE

1. Ask students to explain why we should care about conserving energy. If students have been discussing energy issues covered in the news, review articles that describe energy shortages, non-renewable energy sources, energy costs, energy independence, and health problems associated with pollution and other effects of energy use.

2. Ask students to suggest ways they can save energy. Introduce students to the notion of saving energy by making choices that save energy. Such choices might include taking shorter showers, washing hair in a sink instead of the shower, not leaving water running while washing dishes, defrosting the freezer, closing the refrigerator door as quickly as possible, and turning off lights, televisions, radios, and stereos when no one is in the room.

3. Ask students to decide on one or more ways they will conserve energy for the next week. Post the sample energy contract and help students write out a contract stating their week-long commitment to conserve energy. Collect and save the contracts until the week is over.

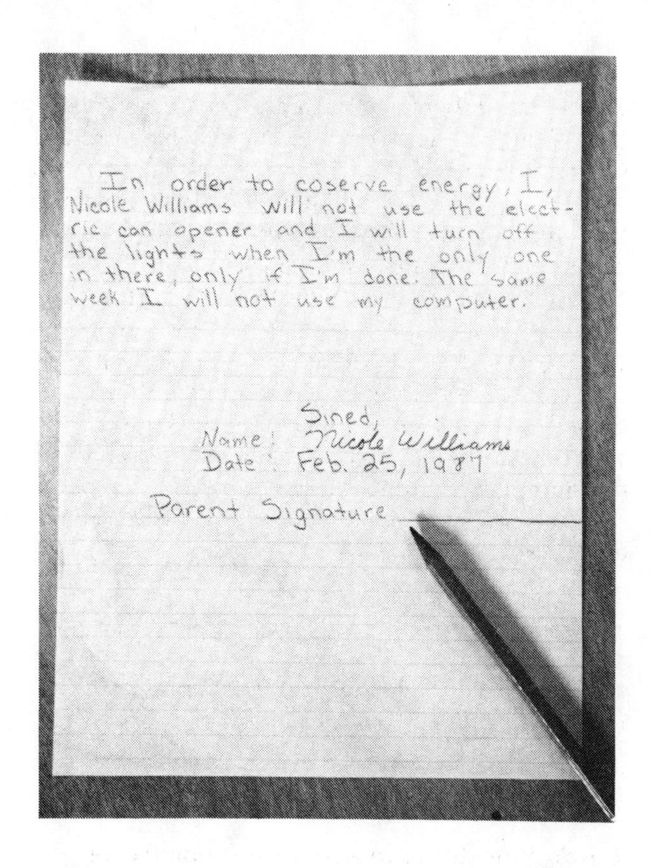

In order to coserve energy, I, Nicole Williams will not use the elect-ric can opener and I will turn off the lights when I'm the only one in there, only if I'm done. The same week I will not use my computer.

Sined,
Name: Nicole Williams
Date: Feb. 25, 1987

Parent Signature

4. Tell students that each night they are to write two or three sentences about how they are saving energy. During the week ask students periodically how they are doing and find out if they are running into any difficulties keeping their contracts.

5. At the end of the week, return the contracts to students. Ask students to re-read their original contract and then write a summary explaining whether they were able to keep to their plan, what difficulties they found, any unusual thing that happened, anything they learned about their habits and use of energy, and how they felt about making choices to conserve energy. Discuss the results (see the discussion questions).

DISCUSSION QUESTIONS

Were you able to follow through with your plan to conserve energy? Why or why not?
Was it easy or hard? Why?
What would make it easier for you to conserve energy?
What do you think might make it easier for other people to conserve energy?

EVALUATION

The students' written work in step five can serve as an evaluation of their understanding.

EXTENSION IDEAS

- Have students work alone or in small groups to design an energy conservation public service announcement. Students can present their announcements to the class. If your school uses a public address system, perhaps several students could present their announcements to the whole school.
- Have students write letters to the editor of the local newspaper about any energy topic they wish. Mail the letters and ask students who get the paper at home to look for letters written by their classmates.

Fostering a Healthy Environment

Third Through Sixth Grades

Introduction to the Unit

All living things, including people, other animals, and plants, share basic needs of food, water, air, shelter, and space. A healthy environment is one that includes these necessities in the quality and quantity required by the particular organism. Throughout this unit students will be learning what living things need for a healthy environment and ways that people can affect the environment. Activities focus on the importance of water, air, and land to living things and on ways human actions influence these physical factors.

The first two activities introduce students to the needs of living things. In the next three activities students learn about the importance of water and about ways that human activities affect water quality. Students then monitor particles that are found in the air and learn how plants satisfy oxygen needs. In the seventh activity the focus shifts to the importance of land; students study the effects of one human activity—littering—on the land. In the final three activities students learn methods for evaluating the quality of an environment, the effects of their own actions on the environment, and attitudes of people in their community toward the environment.

If after completing the unit students express a desire to take positive actions to help the environment, you might consider the extension ideas suggested throughout the unit, many of which are action-oriented. Students could also conduct one of the projects outlined in the Action Project section of this guide. Another possibility is to help students develop their own project which would have personal meaning and provide them satisfaction in doing something beneficial for the environment.

Advance Planning

For the fifth activity, "Oil Spill," you will need to acquire a natural feather for each pair of students. Natural feathers may be a little difficult to find so you should start looking well before you plan to do the activity. A craft store in your area may stock feathers; if so, be sure that they are *natural* feathers; dyed or "fluffed up" feathers will not work. A poultry company is another source of clean feathers. If you have trouble finding feathers, ask students to help you collect them. (The best time to look for feathers is in the late spring when most birds are molting. However, feathers can be found just about any time of the year. Remember that it is illegal to collect the feathers of birds of prey like eagles, hawks, and owls. (The California Department of Fish and Game at 1416 Ninth Street, Sacramento, Calif. 95814 does permit collecting these special feathers for educational purposes if permission is requested in advance.)

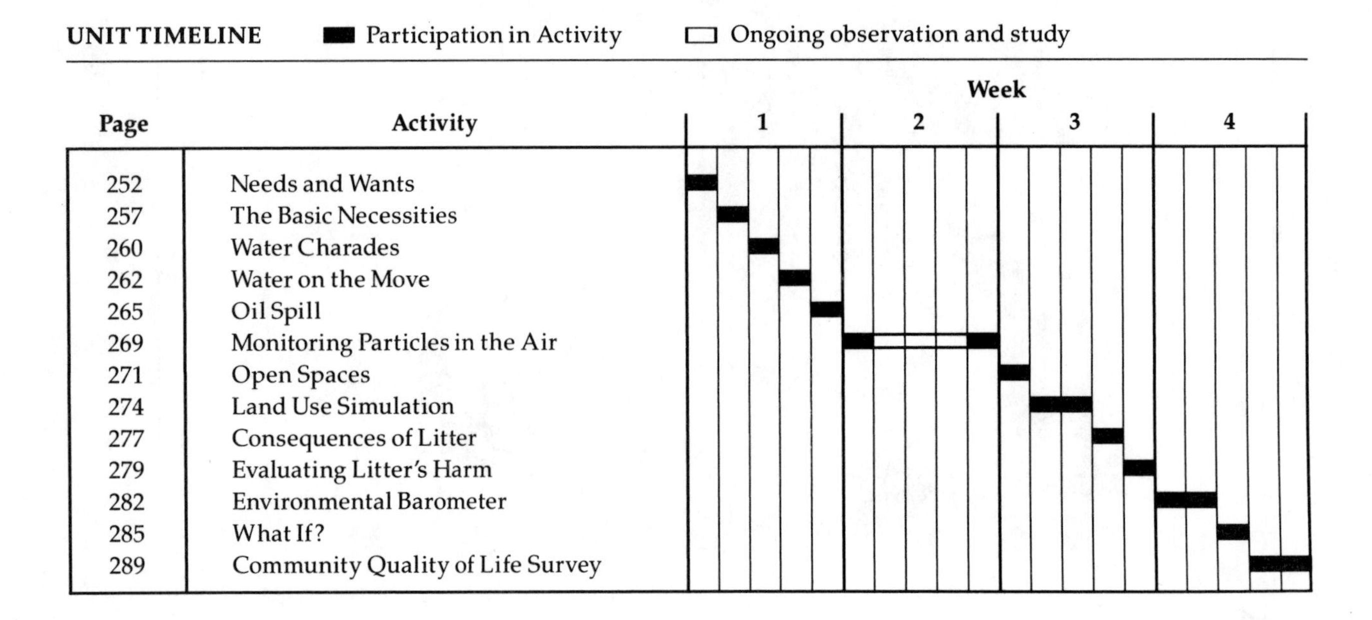

UNIT TIMELINE ■ Participation in Activity □ Ongoing observation and study

Page	Activity
252	Needs and Wants
257	The Basic Necessities
260	Water Charades
262	Water on the Move
265	Oil Spill
269	Monitoring Particles in the Air
271	Open Spaces
274	Land Use Simulation
277	Consequences of Litter
279	Evaluating Litter's Harm
282	Environmental Barometer
285	What If?
289	Community Quality of Life Survey

Resources

Myers, Norman. *Gaia, An Atlas of Planet Management.* Garden City, N.Y.: Anchor Press/Doubleday, 1984. This book analyzes our living planet in terms of land, oceans, elements, evolution, humankind, civilization, and management, each considered from the perspectives of potential resources, crises, and management alternatives.

Samuals, Mike, and Hal Zina Bennett. *Well Body, Well Earth.* San Francisco, Calif.: Sierra Club Books, 1983. The earth's and humankind's healthiness are interconnected, as this sourcebook shows.

The California Water Map. Sacramento, Calif.: Water Education Foundation, 717 K Street # 517, Sacramento, Calif. 95814. The California Water Map is a pictorial representation of naturally occurring and human-made waterways in California. The map and other educational materials are available from the Water Education Foundation.

For Students

Cobb, Vicki. *The Trip of a Drip.* Boston, Mass.: Little, Brown, and Company, 1986. This book describes where tap water comes from and where it goes after it is used.

Giono, Jean. *The Man Who Planted Trees.* Chelsea, Vt.: Chelsea Green Publishing Co., 1982 (original copyright 1954). A man's generosity toward nature and people is the subject of this story.

McLerran, Alice. *The Mountain That Loved a Bird.* Natick, Mass.: Picture Book Studio USA, 1985. A bird and a mountain share an unusual love in this story.

NEEDS AND WANTS

SUMMARY OF ACTIVITY

Students look at pictures of various things and decide whether they are "needs" or "wants," then write poems about things they need in their lives to stay healthy.

Time: 45 to 60 minutes

Setting: Classroom

Materials:
- Scissors
- One set of duplicated copycat pages for each pair of students
- One envelope for each pair of students
- Paper for each student
- Pencil for each student

Subjects: Language arts, science, social studies, math

Key Words: Needs, wants, healthy, survival

RELATED CALIFORNIA FRAMEWORK CONCEPTS

Major natural resources needed by humans include air, water, soil, minerals, plants, animals, sources of energy, and areas of natural beauty. Natural resources are in limited supply. (*Science Framework Addendum*)

There are certain human needs and life experiences that are common to all peoples. (Adapted from *History-Social Science Framework*)

Objects can be classified and sorted using one or more attributes. (Adapted from *Mathematics Framework*)

Writing enables us to communicate our ideas and can lead to a better understanding of ourselves and the human condition. (Adapted from *English-Language Arts Framework*)

OBJECTIVE

Given a set of picture cards, students distinguish between personal wants and needs.

BACKGROUND INFORMATION

People have different ideas about what defines "needs" and "wants" depending on their culture, background, values, and situation. For example, in our culture electricity might be viewed as a need but millions of people around the world live happy and productive lives without electricity. Similarly, a computer might be considered a need by many business people while other people would consider a computer a want, not a need.

Throughout this unit students will be learning what living things need for a healthy environment and ways that people can affect the environment. In this activity students examine things in their lives to determine the differences between "needs" and "wants."

Your students will have different feelings about what is a need or a want—allow them to express their own ideas. Some of the items illustrated in the copycat pages were purposely chosen because they could be viewed as either needs or wants, depending on the student. To help students express their ideas, they create simple poems called cinquains that have five lines. Cinquains are a wonderful way to combine feelings and facts about our world into a poetic image. They are easy to create as well as fun.

Although every person has different ideas about what is necessary to him or her, there are certain basic needs that all humans share, including biological needs (food, water, shelter, and air), social needs (clothing, feeling of belonging, and protection), and spiritual needs (faith, hope, and love). Students will explore some of these needs in this activity. In the next activity students will have the opportunity to consider basic survival needs that are shared by humans, other animals, and plants.

PREPARATION AND LEAD-UP

Make copies of the "Needs and Wants" copycat pages so that each pair of students has a set. Cut the cards along the dotted lines and place each set of cards into an envelope (students can help do this).

PROCEDURE

1. Divide students into pairs. Pass out one envelope of cut-up copycat cards to each pair. Direct student pairs to sort the cards in their envelope into piles so that the things in each pile are alike in some way. Ask students to share with the class the "rule" they sorted by. On the board, begin a class list of ways to sort the objects. Allow students several opportunities to re-sort the objects, encouraging them to look for new ways to sort.

2. Have students put the cards back into the envelopes, then discuss with students the difference between needs and wants. Ask, "Could you live without the things you need? The things you want?" Ask students to sort the cards according to needs and wants, then discuss which things they think are needs, which are wants, and whether different people have different ideas about what they need.

3. Tell students that there are certain things, called basic needs, that everyone absolutely has to have in order to stay alive and healthy. Ask which of the things on the cards are basic needs and list student responses on the board. Ask students if they can think of any other things not on the cards that might be considered basic needs. Add appropriate responses (trees, animals, and love, for example) to the list.

4. Explain to students that they will create poems of five lines called cinquains about one or more of the basic needs listed. Write on the chalkboard the sample cinquains or a cinquain you create. Explain to students the rules for cinquains:

First line:	One word, giving title
Second line:	Two words describing title
Third line:	Three words expressing an action
Fourth line:	Four words expressing a feeling
Fifth line:	One word, a synonym for the title

Sample cinquains:

WATER	*WIND*
Wonderfully wet	*Waving, blowing*
Trickling, roaring, moving	*Moving rain clouds*
It feels so cool	*Nice on my face*
Wetness	*Breath*

Have students work alone or in pairs creating these brief, evocative poems, then ask students to share their creations with the class or in smaller sharing circles.

5. Tell students that the following day they will look at needs that humans, other animals, and plants share.

DISCUSSION QUESTIONS

Why are basic needs important to us?
Are there things people do to protect these basic needs?
What is the difference between a need and a want?
Is there anything that you consider a need that someone 100 years ago (or in another country today) might consider a want?

EVALUATION

Ask students to make a list of people's basic needs.

EXTENSION IDEA

Students write stories about what life would be like without one of the wants they listed.

HOME LEARNING SUGGESTION

(Use as follow-up to this activity)

Ask students, "Do you think adults have the same ideas about needs and wants as kids?" Have students write down and take home a list of the items named on the copycat pages for parents to classify into needs or wants. Students should ask their parents to write "N" next to the things they feel are needs and "W" next to the things they feel are wants. Students should also ask their parents to write down any basic needs missing from the list. Next day in class have students share their findings and help them tabulate the class results. Ask, "Were our predictions right about whether adults have different ideas about needs and wants than children?"

SOURCE OF ACTIVITY

Jorgensen, Eric, Trout Black, and Mary Hallesy. *Manure to Meadow to Milkshake*. Los Altos, Calif.: Hidden Villa, Inc., 1978.
O'Connor, Maura. *Living Lightly in the City*. Milwaukee, Wisc.: Schlitz Audubon Center, 1983.

Copycat Page

NEEDS AND WANTS

(cut cards apart)

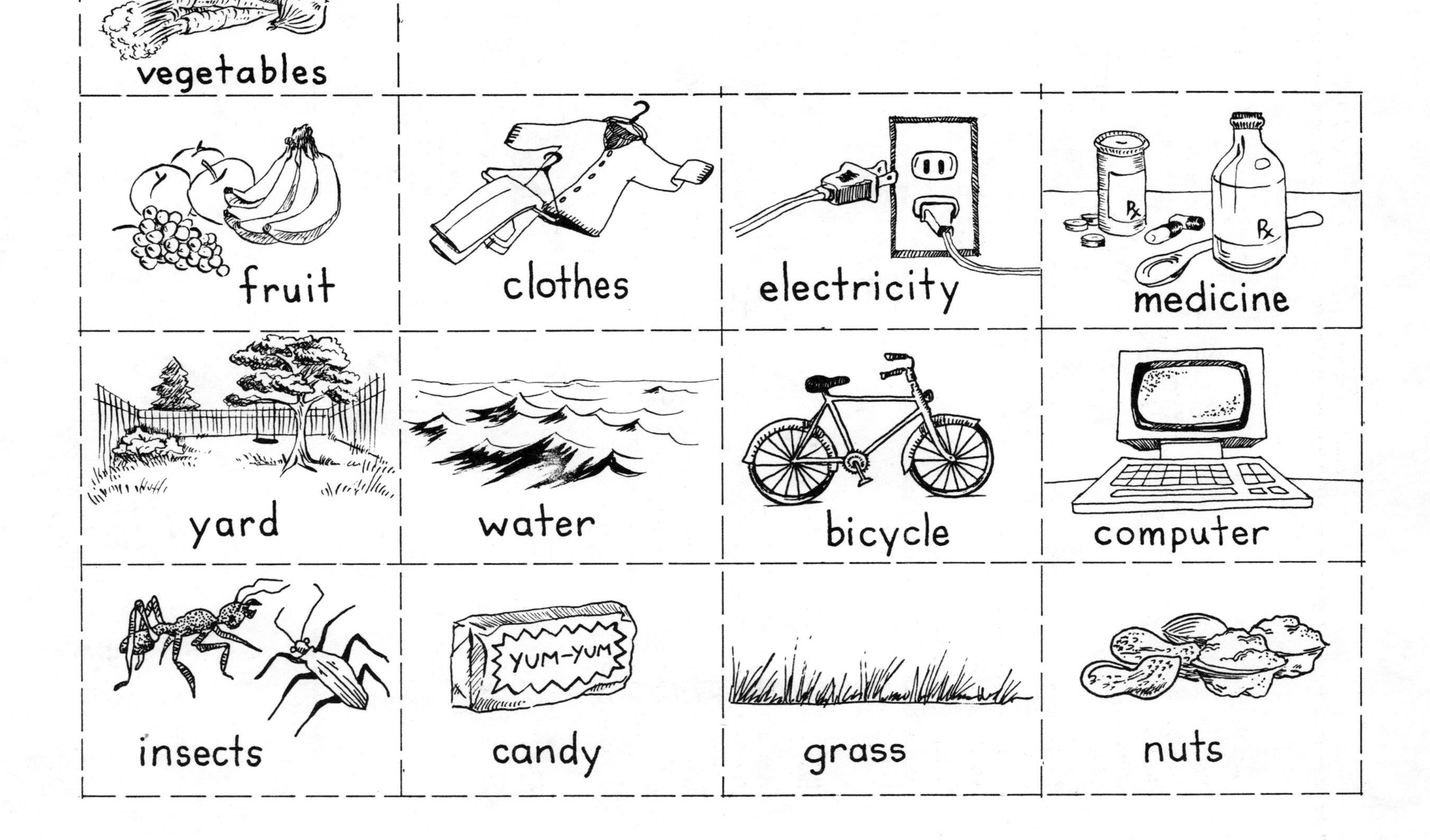

Copycat Page

NEEDS AND WANTS

(cut cards apart)

quiet

friends

car

milk

MILK

MILK

television

sun

warmth

home

dollars

rain

parent

eggs

air

THE BASIC NECESSITIES

SUMMARY OF ACTIVITY

Students list and organize needs of people, other animals, and plants.

Time: 45 minutes

Setting: Classroom

Materials:
- Butcher paper
- Marking pens
- Paper
- Crayons or colored pens

Subjects: Science, language arts, social studies

Key Words: Brainstorming, survival needs, environment

RELATED CALIFORNIA FRAMEWORK CONCEPTS

Living things get things they need from each other and from the environment. (*Science Framework Addendum*)

There are certain human needs and life experiences that are common to all people. (Adapted from *History-Social Science Framework*)

Major natural resources needed by humans include air, water, soil, minerals, plants, animals, sources of energy, and areas of natural beauty. Natural resources are in limited supply. (*Science Framework Addendum*)

Information can be organized by using charts. (Adapted from *Mathematics Framework*)

OBJECTIVE

Through brainstorming, students identify and organize the needs of people, other animals, and plants.

BACKGROUND INFORMATION

All living things depend directly or indirectly on sunlight, soil, and air, and need food, water, shelter, and space in which to live. These needs must be in the quality and quantity required by the particular organism.

In this activity students identify the basic needs of all living things and recognize that these basic needs are similar. Students are also introduced to the term "environment," meaning the sum of all the physical, biological, and other factors that act upon an organism or community and ultimately determine its form and survival. Students begin to think about things that make a healthy environment.

Students will be using a process called "brainstorming" to generate ideas. In brainstorming it is important to generate lots of ideas, even offbeat ones. Ideas should be recorded but not evaluated until as many ideas as possible are generated. Two-time Nobel Prize winner Linus Pauling said, "The best way to get a good idea is to get a lot of ideas." A good way to introduce beginning brainstormers to this process is the DOVE rule:

D—Don't judge;
O—Offbeat ideas;
V—Vast numbers; and
E—Evaluate later.

PREPARATION AND LEAD-UP

Write the headings "People," "Other Animals," and "Plants" on a piece of butcher paper so that a column of words can be listed under each heading. Label another piece of butcher paper "What Is in the Environment?"

PROCEDURE

1. Remind students that the previous day they talked about people's needs and wants. Have students think back to the things they thought were needs and ask, "What do people really need in order to stay healthy?" List students' ideas in a column on the butcher paper under "People." Accept all ideas; save evaluation of ideas and discussion for later.

2. Explain to students that they will be using a technique called brainstorming to generate ideas for the other two columns on the chart. Introduce the DOVE rule.

3. Have students work in groups of four and give paper to each group. Ask each group to make a list of things animals need and a list of things plants need.

4. After the lists are made, ask the groups to go through their lists and cross out the ideas that are not essential needs. Have each group read aloud their revised lists so that you can write their ideas on the chart under the appropriate column (you might want to refer to the chart throughout the unit so write neatly enough that you feel comfortable having the chart posted for several weeks). After all three columns are filled in, ask students if any needs appear on more than one list. Circle items that appear on all three lists.

5. Go through the lists and see if the class agrees that all the items listed are essential, that each item is necessary for survival. Put squares around the items that are essential. Ask, "Are essential needs the same as those that were circled? What seem to be the essential survival needs for people, plants, and animals?" The most basic survival needs should be the same for each of the three groups.

6. Introduce the word "environment" (everything around a living thing that determines its survival). Ask students, "What are some of the things you think might be in an environment?" List responses on the piece of butcher paper labeled "What Is in the Environment?" (examples might include water, air, rocks, land, rivers, lakes, oceans, plants, animals, and soil). Students can add to this list during the unit. Discuss the requirements of a healthy environment (see the discussion questions). Explain to students that over the next few weeks they will be looking at ways that people can help maintain an environment healthy for themselves and for other living things, focusing on water, air, and land.

DISCUSSION QUESTIONS

What things do you think might be true about a healthy environment?

Do people, other animals, and plants need different things in their environment in order to be healthy?
Are the basic things we need in our environment?
What would happen if they weren't in our environment?

EVALUATION

Pass out paper and crayons or marking pens. Have students draw pictures of an environment that include the essential needs of people, other animals, plants, or all three.

EXTENSION IDEA

Have students take a walk to look for a healthy and an unhealthy tree. Discuss how students know the difference and what factors might make trees unhealthy (disease, insects, fire, wind, lightning, pollution, and poor growing conditions, for example). Ask, "What actions can people take to help trees stay healthy?"

HOME LEARNING SUGGESTION

(Use as follow-up to this activity)

Ask students to list all of the things they or their parents do for a houseplant or garden plant to help it stay healthy, and list all of the things they do for a pet (if they have one) to help it stay healthy. Have students circle the things that are on both lists and put a check mark next to those things that people also need. In class discuss how things that live in and around our homes get the things they need to survive and stay healthy, which basic survival needs are provided by us, which are not, and how other animals and plants get the things they need.

WATER CHARADES

If there is magic on this planet, it is contained in water.
—LOREN EISELY

SUMMARY OF ACTIVITY

Students act out charades that demonstrate interactions between water and humans, other animals, and plants.

Time: 30 to 45 minutes

Setting: Classroom

Materials: Set of charade instructions (see preparation and lead-up)

Subjects: Performing arts, social studies, science

Key Words: Water, environment

RELATED CALIFORNIA FRAMEWORK CONCEPTS

Water is essential to all forms of life. (*Science Framework Addendum*)

Major natural resources needed by humans include air, water, soil, minerals, plants, animals, sources of energy, and areas of natural beauty. Natural resources are in limited supply. (*Science Framework Addendum*)

The effect on other populations needs to be considered along with other costs and benefits when human activities that affect the environment are evaluated. (*Science Framework Addendum*)

Dramatizations can be used to express ideas, intentions, or feelings. (Adapted from *Visual and Performing Arts Framework*)

OBJECTIVE

Through pantomime, students demonstrate the importance of water to humans, other animals, and plants.

BACKGROUND INFORMATION

Water is vital to living things because it is essential to the creation and functioning of living cells. As the major component of animal blood and plant sap, water transports nutrients to living cells and carries away waste products. Humans are made up of 70 percent water; a person can dehydrate and die in two or three days without water.

People use water in many more ways than just for drinking. Industry, agriculture, recreation, propagation of fish and other aquatic life and wildlife, hydropower production, navigation, transportation, and waste disposal are some of the other ways we use water.

Even though water covers about 70 percent of the earth's surface, less than 1 percent is in the form that people, other animals, and plants can use. Because there is a limited supply for growing populations, it is important that we care for our freshwater resources.

In this activity, through dramatizations, students focus on the importance of water to people and to other living things. Dramatizations such as these enable students to nonverbally express emotions and feelings about water, and allow students to reflect on all the ways we use and rely on water.

PREPARATION AND LEAD-UP

Copy the following list of suggested scenes and cut into separate strips. Make sure there are enough strips for each pair of students to have at least one.

- Making a thirsty animal happy
- Watering a plant
- A rainy day at school
- The day it snowed
- The year it didn't rain
- A tree or group of trees in a flood
- People rafting down a river
- Someone crossing a river by jumping from rock to rock
- A school of fish swimming
- What it feels like to drink a glass of water when you are really thirsty
- Birds in a birdbath
- A beaver damming a river with logs

- People swimming in a lake
- A person stomping in a puddle
- People ice skating
- A person taking a shower
- Brushing your teeth

PROCEDURE

1. Remind students of the basic survival needs they generated the day before (you might refer back to the brainstorming lists if they are available). Tell students that for the next few days they are going to be looking at one of those needs—water. Divide students into pairs and tell students that they will act out charades that demonstrate interactions between water and plants and animals (including humans). Hand each pair of students one of the strips you have prepared and allow students five to ten minutes to create their charades.

2. Have teams take turns acting out their charades. After each charade have the rest of the class try to guess what was being enacted. As a courtesy to the actors, be sure that each team is through with its charade before you allow others to guess. Ask students in the audience to describe how the scene showed the importance of water to living things. Make a point of calling on cooperative students to go next.

DISCUSSION QUESTIONS

Why is water important to people? To other living things?
Why do we need water?
Do we need to be concerned about the kind of water that is available to us? (For example, will salty, soapy, or dirty water do?)
Do the ways that humans use water create problems for other living things or the environment?
Do you think that we can hurt other living things by the things we put in water by mistake or on purpose?

EVALUATION

Have students pick one of the suggested scenes and write a story about it that shows the importance of water.

EXTENSION IDEAS

- Take a field trip to a water treatment plant to learn step-by-step how water gets to your area. Make a class mural showing where the water for all human uses comes from and where it goes after it is used.
- Begin a bulletin board on the things that people do with and to water. Post a large piece of butcher paper, divided in half. On one half write the title "Water—How do we use it?" On the other half write "Water—What are we doing to it?" Have students draw illustrations or cut out pictures from magazines showing ways people use and need water, and things people do to harm or pollute water.

HOME LEARNING SUGGESTION

(Use as lead-up to the next activity)

Ask students to use the brainstorming technique to develop (with the help of a parent) a list of ways humans use and depend on water (you may need to review how brainstorming is done; refer to the activity "The Basic Necessities"). Tell students that the class will discuss the lists the following day.

SOURCE OF ACTIVITY

Project Learning Tree, "Water You Know." Washington, D.C.: The American Forest Council, 1977.

WATER ON THE MOVE

SUMMARY OF ACTIVITY

Through demonstrations and discussions of water movement, students discover how pollution can travel from one place to another.

Time: 20-minute introduction, 15-minute discussion and observation later

Setting: Classroom (or near a natural body of water outdoors)

Materials:
- Basin or jars of water
- Food coloring
- Stalks of celery (or white carnations)
- Map of California
- Small quantity of popcorn, dried leaves, or twigs (optional)

Subject: Science

Key Words: Water pollution, water cycle, motion, prediction

RELATED CALIFORNIA FRAMEWORK CONCEPTS

Major natural resources needed by humans include air, water, soil, minerals, plants, animals, sources of energy, and areas of natural beauty. Natural resources are in limited supply. (*Science Framework Addendum*)

Conservation of resources is an ethical concern of individuals and societies. (*Science Framework Addendum*)

The effect on other populations needs to be considered along with other costs and benefits when human activities that affect the environment are evaluated. (*Science Framework Addendum*)

OBJECTIVE

Through laboratory demonstrations, students observe the movements of water.

BACKGROUND INFORMATION

Water is constantly on the move. It evaporates from oceans into the atmosphere, falls as rain or snow, and eventually returns to oceans through a drainage system of streams and rivers. This sequence of water movement is called the water cycle.

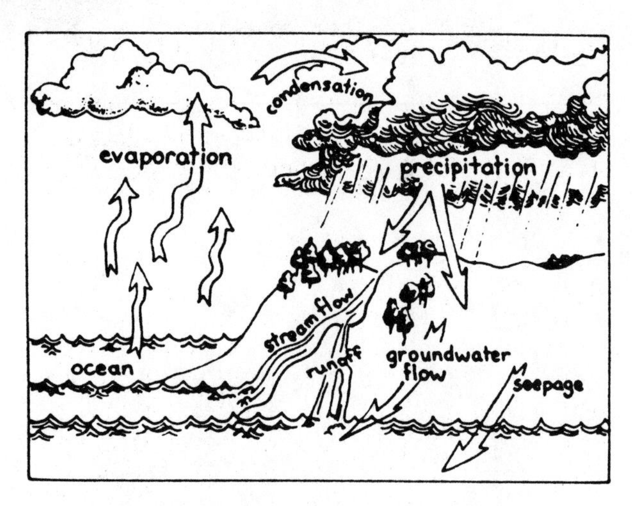

The water cycle

As water moves over the surface of land and underground, it picks up a variety of foreign substances. Depending on its speed and volume of flow, water may pick up and carry particles ranging in size from molecules to large boulders.

Some substances picked up by water can improve its quality by giving it a pleasant taste and by adding minerals and other elements beneficial to the health of plants and animals. Other substances may be harmful. A pollutant is something that doesn't belong in the water and is harmful in some way. A pollutant can also be excessive amounts of a substance that in small quantities is a good thing; for example, too much nitrogen or phosphate in water causes excessive growth of algae. Some types of pollution are easy to see while others are invisible.

An unfortunate side effect of human population growth and technological advances has been the increased pollution of our streams, rivers, lakes, groundwater supplies, and even the oceans. Heavy use of fertilizers and pesticides, inadequate treatment of industrial wastes, oil spills, and dumping of raw sewage have seriously polluted our freshwater resources.

This activity introduces students to the notion that water moves. Because water moves, water pollution can travel from one place to another.

PREPARATION AND LEAD-UP

Explain the water cycle to students. Although they will learn more about the cycle in this activity, students should have a general idea of how water moves.

PROCEDURE

1. Divide students into groups of four and ask students to share with their group the lists of ways that humans use and depend on water that were generated in the previous day's home learning suggestion. As a class discuss, "Why should we be concerned about the ways people use water? Do any of the ways people use water cause it to become dirty or harmful?"

2. Ask students, "How do you think water moves from place to place?" Demonstrate that even relatively still water is in motion by dropping food coloring into jars of water or large basins (as an option you can place popcorn, dried leaves, or small twigs—anything that is biodegradable and aesthetically harmless—into a natural body of water), then watch it travel.

3. Explain to students that even water we cannot see because it is inside living things is in motion. To demonstrate how water transports other substances both harmless and harmful to plants, tell students that you will place a stalk of celery (or a white carnation with a stem) into a jar of water that contains plenty of food coloring. Ask students what they think will happen. Have them predict how long it will take.

4. Check back in an hour or so to see how the coloring has traveled through the veins of the celery or flower. Discuss how water moves and transports substances throughout the environment (see the discussion questions).

5. Have students look at a map of California. Point to a location on one of California's rivers and have students suppose that a factory dumped toxic waste into the river at that spot. Ask, "Where would the pollution go? What cities and towns would be affected?"

DISCUSSION QUESTIONS

How does water move from place to place?

If someone puts something harmful in a river, do you think that the harmful material would stay in one place? Where would it go?

What does pollution mean?

Why should we be concerned about pollution?

Farmers use many pesticides and other chemicals to help them grow food. Could some of those chemicals get into our food?

EVALUATION

Indicate a different location on the map of California where a river has been polluted. Have students write a story about where the pollution goes and which cities and towns are affected.

EXTENSION IDEAS

- Have students experiment to determine how a plant will grow when subjected to different kinds of water (such as tap water, salt water, soapy water, or rain water). Students should use at least two plants for each type of water chosen. Plants should be the same species and all other growing conditions (like light and temperature) should be the same—the only variable should be the kind of water used for watering. Students can observe and record observations daily over a period of two to three weeks.
- A stream table is a valuable tool for exploring the movement and effects of water. Use either a commercial stream table or prepare a wooden or cardboard box about 60 centimeters (two feet) or longer and at least 30 centimeters (one foot) wide. Set it up outside.

  Make a small hole at one end for water drainage. Have on hand soil, sand, rocks, twigs, and other materials to place in the stream and blocks for changing the angle of the flow. Allow students time to explore ways to change the flow of water in the stream table. Other explorations might include work in flow dynamics, ocean currents, the effects of islands, changing land forms, sedimentary rock formation, and wind flow. Movement of materials by wind or glacier modeling is another possible subject for study.

HOME LEARNING SUGGESTION

(Use as follow-up to this activity)

Ask students to find out (with the help of a parent) what happens when rain falls on the roofs of their houses. Where does the water go? Students might make a sketch with arrows indicating the direction of water flow.

OIL SPILL

SUMMARY OF ACTIVITY

Students conduct experiments using oil, detergent, and feathers to determine the effects of environmental pollution on birds.

Time: 45 to 60 minutes

Setting: Classroom

Materials:
- Cooking oil
- Water
- Dishwashing liquid
- Several deep containers of water
- Several paper cups of oil
- One eye dropper
- Duplicated copycat page for each pair of students
- One shallow container for each pair of students
- One hand lens for each pair of students
- One natural feather for each pair of students (in the introduction to this unit are suggestions for finding feathers)
- One eye dropper (optional)

Subjects: Science, math, social studies, language arts

Key Words: Pollution, oil spill, trade-off, detergent

RELATED CALIFORNIA FRAMEWORK CONCEPTS

The effect on other populations needs to be considered along with other costs and benefits when human activities that affect the environment are evaluated. (*Science Framework Addendum*)

Pollutants carried into oceans and lakes affect living things and need to be controlled by individual behavior and public policy. (*Science Framework Addendum*)

Conservation of resources is an ethical concern of individuals and societies. (*Science Framework Addendum*)

Data can be collected, organized, represented, and interpreted using lists, tables, and graphs. (Adapted from *Mathematics Framework*)

OBJECTIVE

Students conduct an experiment to observe the effects of oil, water, and detergent on bird feathers.

BACKGROUND INFORMATION

Although the effects of environmental pollution often are difficult to see, a major oil spill gives dramatic evidence of the impact on wildlife. Feathers are damaged, embryos are killed when oil seeps into eggs, fish suffocate because their gills become clogged, and marine and land animals die from ingesting food and water contaminated by oil.

People attempt to prevent oil spills and "clean up" after spills take place. Their actions are not always successful and sometimes without knowing it their assistance does more harm than good. For instance, the process of using detergents to clean oil from the feathers of birds caught in a spill can damage the birds' feather structure and arrangement (the birds' waterproofing). Birds may also be more susceptible to disease during this time of stress and may be weakened so that it is more difficult for them to secure food and water. Obviously, the quality of food and water sources also may be affected.

Oil spills are one way water is polluted. There are many other ways, including oil and grease that are washed from cars into city streets, then dumped into storm sewers and end up in streams; pesticides that are washed off farm crops and soils by rain and make their way into streams and rivers; and industrial waste water that is discharged directly into streams or rivers.

In this activity students examine some of the possible consequences of pollution. The activity takes place in a laboratory-like setting.

PREPARATION AND LEAD-UP

Place water and oil separately into several different deep containers and position the containers so they will be easy for students to get to. Organize the remaining materials so they can be distributed quickly.

PROCEDURE

1. Tell students that today they will be investigating some of the ways that one type of water pollution affects living things. Ask students, "What is an oil spill? Have you ever seen pictures of one? What causes an oil spill? What kinds of problems do you think an oil spill might cause?" Tell students that they are going to be looking at ways that pollution like oil affects wildlife. Distribute the copycat page and briefly review it so that students know the lab activities they will be doing.

2. Divide students into pairs. Supply each pair with an eyedropper, a small container of oil, and a shallow pan filled with water. Instruct students to add from one drop to a dropper full of cooking oil to their container (alternatively you could add the oil to each container yourself). Have students observe the interaction of oil and water. Ask, "What happens to the oil? Does it stay in one place?" Have students record their observations on the copycat page, then dump the water into the sink.

3. Explain to students that they also will be observing how water, oil, and detergent affect feathers. Provide each pair of students with a natural feather. Demonstrate to students the steps they will take and have them work with their partners as follows:

First, students examine their feather with a hand lens and sketch what they see (or write a description) on their data sheet.

Second, students dip the feather into water for one or two minutes. When they remove the feather they examine it again with the hand lens. Students then sketch the feather and compare the sketch with their first sketch (or write a description and compare).

Third, students place the feather in oil for one or two minutes. When they remove the feather they examine it with the hand lens. Students sketch the feather again and compare the sketch with the other sketches (or write a description and compare).

Last, students clean the feather with detergent, rinse it in water, and dry it. They examine

the feather with the hand lens, sketch it, and compare the sketch with previous sketches (or write a description and compare).

4. Discuss all lab results. Ask, "What happened to the oil when it was placed on top of water? Did it stay in one place? How might the properties of oil affect wildlife? People? What changes did you observe after your feather was exposed to water? To oil? To detergents? What effect could these changes have on normal bird activity?"

DISCUSSION QUESTIONS

How else might birds be affected by an oil spill?

What other possible impacts might there be on other wildlife species, on humans, or on the environment?

Do we have to choose between oil and birds? What are some alternatives?

What are other examples of pollution that can have harmful effects for wildlife, people, and the environment?

EVALUATION

Students describe some possible effects of oil on birds.

EXTENSION IDEAS

- Repeat the feather experiment using a variety of oils—cooking oil, motor oil, crude oil. Compare the effects.
- Study the effect of oil on aquatic plants. Put some aquatic plants (available from tropical fish stores) into two aquariums or large jars filled with water. Pour a generous amount of oil or grease into one of the containers (keep the other container of plants as a control). Treat the plants the same and observe them for two weeks. What effect has the oil or grease had on the plants?

HOME LEARNING SUGGESTION

(Use as follow-up to this activity)

Ask students to investigate (with the help of a parent) where run-off from their driveway goes. Ask, "If there were an oil leak from a car, where would the oil go?"

SOURCE OF ACTIVITY

Adapted from *Project Wild*, "No Water Off a Duck's Back." Boulder, Colo.: Western Regional Environmental Education Council, 1985.

Names ______________________________

____

OIL SPILL DATA SHEET

1. Observations of oil in water:

2. Observations of feathers:

Dry feather	*Feather dipped in water*	*Feather dipped in oil*	*Feather dipped in detergent*

MONITORING PARTICLES IN THE AIR

SUMMARY OF ACTIVITY

Students set out paper coated with petroleum jelly to collect particles in the air.

Time: Two 30-minute periods four (or more) days apart

Setting: Classroom, outdoors

Materials:
- Petroleum jelly
- Tape
- Paper towels
- String
- Hole punch
- Two five-centimeter (two-inch) squares of waxed paper for each student
- Two five-centimeter (two-inch) squares of cardboard for each student
- Hand lens for each student

Subjects: Science, math

Key Words: Dust particle, pollution, air pollution

RELATED CALIFORNIA FRAMEWORK CONCEPTS

Major natural resources needed by humans include air, water, soil, minerals, plants, animals, sources of energy, and areas of natural beauty. Natural resources are in limited supply. (*Science Framework Addendum*)

Conservation of resources is an ethical concern of individuals and societies. (*Science Framework Addendum*)

OBJECTIVE

Through sample collecting, students identify air particles and compare the kinds and number of particles found in different locations.

BACKGROUND INFORMATION

In previous activities students have studied ways that humans use and rely on water and some ways that humans harm water sources. In this activity students are introduced to ways that people pollute the air. Students are provided an opportunity to monitor their own environment by sampling particles in the air around their classroom and home.

Particles in the air can be harmful because they get into lungs, make things dirty, and coat plants so that it may be difficult for them to grow. Air pollution has harmed trees in forests around Los Angeles and other cities.

Most air pollution is caused by burning something. Major sources of air contaminants are automobiles, airplanes, industrial plants (like cement factories, steel mills, and chemical processors), electric power generators, heating systems (of homes, offices, factories, and schools), and pesticides.

PREPARATION AND LEAD-UP

Cut two five-centimeter (two-inch) squares of cardboard and of waxed paper for each student.

PROCEDURE

1. Remind students of the list of basic needs they generated in "The Basic Necessities" activity. Review with them what they have learned about water. Tell them that over the next few days they will be studying another need—air. Ask, "Do you think air moves from place to place? How do you know? How can you observe air moving?"

2. Students can see air moving dust particles in a stream of light or feel air moving when they blow on their hands. Ask, "Do you think the air we are breathing has been somewhere else? Do you think it will travel far away after it's been here? If there is something harmful in the air, does it stay in one place?" Tell students that they will be collecting particles in the air to find out more about air movement and air pollution.

3. Demonstrate to students how to make a "sticky square," which they will use to sample dirt and dust particles. First, have students label a cardboard square with their name and tape the waxed paper square to the cardboard. Next, cover the waxed paper with an even coat of petroleum jelly

(a messy process). Finally, place the square in a place where it will be undisturbed for a week.

4. Help students place their "sticky squares" so that the squares are distributed among a variety of places both inside and outside the classroom. Students can also tie a piece of string through punched holes and hang the squares (in the home learning suggestion students will place their other square somewhere at home).

5. At the end of a week examine the squares with a hand lens or magnifying glass. Count the number of particles collected on each square. Compare different particles on each square. Compare differences depending on the location of squares.

DISCUSSION QUESTIONS

Which places had the most particles?
Which places had the fewest particles?
What do you think the particles are?
Do all of the particles look the same?
Where do you think the particles come from?
How might the particles be harmful?
If something harmful gets into the air, does it stay in one place?
Are there any natural causes for things in the air?
Are there ways we could cut down on the number of particles in the air?

EVALUATION

Have students write a paragraph describing what they discovered from their squares.

EXTENSION IDEAS

- Attach cloth smeared with petroleum jelly to the tail pipe of several cars. Have the driver of each car start the motor and idle the engine for three minutes. Compare residues noting the make, model, and year of each car.
- Have students look for things on their way to and from school that cause air pollution. The class can make a master list of all these "air polluters."

HOME LEARNING SUGGESTION

(Use as a part of this activity)

Have students make a "sticky square," put it in a sandwich bag, and take it home to place it somewhere inside or outside their homes (if students have petroleum jelly at home they can apply it to the waxed paper there). After one week ask students to collect their squares and record the kind and number of particles they observed. Students can bring the squares to class (in a sandwich bag) for discussion.

SOURCE OF ACTIVITY

Greenbox, "Drifters and Drop-outs." Eureka, Calif.: Humboldt County Office of Education, 1975.

OPEN SPACES

SUMMARY OF ACTIVITY

Students demonstrate how large an area of grass is needed to provide the daily oxygen required by the class and discuss reasons why open spaces are important.

Time: 45 minutes

Setting: Classroom

Materials:
- Geranium, begonia, or wandering jew plant
- Magnifying lens
- White string, six meters (20 feet) per student

Subjects: Science, math

Key Words: Stoma (plural—stomata), open space, oxygen, carbon dioxide

RELATED CALIFORNIA FRAMEWORK CONCEPTS

Major natural resources needed by humans include air, water, soil, minerals, plants, animals, sources of energy, and areas of natural beauty. Natural resources are in limited supply. (*Science Framework Addendum*)

Estimating answers to computational problems can help people decide whether a proposed numerical answer is reasonable. (Adapted from *Mathematics Framework*)

Conservation of resources is an ethical concern of individuals and societies. (*Science Framework Addendum*)

OBJECTIVE

Students estimate and verify the amount of outdoor space necessary to meet the oxygen needs of the entire class.

BACKGROUND INFORMATION

Plants are an important aspect of open spaces because they produce oxygen, which living things need. An area of 2.25 square meters of grass (25 square feet) provides enough oxygen to meet a person's daily requirements (0.7 square meters [7 square feet] of trees provides the same amount of oxygen).

Plants have the ability to use their green pigment, chlorophyll, to manufacture food out of carbon dioxide and water using energy from sunlight. This process is called photosynthesis. During photosynthesis, oxygen is given off. The openings through which the gases pass, located in the plant's leaves or stems, are called stomata. A strong hand-magnifier or a low-power microscope will show the stomata clearly on the underside of the leaves of a geranium, begonia, or wandering jew.

Helping to supply oxygen needs is but one reason why open spaces are important. Open spaces provide a habitat for wildlife and native plant species. Open spaces also provide areas for water to collect as reservoirs for people or as water supplies for plants and wildlife. In addition, open spaces provide places for recreational activities like hiking, jogging, fishing, and bird watching, as well as aesthetically pleasing places where community members can relax and reflect.

In this activity students are introduced to the idea that open spaces are necessary because they help satisfy the oxygen needs of people living in a community. In the following activities students will look at land use management and how human activities affect the health of the land.

PREPARATION AND LEAD-UP

Cut a piece of string six meters (20 feet) long for each student. Use string that is white or another color that will show up against the ground; brown twine tends to disappear.

PROCEDURE

1. Discuss the importance of oxygen to plants and animals. Show students the stomata of leaves of a geranium, begonia, or wandering jew, using a strong magnifying lens. Explain that oxygen made by the plant exits through the stomata and that almost all oxygen we breath is made by plants.

2. Have students guess how much grass they think is necessary to provide a person's daily oxygen needs. Tell students that each person's daily oxygen requirement is about the amount of oxygen given off by a square of grass that is 1.5 meters (5 feet) on each side (the area is 2.25 square meters or 25 square feet).

3. As a class, estimate how large an area would be required to supply the oxygen for all students in the class. Go out on the ball field or any space near the school where each student can lay out a 1.5-meter by 1.5-meter square of string (five-feet by five-feet square). Help students lay out their string so that the spaces are adjacent to each other, not overlapping. Have students stand at the perimeter to see how large an area the class as a whole would need. Compare the actual area with class estimates.

4. In the classroom discuss whether it is important that open spaces exist in people's communities. Help each student estimate how much open space is needed to supply all students in the school with oxygen.

DISCUSSION QUESTIONS

Where do people living in the city get their fresh air supply?

We need open space for air; why else do we need open space?

What are some open spaces in our neighborhood or city?
How do open spaces like parks or public lands make you feel?
What do you like to do in open spaces?

EVALUATION

Have students draw pictures or write stories about why open spaces are important to them.

EXTENSION IDEAS

- Using maps of the community, have students estimate the total area of land devoted to public parks and open space. Discuss whether this amount is sufficient for community needs, more than sufficient, or insufficient.
- Look for and learn songs that reflect people's need for land and space. "Don't Fence Me In" and "This Land Is Your Land" are two examples.

HOME LEARNING SUGGESTION

(Use as follow-up to this activity)

Ask each student to estimate the amount of open space needed to provide oxygen for his or her family.

SOURCE OF ACTIVITY

Busch, Phyllis S. *The Urban Environment*. Chicago, Ill.: J. G. Ferguson Publishing Co., 1975.

LAND USE SIMULATION

SUMMARY OF ACTIVITY

Students represent interest groups at a city council meeting and make a land-use planning decision concerning a lake.

Time: Two 30- to 45-minute periods

Setting: Classroom

Materials:
- Chalkboard or piece of butcher paper
- One large piece of butcher paper for each interest group
- Crayons or marking pens for each interest group

Subjects: Social studies, science, language arts, art

Key Words: Simulation, point of view, interest group, wildlife

RELATED CALIFORNIA FRAMEWORK CONCEPTS

Major natural resources needed by humans include air, water, soil, minerals, plants, animals, sources of energy, and areas of natural beauty. Natural resources are in limited supply. (*Science Framework Addendum*)

The effect on other populations needs to be considered along with other costs and benefits when human activities that affect the environment are evaluated. (*Science Framework Addendum*)

We can participate as citizens of our nation, state, and community in decisions that affect us all. (Adapted from *History-Social Science Framework*)

Visual art media can be used to translate ideas, feelings, and values. (Adapted from *Visual and Performing Arts Framework*)

Talking and listening are important ways by which people communicate with and learn from each other. (Adapted from *English-Language Arts Framework*)

OBJECTIVE

Students make land-use recommendations after participating in a simulation activity.

BACKGROUND INFORMATION

In the previous activity students looked at reasons why it is important for communities to have open spaces. In this activity students play the role of a city council that must decide on the best plan for using a piece of land. The activity emphasizes the complexities of decision making where people of different viewpoints are affected, and helps students build on their understanding that different people have different wants and needs. This activity also allows students the opportunity to assume the perspective of another person and compare it with their own perspective, a skill that students at this age are beginning to acquire.

Simulations like this are operating models of real-life situations. In a simulation students evaluate the consequences of decisions before they are actually carried out. Students interact with each other in the decision-making process, developing skills they will need later to take active roles in their communities.

Because students may become emotionally involved in their roles, and take the outcome personally, the teacher should give students the opportunity following the simulation to vent any frustrations or hurts they feel or express any concerns they have about the reality of the situation. This will also help students relate what was learned to real life.

PREPARATION AND LEAD-UP

Copy the following map on the board or on a piece of butcher paper.

PROCEDURE

Day One

1. Tell the class, "Oso Lake is a small lake outside Daily City. Recently the lake and a small area of land around the lake were donated to Daily City by a wealthy citizen. There are no roads to the lake, only trails. The city has to decide how the lake and land are to be used in the future. What should the city do?"

2. Have students brainstorm possible ways that the lake and land could be used and list the ideas on the board. Help students group ideas that are similar and give a title to each group (like "hous-

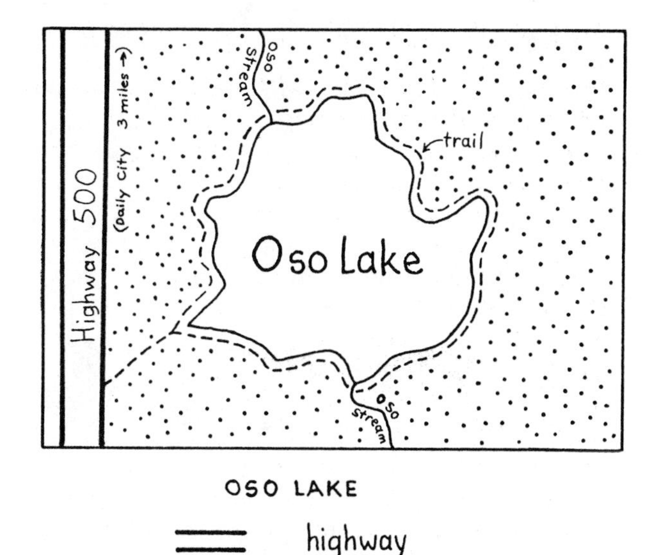

OSO LAKE

highway
trail
donated land

ing," "recreation," or "stores"). Form as many citizen interest groups as categories, and allow students to choose which group they want to join.

Alternatively, tell the class that there are three different special interest groups. One group, the Anderson Development Company, wants the city to sell the land to it so that the company can build condominiums around the lake and a road to the lake. Another group, the Neighborhood Park Alliance, wants the city to develop the lake into a park by building a boat launch, fishing pier, play fields, and a road into the park. The last group, the Wildlife Association, wants the lake and the land around it set aside for a wildlife refuge. Divide the class into groups representing these three interests.

3. Tell students that each interest group will have 20 minutes to draw a map of its plan for the lake area and to prepare a two-minute presentation that will be made to the city council. The presentation must be made by more than one person. Distribute paper and markers to each group.

4. About 10 minutes after the groups have begun their planning, pull one or two students from each group to form the city council (because these students will have spent some time with a group, they will identify with the group's plan, making the decision-making process more interesting and realistic than if the students had not worked with an interest group). The city council must decide on the best plan for the lake. While the groups continue to plan their presentations, the council should plan the hearing procedures. Who will testify first? In what order? Where will the council sit? Where will the presenters sit? What will be the council's strategy for deciding the best plan?

5. Fifteen minutes into the planning, remind groups that they have only five minutes left. When the time is up, collect the plans and explain to students that the city council meeting will be held the next day.

Day Two

6. Have city council members sit as planned. Appoint a timekeeper to cut off presentations after two minutes. After all presentations have been made, the city council may ask questions (allow only five to ten minutes for questions).

7. Allow the council to meet briefly (five to ten minutes) to reach a decision. While the council meets, each group can develop a list of things they think the decision should be based on.

8. The city council announces its decision. The council also gives reasons why it reached the decision it did.

9. Help students come out of the simulation. Ask, "How did your group work together; did you work as a team or individually? How did you feel about the city council's decision? If your plan wasn't chosen, how did you feel about it? Did you feel that the selection process was fair? Why or why not? Did people in the city council find it difficult to select a plan? If so, why? Do you think this activity was realistic? Why or why not?"

DISCUSSION QUESTIONS

How would each of the plans have affected air quality? Water quality?
How would each of the plans have affected the plants and wildlife in the lake area?
Are there any other possible solutions to this land-use problem?
Can you think of a plan that would benefit both people and wildlife?

EVALUATION

Have each student write a position paper describing how they think Oso Lake and the land around it should be used and why. Students may wish to include a map of their plan.

EXTENSION IDEA

Find out how land-use decisions are made in your area. Have students write short papers describing the process or, better yet, have students interview local council members about a recent land-use issue.

HOME LEARNING SUGGESTION

(Use as follow-up to this activity)

Ask parents to help their child find a land-use issue that is of current concern in your own region. This issue can be one that the parent knows about or one that is found by looking in the newspaper or at local television news.

CONSEQUENCES OF LITTER

SUMMARY OF ACTIVITY

Students take a journey to a special place using guided imagery, then experience how they feel if their special place is changed.

Time: 30 to 45 minutes

Setting: Classroom

Materials:
- Drawing paper
- Crayons or colored pens

Subjects: Language arts, social studies, art, science

Key Words: Guided imagery, litter, consequences

RELATED CALIFORNIA FRAMEWORK CONCEPTS

Major natural resources needed by humans include air, water, soil, minerals, plants, animals, sources of energy, and areas of natural beauty. Natural resources are in limited supply. (*Science Framework Addendum*)

Conservation of resources is an ethical concern of individuals and societies. (*Science Framework Addendum*)

The effect on other populations needs to be considered along with other costs and benefits when human activities that affect the environment are evaluated. (*Science Framework Addendum*)

Visual art media can be used to translate ideas, feelings, and values. (Adapted from *Visual and Performing Arts Framework*)

Talking and listening are important ways by which people communicate with and learn from each other. (Adapted from *English-Language Arts Framework*)

OBJECTIVE

Through guided imagery and art, students express the emotional impact of environmental damage.

BACKGROUND INFORMATION

In the previous activity students were introduced to the idea that people have different views about how land should be used. In this activity students look at how consequences of people's actions toward the land can affect other people.

The guided imagery in this activity enables students to begin to understand that everyone has a special place he or she is emotionally attached to. This emotional attachment is the reason people get so upset over environmental issues. Guided imagery is a good way to allow students to use their imaginations; it also enables students to go on imaginary journeys even if they are unable to take real ones.

PROCEDURE

1. Take your students on a guided imagery journey of a special place. "Close your eyes and think of a place that is special to you . . . It might be in your backyard or a place you go on vacation every year . . . It is a place where you can think and where you enjoy being . . . Think about the smells of that place, the sounds you might hear, the things you see around you . . . Now imagine that while you are in your special place, someone walks by and throws an empty soft drink can on the ground . . . Imagine how you feel . . . Now imagine that someone else walks by and throws a bunch of hamburger wrappers and empty milkshake cups on the ground . . . Imagine that you don't move from where you are, but think about how you feel . . . Now imagine that someone comes by your special place and empties a huge garbage can full of garbage right in the middle of your special place so that there is a huge pile of trash in your special place . . . Imagine how you feel . . . Think about how your special place looks now and remember what you see and feel . . . When you are ready, open your eyes."

2. Distribute pieces of drawing paper and crayons or marking pens. Instruct students to draw a line down the middle of their paper. Have students draw two pictures. On one half of the paper a picture of their special place before the litter and on the other half a picture that includes the litter.

3. Discuss with students what they experienced in their guided imagery. Ask volunteers to share their drawings.

DISCUSSION QUESTIONS

How did you feel when your special place was littered?
Do you think that most people have a special place that they care about?
Can you think of things that people sometimes do that affect another person's special place?
What are other things people do that affect the environment?

EVALUATION

Students describe how the littering events made them feel.

EXTENSION IDEA

Have students study litter by selecting an area of ground at school about 50 meters by 50 meters (160 feet by 160 feet). Instruct students to collect all litter found at the site, recording the size, location found, and type of litter. Two weeks later repeat the exercise to determine the types and amount of litter that accumulates. Students can then investigate the effects of "Please Do Not Litter" signs on the site, comparing litter buildup with and without the signs.

HOME LEARNING SUGGESTION

(Use as follow-up to this activity)

Have students conduct the guided imagery exercise with a parent. Direct students to lead their parents on a similar trip using the same guided imagery. Students then ask their parents to draw two pictures, one showing their special place before the littering and one afterwards. In class discuss parents' reactions to the littering events. How were they different? How were they the same? Do adults and children both have special places that they care about?

EVALUATING LITTER'S HARM

SUMMARY OF ACTIVITY

Students collect and evaluate litter in terms of its possible harm.

Time: 45 minutes (minimum)

Setting: Classroom, schoolgrounds, or park

Materials:
- One six-pack holder from canned drinks
- Plastic litter bags for each group of four students
- Newspaper for each group of four students
- At least one small to medium-sized (thin) rubber band for each student

Subjects: Science, math, language arts, social studies, art

Key Words: Litter, pollution

RELATED CALIFORNIA FRAMEWORK CONCEPTS

Major natural resources needed by humans include air, water, soil, minerals, plants, animals, sources of energy, and areas of natural beauty. Natural resources are in limited supply. (*Science Framework Addendum*)

The effect on other populations needs to be considered along with other costs and benefits when human activities that affect the environment are evaluated. (*Science Framework Addendum*)

Conservation of resources is an ethical concern of individuals and societies. (*Science Framework Addendum*)

Using one or more attributes, objects can be classified and sorted by observing similarities and differences, describing and recording relationships, and making generalizations. (Adapted from *Mathematics Framework*)

OBJECTIVE

Students collect litter and identify ways in which it may be harmful to living things.

BACKGROUND INFORMATION

In the previous activity students were exposed to some of the emotional and aesthetic impacts of litter. In this activity students learn that environmental pollution affects all forms of life. It is unsightly and also dangerous to animals.

Birds with long bills often get monofilament fishline wrapped around their bills, which prevents them from eating. They starve to death. The line also gets tangled in wings, so birds cannot fly.

Sometimes fish and birds are caught in the loop portions of plastic six-pack holders. Animals can exhaust themselves struggling to get free. If they don't get free and continue to grow, the loop can eventually strangle them because it doesn't stretch. These loops also get tangled around the feet of waterfowl.

Deer and other animals cut their tongues on half-opened cans. Sometimes smaller animals get their heads stuck inside the cans and can't eat.

Mice and chipmunks crawl into opened bottles and may get trapped inside, unable to get a footing on the slippery glass to push themselves out through the small opening. Broken glass from bottles and other glass objects can injure people, pets, and wildlife.

Wildlife, including fish, can be injured or killed by bottle caps or pop tops. Cigarette butts, cellophane wrappers, and styrofoam can cause internal problems if eaten.

PREPARATION AND LEAD-UP

Select a site. Mark boundaries for litter collection.

PROCEDURE

1. Divide the class into teams of four. Have students use plastic bags to collect litter from schoolgrounds, a park, or a vacant lot. Remind students of proper outdoor behavior and instruct them not to take things out of garbage cans.

2. Have groups dump the contents of their bags onto newspaper and classify the specific items of litter into categories. Each group should decide how it will classify the objects. Possible categories include size (small, medium, large); kind (glass, metal, paper, plastic, organic); and location found

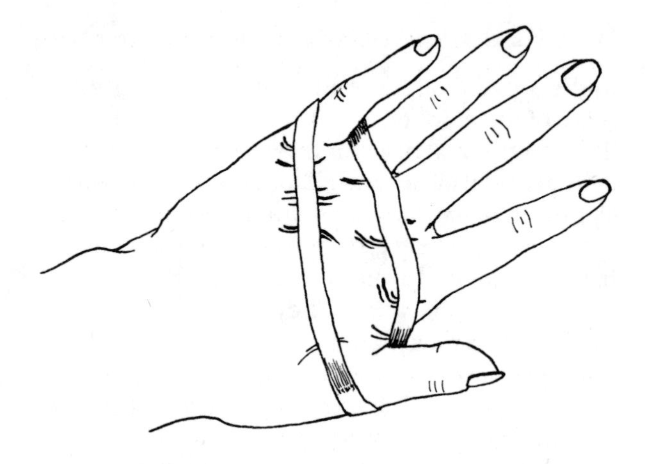

(open area, vacant lot, near a tree). Each group can tally the number of items it found in each category.

3. Throw the litter away, then discuss the effects of litter on people and wildlife. Ask, "In what ways do you think litter might be harmful to people? Does litter affect people in other ways? How do you think litter might affect wildlife?"

4. Show students the six-pack holder and ask them to think of ways this type of litter could be dangerous to wildlife. Explain that students will demonstrate how the holder might affect a duck.

5. Distribute a rubber band to each student and ask students to hold their left hand up, in front of their face with the back of their hand facing them. Have students use their right hand to hook the rubber band over the "baby" finger of their left hand and stretch it over the thumb of their left hand. The rubber band should be taut and resting across the knuckles of the left hand. Have students place their right hand on the bottom of their left elbow.

6. Now ask students to imagine that they are a duck that has the plastic ring of a six-pack holder around its neck. Have students try to free themselves from the rubber band following this rule: Students cannot use their hands, teeth, face, or other body parts to help them.

7. One or two students may free themselves in 10 to 20 seconds, but most will have difficulty. Discuss how the duck might feel after struggling all morning to free itself. Ask, "How will it feel if it misses breakfast? Lunch? Dinner?"

8. Explain to students that one way to eliminate the harm of six-pack holders is to cut each ring open with a pair of scissors. Demonstrate this.

9. Talk with students about other ways that litter is harmful to wildlife (see the background information). Ask, "Should people be more careful about not littering?"

DISCUSSION QUESTIONS

How can people be taught about the dangers as well as the ugliness of littering?
What do you think might encourage people to eliminate litter?
What can we do to eliminate or reduce litter?

EVALUATION

Students name two ways that litter can harm wildlife and two things they can do to eliminate these dangers. Alternatively, students propose what they consider to be one of the most effective ways to reduce or eliminate litter.

EXTENSION IDEAS

- Help students set up a recycling center in your school. Investigate who will buy and recycle the things you collect. Figure out how to get recyclable items to the dealer. Find out in what form the dealer will take the materials. (Does glass need to be separated by color? Must labels be removed from cans and glass? Do cans need to be flattened? How should newspaper be bundled?) Find a space to store the collected materials and decide which materials (paper, glass, aluminum, tin cans) the class will collect. Have the class prepare a flyer showing people how to process the materials before bringing them to your center. Make the center a safe place to work. Post these safety rules: Don't leave glass around where it can get broken accidentally. Be careful opening cans. Wear special clothing to protect yourself.
- Bury different types of litter to find out what happens to it. Make a list of exactly what was buried. After about a month, have students dig up the litter and examine what they found.

SOURCES OF ACTIVITY

Adapted from *Project Wild*, "Litter We Know." Boulder, Colo.: Western Regional Environmental Education Council, 1985.

Going Wild (*Project Wild* Newsletter), Vol. 2, No. 1. Sacramento, Calif.: California Department of Fish and Game, 1986.

ENVIRONMENTAL BAROMETER

SUMMARY OF ACTIVITY

Students go outside to observe and count or estimate wildlife in an area, then do the same in another setting and compare their findings.

Time: One 30- to 45-minute period and one 15- to 30-minute period on two different days

Setting: Classroom, schoolyard, or park

Materials:
- Writing materials
- Poster board or construction paper
- Crayons or marking pens

Subjects: Science, math

Key Words: Evidence, wildlife, environmental quality, habitat

RELATED CALIFORNIA FRAMEWORK CONCEPTS

Major natural resources needed by humans include air, water, soil, minerals, plants, animals, sources of energy, and areas of natural beauty. Natural resources are in limited supply. (*Science Framework Addendum*)

The effect on other populations needs to be considered along with other costs and benefits when human activities that affect the environment are evaluated. (*Science Framework Addendum*)

Conservation of resources is an ethical concern of individuals and societies. (*Science Framework Addendum*)

Data can be collected, organized, represented, and interpreted using lists, tables, and graphs. (Adapted from *Mathematics Framework*)

OBJECTIVE

Students compare the healthiness of two environments by conducting a census of living things.

BACKGROUND INFORMATION

Some species of animals adapt easily to difficult conditions. Other animals are so specialized that they can find the food, water, shelter, and other things they need in specific environments only.

The abundance or scarcity of wildlife is an important indicator of the overall health of an environmental area. If there are few wild animals or little evidence of wildlife, basic needs like food, water, and shelter are probably in short supply. The kinds of wildlife present are also important indicators. Birds of prey, for example, are high on the food chain. If they are present it indicates that there is a variety of other animals and plants in the area. The greater the diversity of animals living in an environment, the more likely it is that the environment satisfies the needs of many kinds of animals.

In the previous activities, students have looked at ways that human actions affect the environmental health of an area. In this activity, students observe the abundance of wildlife in two areas to compare the quality of the environments.

Several possibilities may arise while doing this activity. Your school may be in an area where there are few, if any, wild animals present and students may not have access to an area that has much wildlife. If there is no significant difference between students' observations in the two settings, you can still talk with students about what this means. It is also possible that your school is in an area that is as full of wildlife as any other setting in the area. Again it is all right if there is no significant difference in the number and variety of wildlife observed in each area. You may choose to make the observations in one setting only, analyzing the quality of that environment without comparing it with another.

Help your students look for evidence of wildlife as well as actual wildlife. Webs, chewed leaves, shells, tracks, feathers, dead insects, scat, bird song, and holes in trees and in the ground are signs of wildlife that live in the area.

PREPARATION AND LEAD-UP

Select a study site in the schoolyard. Students will investigate their own backyards as the second study site (see the home learning suggestion). As an option to students investigating their own yards, you may select a second study site in another area, such as a park or vacant lot, that is more or less abundant in wildlife than the school site.

PROCEDURE

Day One

1. Remind students of the things that animals and plants need to stay healthy. Discuss possible ways of determining whether an environment is a healthy one for living things. Explain that one way to determine the quality of an environment is to study how many kinds of animals are able to live there. Tell students that they will be making observations about the quality of the school environment by looking for wildlife. Ask, "What kinds of wildlife do you think we'll be able to observe in the school's environment?" (Make sure students understand that wildlife includes squirrels, birds, insects, bugs, spiders, and worms, as well as larger animals.) "What kinds of evidence of wildlife do you think we might observe?"

2. Review proper outdoor behavior with students. Remind students that they are to observe only and are not to disturb plants and wildlife. Students should work quietly so that wildlife will not be scared off and so that other classes are not disrupted.

3. Take your students on the schoolgrounds to do a wildlife count. Students should work alone or in pairs and have writing materials. Ask each student or pair of students to find a spot, sit quietly for 10 minutes, and observe (being quiet increases the likelihood of seeing wildlife, although insects and most city birds can still be observed even if students are somewhat noisy). Students should record the kinds and numbers of any wildlife they see.

Explain to students that they do not need to know the names of animals they see. Students can either draw a sketch of animals they observe or make up a name that describes the animal, like Big Brown Bird. Students can include evidence of wildlife (like spider webs, feathers, or chewed leaves), in addition to actual sightings.

Kind of Animal or Evidence	Number Seen
Ant	卌 I
Bluebird	I
Squirrel	II
Spiderweb	III

4. Collect the students' information on one master chart. This chart should list all of the kinds of animals or evidence of animals observed and the number of each animal seen.

5. Have students investigate their own backyard (see the home learning suggestion). Alternatively, you can take students to a second setting of your choice and repeat the process, with each student sitting quietly for 10 minutes, then recording his or her observations.

Day Two

6. Make a master chart of the information from the second environment. Use the same format as on the previous day.

7. Compare the information from the two charts (see the discussion questions). Talk about whether it is realistic for every environment to be a good home (habitat) for varieties of wildlife. Discuss the possibility and appropriateness of improving environments as wildlife habitats and homes for people. Tell students that on the following day they will look at some of their own activities to see how these activities affect the environment.

DISCUSSION QUESTIONS

Was there any difference between the two settings? Why or why not?

Which environment seemed to have the most variety of wildlife?

Which environment had the most of any one kind of wildlife? (For example, which environment had the most birds?)

What kinds of food, water, shelter, and space were in each setting to support the survival needs of wildlife?

If there were few animals (or many), what might this tell us about the quality of the environment?
What is environmental quality?
Can wildlife be an indicator of environmental quality?

EVALUATION

Students make a list of things we do in cities and towns that tend to decrease the number and kinds of wildlife that live there. Students also list things we do in cities and towns that tend to increase the numbers and kinds of wildlife there.

EXTENSION IDEA

Repeat the activity in another season. Compare the results.

HOME LEARNING SUGGESTION

(Use as follow-up to this activity)

Ask students to spend about 10 minutes at home in their own backyards or in a park near their house, observing the wildlife they find there. Ask students to record their findings on a data sheet like the one they used for their earlier observations.

SOURCE OF ACTIVITY

Adapted from *Project Wild*, "Environmental Barometer." Boulder, Colo.: Western Regional Environmental Education Council, 1985.

WHAT IF?

SUMMARY OF ACTIVITY

Students analyze activities they enjoy doing to see how these activities affect the environment.

Time: 30 to 45 minutes

Setting: Classroom

Materials:
- "What If" copycat page
- Pencils

Subjects: Science, math, social studies, language arts

Key Words: Environment, disaster

RELATED CALIFORNIA FRAMEWORK CONCEPTS

Conservation of resources is an ethical concern of individuals and societies. (*Science Framework Addendum*)

The effect on other populations needs to be considered along with other costs and benefits when human activities that affect the environment are evaluated. (*Science Framework Addendum*)

Data can be collected, organized, represented, and interpreted using lists, tables, and graphs. (Adapted from *Mathematics Framework*)

OBJECTIVE

Students identify and analyze favorite activities in terms of the effect on the environment.

BACKGROUND INFORMATION

In previous activities students have studied how human actions affect the quality of the environment. In this activity students look at their own actions to see how they might affect the environment. By thinking about their actions, students begin to think about lifestyle choices that do the least harm to the environment.

PREPARATION AND LEAD-UP

Reproduce the copycat page.

PROCEDURE

1. Remind students of their findings in the "Environmental Barometer" activity. Ask, "Do you think our actions affect the environment? If so, how?" Number from one to ten down the left side of the chalkboard, then make four columns across the top labeled "Air," "Water," "Land," and "What If?" Next to the first few numbers list sample activities that children enjoy doing.

2. As a class, decide whether the first activity has any effect on the air, positively or negatively. If it affects the air positively, put a plus mark (+) under the "Air" column. If it affects the air negatively, put a minus mark (−). If the activity does not have an effect, leave the column blank. Discuss the students' perceptions about how the activity helps or harms the air.

3. Decide as a class whether the same activity affects the water, either positively or negatively, and place a plus or minus mark in the "Water" column (or leave the column blank if the activity has no effect). Discuss the students' perceptions about how the activity helps or harms water. Repeat the same process for the "Land" column.

4. Ask, "What if half the world's population were to do this activity at any one time?" There are three choices: W = Wonderful, D = Disaster, or OK. Decide as a class which symbol (W, D, or OK) to place in the "What If?" column.

5. For each of the other activities listed on the board, decide as a class whether the activity affects the air, water, or land and put plus or minus marks in the appropriate columns. Decide "what if" half the world's population were to do each activity at any one time.

6. Hand out the copycat page and ask each student to make a list of activities he or she enjoys doing. Lists can include activities done after school, on weekends, or during vacations. Students then decide whether their own activities affect the air, water, and land, and "what if" half the world did each activity at one time.

7. Divide students into groups of four. Have students share their lists with their group.

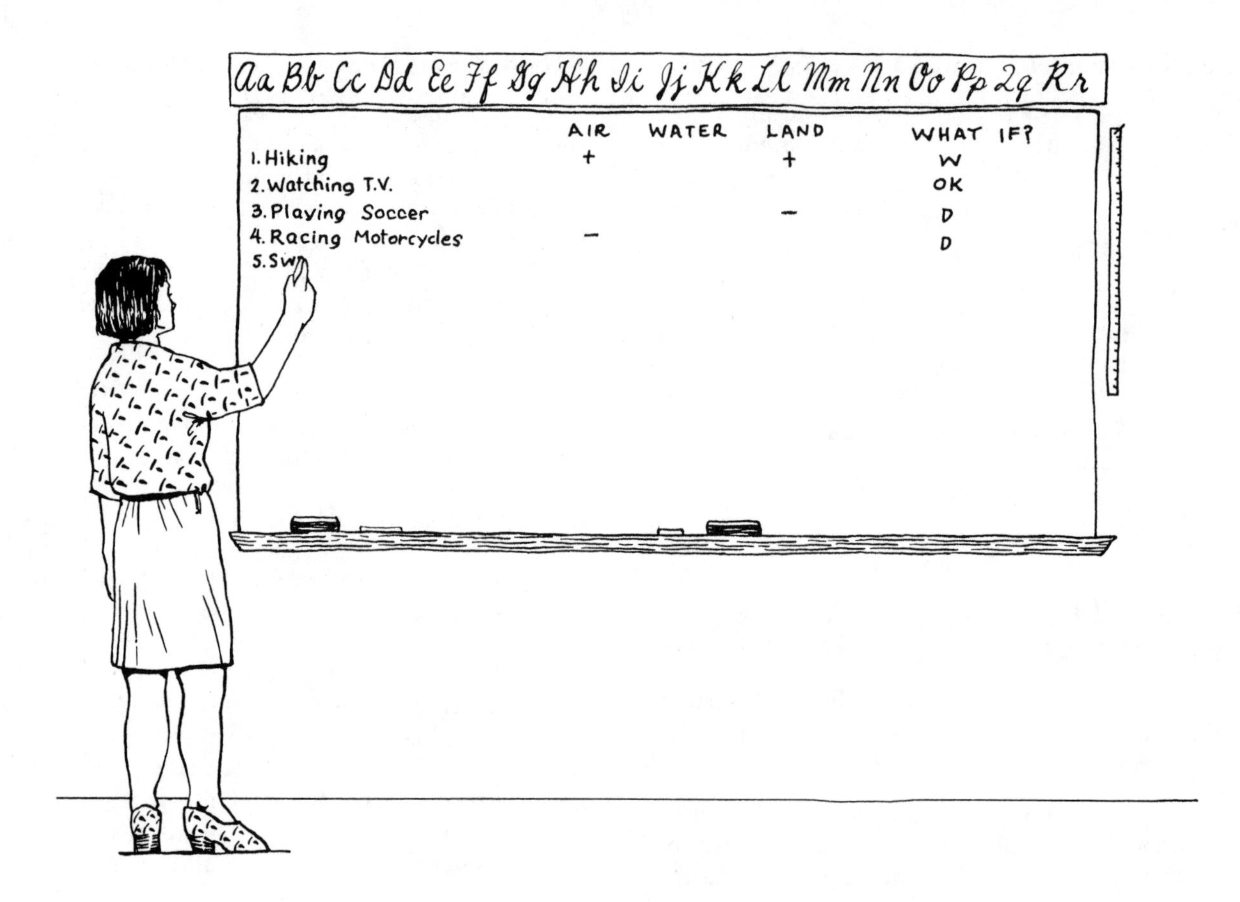

DISCUSSION QUESTIONS

Which of our activities are harmful to the air? To water? To land?

Which of our activities do not harm the air? The water? The land?

Do you think we should think about how our actions affect the air, water, and land? Why?

Could some of our activities be changed so that they do less damage to the environment? Which ones?

EVALUATION

Ask students to choose one of the activities listed and write a story or draw a picture about what it would be like if half the world did the activity. Ask, "What would the world be like? What would be the effect on people? On other animals? On plants? How would the air, water, and land be affected?"

EXTENSION IDEAS

- Divide students into groups of four and give each group a set of stones, sticks, eucalyptus pods, leaves, cones, or other natural objects (the objects can be different for each group). Challenge students to invent a game they could play with the objects. Games should have at least three rules and a title.
- Have students produce a play based on the book *The Day They Parachuted Cats on Borneo*, by Charlotte Pomerantz. This story, which is written in verse and illustrated as a play, dramatizes how the environment can be affected when the consequences of our actions are not fully anticipated.

HOME LEARNING SUGGESTION

(Use as lead-up to the next activity)

Ask students to look for activities in their neighborhood or community that seem to help or hurt the environment or wildlife and activities that do not seem to affect the environment. Ask each student to come to school the next day prepared to share at least one example.

RESOURCE

Pomerantz, Charlotte. *The Day They Parachuted Cats on Borneo.* Reading, Mass.: Young Scott Books, 1971. This play tells the true story of what happened when DDT was sprayed on farmers' huts in Borneo.

SOURCE OF ACTIVITY

Jorgensen, Eric, Trout Black, and Mary Hallesy. *Manure to Meadow to Milkshake.* Los Altos, Calif.: Hidden Villa, Inc., 1978.

Copycat Page

Name ____________________

What If?

List 10 activities that you enjoy doing after school, on weekends, or during vacation. Next to each activity, in the appropriate column, put a plus (+) if the activity affects the air, water, or land in a positive way. Put a minus (–) if the activity affects the air, water, or land in a negative way. If half the world were to do this activity at one time, decide whether it would be Wonderful (W), a Disaster (D), or okay (OK), and put the appropriate abbreviation in the "What If?" column.

Activity	*Air*	*Water*	*Land*	*What If?*
1				
2				
3				
4				
5				
6				
7				
8				
9				
10				

COMMUNITY QUALITY OF LIFE SURVEY

SUMMARY OF ACTIVITY

Students survey members of their community to determine attitudes about the environmental quality of the community.

Time: 45 minutes to formulate survey; time to conduct survey (varies); 30 minutes to process survey

Setting: Classroom, home

Materials:
- Copies of survey questions for each student
- Clipboard or other hard writing surface for each student

Subjects: Language arts, math, science, social studies

Key Words: Survey, open-ended, multiple-choice, evaluation, opinion, attitude, environmental quality

RELATED CALIFORNIA FRAMEWORK CONCEPTS

Data can be collected, organized, represented, and interpreted using lists, tables, and graphs. (Adapted from *Mathematics Framework*)

The effect on other populations needs to be considered along with other costs and benefits when human activities that affect the environment are evaluated. (*Science Framework Addendum*)

Major natural resources needed by humans include air, water, soil, minerals, plants, animals, sources of energy, and areas of natural beauty. Natural resources are in limited supply. (*Science Framework Addendum*)

People can appreciate and preserve the beauty of their community and improve the quality of life in it. (Adapted from *History-Social Science Framework*)

Talking and listening are important ways by which people communicate with and learn from each other. (Adapted from *English-Language Arts Framework*)

OBJECTIVE

Students conduct and evaluate a survey of attitudes related to local environmental quality.

BACKGROUND INFORMATION

Throughout this unit students have been learning about what living things need for a healthy environment and about ways that people affect the environment. In this activity students take what they have learned and use their knowledge and interests to formulate a survey. The survey can serve as a review of the concepts studied and also help students find out more about their community and about the attitudes of the people living there.

In general it is better to have a short survey with good questions than a long survey. When formulating and selecting questions for a survey, keep in mind the various forms questions can take. Yes/no or multiple-choice questions are easy to evaluate but open-ended questions often produce more interesting information. A mix of yes/no, multiple-choice, and open-ended questions may be best.

Some sample questions for surveys are:

Do you think people can hurt other living things by the things we put in water? (yes/no)

Do you think water pollution is a problem in our community? (yes/no)

Do you think air pollution is a problem in our community? (yes/no) Why or why not?

What do you think is the biggest cause of air pollution in our community?

What do you think might be done to eliminate litter problems in our community?

Do you think there is enough open space in our community? (yes/no)

What do you think is the most important reason for having open space? (a) Recreation (b) Fresh air (c) Solitude (d) Other

PREPARATION AND LEAD-UP

Decide how many surveys you want each student to conduct and whether you want students to work individually or in pairs. Decide whether it is most appropriate for students to interview friends, family members, other members of the community, or a combination of people.

PROCEDURE

1. Introduce the activity by asking students what they found out from the previous day's home learning assignment. Ask, "What kinds of actions do people take that directly affect the environment or wildlife? Which actions, if any, seem harmful? Which seem helpful? Which seem to have no effect? How do you think people feel about the environment and about their actions toward the environment?" Ask students if they can think of ways to find out more about what people think about the environment. If no one mentions a survey, suggest taking one.

2. To introduce students to how a survey works, take a quick survey of the class on a question like "Does your family have a pet?" Discuss with students what kinds of things they found out from this short survey. "Is most of our class from families that have pets? Do you think most of the families from our school have pets? What kinds of questions might we ask to find out more about what it is like to have a pet?"

3. Discuss what students want to find out about their community or about what people think about the environment. You might begin by giving students sample questions from the background information. Discuss the different forms students' questions might take. Decide as a class if the survey will contain yes/no, multiple-choice, or open-ended questions.

4. Divide students into groups of four and have each group brainstorm questions they might ask in their survey. When groups are finished, ask each group to select its two or three favorite questions.

5. Have groups help you write their selected questions on the board. Ask whether there are any questions that are the same and help students eliminate duplicates (be careful that all of the ideas are preserved). As a class, take a look at the questions. Determine if there are too many or too few questions, and whether there is a mix of multiple-choice and open-ended questions. If there are too many questions, students can vote on the questions they want most or you can decide which questions you feel are most appropriate for the survey.

6. After the survey questions have been decided, introduce survey etiquette to students. This means that if people say they don't want to do the survey, don't force them to, and thank them anyway; accept all ideas presented; don't laugh or react in any way (you are trying to find out what people think, so make them feel comfortable about being honest); don't try to change people's minds.

7. Select two students to act out taking a survey, following the survey etiquette rules. You may want to choose students who are self-confident or have strong egos.

8. Make enough copies of the survey questions so that each student (or pair of students) can conduct the number of interviews you have decided will be appropriate. Give students enough time to conduct the surveys.

9. After students have conducted the surveys, help the class graph the responses to yes/no and multiple-choice questions. Help students compile the responses from open-ended questions.

DISCUSSION QUESTIONS

What things did most of the people we surveyed agree on?
What else did we learn?
Was there anything that surprised you?

EVALUATION

Students report what they found out from their survey. Reports can be written or oral.

EXTENSION IDEAS

- Have students conduct the same survey among classmates and compare responses to the responses of the other people surveyed. Ask, "How were the results the same? Different?"
- Have students create posters that address issues from the survey and display the posters throughout the school. Students might conduct the survey again to see how their posters affect the attitudes or understanding of other students. Ask, "Are posters a good way to get information to people? Do posters help change people's attitudes? What other ways are there of getting information to people?"
- Based on the information from the survey, help students decide on an action they can take to improve the environmental quality of their school or neighborhood. Refer to the "Action Project" section of this guide for specific ideas.

Action Projects

Fifth and Sixth Grades

Introduction to Action Projects

Everyone, adult and child alike, has the ability to make positive contributions to the environment. The instructional units in this guide provide students with a fundamental understanding of environmental concepts. Through the following "action projects," students are taken from awareness to action, to see for themselves that they can make a difference.

In action projects students solve a problem or improve a situation. This extends students' learning beyond the four walls of the classroom. Students also begin to see past their own personal needs and desires. They look for ways that their actions can benefit the other inhabitants of their world—people, other animals, and plants.

Because you will need to guide students throughout the project and help them select actions that are realistic, positive, and possible, a successful action project may tax a teacher's initiative and energy. The benefits will be well worth your efforts, however, as you will see students transformed by the knowledge that they can affect the environment.

An action project can be an ongoing, continual process; students investigate a project or problem, take an action, then reflect on their action. The reflection can lead to ideas about future investigations and actions to take. This cycle of investigation → action → reflection → investigation is used in the action projects here.

These action projects are meant to spark your imagination and do not represent the only, or even the best, projects you can undertake. They are merely examples of the kinds of projects you and your students might develop. The most exciting projects may come from students themselves. A simple comment from one student voicing concern about the school environment might lead to a satisfying project that holds personal meaning for the entire class.

The action projects were chosen because they tie in with particular units in this guide (see the following list). The projects are meant to be flexible, though. You can conduct them without having done the corresponding unit, or you can adapt them to meet the specific needs and interests of your class. Each action project is designed for a specific grade level, but most of the projects are appropriate for more than one grade.

Action Project	**Unit**
Planting Container Gardens	Diversity of Life (K–1)
Cleaning Up School Litter	Homes and Habitats (1–2)
Improving Our Parks	The Earth Supports Life (2–3)
Improving the School Playground	Communities and Cultures (3–4)
Cultivating Native Plants	Adaptation and Variation (4–5)
Establishing an Energy Task Force	Energy (5–6)

PLANTING CONTAINER GARDENS

BACKGROUND INFORMATION

In the unit "Diversity of Life," kindergarten and first-grade students are introduced to the idea life has many different forms. Ancient Chinese believed that working in harmony with nature to increase the natural yield helped them find real satisfaction and sense more clearly the meaning of life. Much can be learned from caring for the green things of this world. A container garden can be an ideal way to expand students' understanding of life and life processes.

Container gardens have many advantages over usual garden plots; they are more flexible, take up less space, require fewer tools, are less work, are portable, and are almost instantly rewarding. Also, they can be as large or as small as you desire. They can make a rooftop or parking lot attractive and they can turn a dusty asphalt corner of the playground into a pretty, green garden.

There are several things that you should consider when planning a container gardening project with your students. The location of the garden is most important. Water is a basic requirement so the garden should be situated close enough to a water faucet to be reached by a hose. The garden also should be in a spot that receives a minimum of six hours of sunlight (this is mandatory for most vegetables and many flowers). An advantage to smaller containers is that they can be moved around, if necessary, to take advantage of good sunlight. The garden also should be situated so that it is accessible to students yet is secure. If necessary, small containers and containers with wheels can be moved indoors at night to prevent vandalism or theft.

You should decide whether the containers will be communal or individual. In a communal garden students share the work of cultivating, planting, and harvesting all the containers. A communal garden encourages group participation and cooperation and ensures that every student receives something from the harvest. Individual containers enable students to take responsibility for their own containers. They can be used to compare different varieties of plants or to allow for the special needs of individual students.

Annuals will provide the most dramatic results in your garden; they grow and produce quickly during a single season. Annuals require a constant supply of moisture and nutrients to fuel their work, however. Check with a local nursery or gardening association to find out specific varieties you should consider planting. Most vegetables are annuals; you might try beans, beets, broccoli, carrots, swiss chard, cucumbers, eggplant, kale, lettuce, green onions, parsley, peas, peppers, radishes, cherry tomatoes, or strawberries. Try planting some flower seeds as well—bachelor's buttons, calendula, cosmos, snapdragons, sweet alyssum, and sweet peas are easy to grow from seeds.

INVESTIGATING THE TOPIC

Discuss with students the advantages of container gardens. The class might visit a local vegetable garden center or nursery so that students can see vegetables growing in containers and flats.

Also discuss the needs of a container garden and help students investigate the best place for the containers. Have students check possible sites on different days and at various times to determine where the sun shines most. Help students locate a water faucet.

TAKING ACTION

Students can collect containers from parents, friends, and local merchants. Containers should hold at least three gallons of soil for large or deep-rooted plants like tomatoes, squash, and melons. They should hold one and a half gallons of soil for smaller plants like lettuce, onions, and flowers. Containers should have drainage holes on the bottom, and should be made of a material that won't rot or deteriorate before the plants have matured. Baskets, garbage cans, plastic pails, whiskey barrels, wooden boxes, and clay pots all make good containers.

Students should place small stones in the bottom of the containers for drainage, then fill the containers with soil (use commercial planter mix or a homemade mix of 50 percent organic matter —such as peat moss or compost—and 50 percent sand). Commercial fertilizer should be added. Help students sow seeds directly into containers, following seed package directions. Thin the seedlings as recommended on the package.

Help students develop a system to check periodically whether the plants need water. It is better to water according to plants' day-to-day needs rather than by a set schedule. The soil should never become parched. Infrequent deep watering is better than shallow watering, since it prevents alkali buildup in the soil. During hot, dry weather students may need to water containers almost daily.

REFLECTING ON THE PROJECT

After the plants have matured, cut the flowers and compare the flowers of different plants. Eat and compare the vegetables, too. Let some of the plants go to seed so that students can observe an entire life cycle from seed to seedling to plant to seed. Ask, "What did we have to give the plants for them to grow and produce? What did you like about our garden? What didn't you like?" Have students draw pictures of a seed, a seedling, and a plant. Students can make a class picture book that describes the various steps of their project.

RESOURCES

Bremner, Elizabeth, and John Pusey. *Children's Gardens: A Field Guide for Teachers, Parents and Volunteers.* Berkeley, Calif.: University of California Cooperative Extension Common Ground Garden Program. This guide provides handy tips on working with children in gardens.

Ocone, Lynn. *The Youth Gardening Book.* Burlington, Vt.: Gardens for All, 1983. Information on starting and maintaining conventional and container gardens is included in this book.

Sunset Container Gardening, by the editors of Sunset Books and *Sunset Magazine.* Menlo Park, Calif.: Lane Publishing Co., 1984. Container gardening is described and illustrated in this reference book.

For Students

Oechsli, Helen, and Kelly Oechsli. *In My Garden: A Child's Gardening Book.* New York: Macmillan Publishing Co., 1983. This children's book explains the various steps for cultivating a garden.

CLEANING UP SCHOOL LITTER

BACKGROUND INFORMATION

In the unit "Homes and Habitats," first- and second-grade students are introduced to the idea that every living thing needs a special place to live (a "habitat") and that humans can manipulate their habitat to make it more livable. One way students can improve an important component of their habitat, the schoolgrounds, is through a litter cleanup project. A litter cleanup project has immediately visible results, enables students to see that their actions can benefit others, and teaches students that they can choose actions that improve their environment.

An important element of this project is to encourage the rest of the school to participate in the cleanup effort. Students who spend time improving the schoolgrounds could be discouraged if others in the school do not help keep it clean. Before your class begins the cleanup, you may want to tell the school principal, maintenance staff, and other teachers of the project and gain their support. You might also locate a recycling center in your community that will take any recyclable litter your students find. Find out whether the center gives cash for recyclables and how the center wants the items to be prepared (for example, aluminum cans may need to be crushed or newspapers bundled).

INVESTIGATING THE TOPIC

Take your students for a walk around the school. Have them look for litter on the school property. Ask, "Where does most litter seem to collect? Why do you think it collects there? Does the wind blow the litter to that spot? Are trash cans too far away for people in that area to get to? What kinds of litter do you see? Is any of the litter from off-campus sources?" (Maybe people walk by and throw their litter on the schoolgrounds.) Depending on the answers, students might recommend to the principal that a trash can be placed in the trouble areas or that a sign be put up encouraging people in the neighborhood to help keep the schoolgrounds clean by placing trash in trash cans rather than littering. Each student could draw a picture of the schoolgrounds with litter, then envision what the grounds would look like without the litter and draw a picture of that.

TAKING ACTION

Provide teams of students with large plastic bags to clean up the litter around the schoolgrounds. You might hold a contest to see which team can clean up the most litter, with inexpensive prizes for the winning team. Be sure students understand they cannot take anything out of trash cans.

After picking up the litter, the class might separate recyclable items (cans, bottles, and paper) from non-recyclable items. Explain to students that the recyclable materials can be reused and that there are people in the community who process these materials. Have students sort the recyclable items according to the specifications of the recycling center, then help students take the recyclable items to the center. If the center gives cash for recyclables, help students decide how the money they earned will be spent (unless you recycle many pounds of cans or paper, the earnings probably will be small).

The class may wish to write an announcement or a letter to other classes to inform the rest of the school about the cleanup. Students can make posters to encourage other students not to litter and to pick up any litter that they see.

REFLECTING ON THE PROJECT

After the cleanup, ask students, "How did it feel to do something good for the school? Do you think you changed your behavior? Do you think you changed other students' behavior? Why is it hard to change behavior? Why should we put trash in trash cans? Is there anything else we could do to improve our school?"

RESOURCE

For Students

Luther, Sallie. "Adventures of Ranger Rick," *Ranger Rick*, April 1987, pp. 28–31. This story, suitable for reading aloud, describes the cleanup project of Ranger Rick and his friends.

IMPROVING OUR PARKS

Wildness cannot be programmed or created; it can only be accepted, and perhaps gently encouraged.
—MALCOLM MARGOLIN

BACKGROUND INFORMATION

In the unit "The Earth Supports Life," students are introduced to the notion that all life ultimately relies on the earth. A habitat improvement project undertaken at a local park can help students understand this more deeply. Parks provide habitats for many kinds of wildlife that could not otherwise survive in or near human communities. Some parks, particularly those that are more "natural" or "wild," offer special programs that allow classes to work on a wildlife improvement project. In most cases, a class works in the park for one day under a park employee's supervision. Projects may include clearing brush to improve wildlife habitat, building check dams to reduce stream erosion, building brush piles to provide cover for wildlife, or planting native plants to attract wildlife.

Your first task is to find a naturalist or ranger who is willing and able to work with your class. You and the ranger will probably need to collaborate on a project that is both appropriate for your class and important for the park. It may seem that the park is getting a good deal by having your students do the work; however, it will take the ranger as long to do the project with the help of your students as it would without them. The park is not getting free labor; rather it is providing an educational experience.

Transportation to the park is an important consideration. School buses or parent drivers may be available, though many state and local parks are served by public transit and this may be easier to coordinate. If you decide to use public transportation, plan the route in class and let students see it on a map. Pick out interesting sites you will pass along the way, tell students about them beforehand, then have students look for them during the trip. Discuss the environmental benefits of public transportation; after all, getting to the park can be a lesson in environmentally concerned action itself.

INVESTIGATING THE TOPIC

If possible, arrange to have the class interview the ranger who will be working with you. Have students choose questions they want to ask, help compile them, and send a copy to the ranger in advance. Be sure to find out what animals live in the park. Ask the ranger to explain the project the class will be doing.

Also, you may want to arrange for the class to visit the park before the day of the actual project so that students can explore. Have students prove to themselves that animals really live there. Since most animals are too shy or timid to allow a group of noisy children to get even a glimpse of them, students can search for nests, feathers, spider webs, burrow holes, chewed leaves, tracks in mud or sand, scat, and other evidence of animals. If park rangers permit, students can make plant prints or drawings.

Before you take students to the park for the first time, make sure they understand practical considerations. They should wear sturdy shoes and old clothing. They will need to bring a big lunch and lots to drink, as they will probably get especially hungry and thirsty while outside. Also, address any fears students have. Discuss which fears are reasonable (worrying about poison oak) and which are unfounded (fear of grizzly bears, which have been extinct in the state of California since 1922). This will not do away with all of their worries but it should eliminate many of them.

TAKING ACTION

Help students prepare for the project by discussing what they will be doing and why it is important. Ask, "How will this project help the park? How will it help the animals? The plants? The park visitors? You?" You may want to have students act out or draw what they think will happen in the park.

While the class is working in the park, allow opportunities for students to explore the area. They may make several exciting discoveries about the animals and plants there.

REFLECTING ON THE PROJECT

Discuss the day in the park. Ask, "How did it feel to be in the park? How did it feel to do the work? What did you see? Hear? Smell? How might your work change the park for wildlife, plants, and people?" Have students draw and write about their day in the park. Compile a class book of their artwork and writing. Send letters of thanks to the ranger.

After a month or two have passed, the class might visit the park again to see what the project site looks like. Alternatively, you can invite the ranger to report back to the class.

RESOURCE

Margolin, Malcolm. *The Earth Manual: How To Work On Wild Land Without Taming It.* Berkeley, Calif.: Heyday Books, 1985. Written by a former park ranger, this book provides specific information for improving habitats for wildlife.

IMPROVING THE SCHOOL PLAYGROUND

BACKGROUND INFORMATION

In the unit "Communities and Cultures," students learn how communities meet the needs of inhabitants. A playground is one of the few community places dedicated solely to children, yet often playgrounds do not meet the needs of the people for whom they are intended. It is important for children to have safe play environments that are accessible to all and that offer each child a variety of experiences.

Before tackling a playground project, you should consider the scope of the project you wish to pursue. The class may simply survey the existing school playground and make recommendations to improve its safety, then seek funding from the Parent Teacher Association (P.T.A.) or school board to actually carry out the improvements. Alternatively, the class might suggest additional improvements for the playground such as planting flowers or other plants, painting benches, scrubbing graffiti off walls, or designing a mural for a nearby wall. The class might design a piece of play equipment for the playground, either individually or in groups, using scrap materials like old tires. Or the class might undertake an elaborate project such as designing an entire new play environment. Keep in mind that designing a whole playground can be a huge job; you will probably want to start small by encouraging your students to focus on one element of the playground.

Before students have decided on a specific project, you might investigate and consider possible funding sources for your students' playground improvement project. Possibilities include the local school board, the P.T.A., a local service club, or the police department.

INVESTIGATING THE TOPIC

Students can begin their investigation by mapping the school and playground. Help students use a grid to lay out their maps. The maps can be simple, using symbols to represent various elements (for example, play equipment can be designated by squares, trees by circles, and various ground covers by dots or stripes).

Students might then determine where the playground is safe. Ask students, "Are there any things poking out of play equipment that could trip or cut you? Is there padding underneath the equipment? Is it enough? If there are swings or rings, are the S-hooks by which they hang closed rather than open? Are there any holes or spaces in the equipment between four and seven inches across?" (Heads, limbs, or fingers could get caught in these holes.)

Students might also survey other students to find out what they like about the playground and what needs to be improved. Survey questions might include: "Where is your favorite place to play? How is it similar to the school playgound? How is it different? What do you like about the school playground? What don't you like about it? What would you like to see changed? Are there any places in the school playground where you can play by yourself? Are there places to play with other students? Do you feel safe playing in the playground? Is there anything you think is dangerous about the playground? Do you know the rules for playing on the playground? Do you think the rules are worth obeying?"

TAKING ACTION

After investigating the play area, students brainstorm actions they might take to improve the playground. Encourage students to begin small and help them decide on an action that will be feasible and satisfying.

Have students prepare a report of their findings and of their priority project. This report might be presented to the principal, school board, or P.T.A. for funding. The report should include background information (how students became interested in this project and information about the school and when it was built), method of study (describing the investigations students undertook), what students found out (with a map of the school playground that indicates problem areas), recommendations (listing the priority project and future projects that may be undertaken), and a description of the priority project (noting who should get involved, how much the project will cost, who will do the work, and how the project will benefit the school).

Help students present the report to the principal, school board, or P.T.A. If the person or group is not able to provide funding, ask for suggestions of other possible sources. It is worth pursuing other sources so that students feel the satisfaction of seeing their recommendations carried out and also learn how the community and community projects work. When funding has been granted, help students follow through on the project.

REFLECTING ON THE PROJECT

After the project has been completed, discuss with students what they learned from the experience. Ask, "How did it make you feel to do something for our school? What did you like about the project? What was difficult? What did you learn about how our community works? Would you want to tackle another project to improve the playground further? What could we do next?" Students might conduct a survey to find out how other students feel about the playground after the project.

RESOURCES

It's Your Environment: Things to Think About—Things to Do. Environmental Action Coalition, Inc. New York: Charles Scribner's Sons, 1976. Written for older children, this book suggests ways to improve playgrounds and communities.

Play For All News, published by PLAE, Inc., 1824 Fourth Street, Berkeley, Calif. 94710. This is a quarterly newsletter on children's play environments and programs.

CULTIVATING NATIVE PLANTS

BACKGROUND INFORMATION

In the unit "Adaptation and Variation," students investigate ways adaptations help animals and plants survive. By growing California native plants, students can learn firsthand about adaptation and variation among plants.

During the California drought in 1976 and 1977, many home gardeners appreciated the ability of native plants to survive, even thrive, on only rainwater. California native plants are adapted to the state's climate, which in most areas means little or no rain during summer. Various native plants have also adapted to survive fog, salt spray, desert heat, snow, and particular soil conditions. Shrubs such as coyote bush, which usually grow in hot, dry areas, have small, tough leaves that conserve the plant's moisture. The small leaves expose little surface area to the drying effects of the sun's rays and the tough exterior of the leaves minimizes moisture loss. In contrast, thimbleberry bushes grow along cool, shaded stream banks. Thimbleberry leaves are soft and large to capture filtered sunlight so that photosynthesis can take place.

Annual plants, which include many of California's colorful wildflowers, have adapted to winter rain and summer drought conditions by sprouting and flowering quickly with the winter rains, then going to seed and dying as the dry season begins. The seeds lie dormant through summer and germinate with winter rain.

Each area of California supports its own native plants. The local chapter of the California Native Plant Society or a nursery that sells native plants are good places to find out what grows naturally in your area. For showy color in the spring, plant annuals (many will reseed themselves and come back again the following spring). If you want to establish a more permanent native plant garden, plant perennials (plants that live for more than two years) along with annuals.

Fall is the best time to plant seeds because the ground is still warm from the summer sun (warm soil encourages root growth) and winter rains are not far off. Early winter is the best time to transplant larger plants from containers because the rain should provide enough water (unless it is a dry year). Annual flowers will bloom longer if they get some water after the rains stop in the spring. Perennial plants need extra water for the first summer or two until their root systems are well established.

Weeding is not a glamorous part of the project but is vital for success and provides educational opportunities. Most plants we consider weeds are not natives; they were brought here by early Europeans. Weeds are usually fast growing and can quickly overcome slower-growing native plants. Have students weed thoroughly before planting and continue weeding as needed. If the soil is hard and dry, you may need to soak it first in order to make weeding easier. As seeds begin to sprout, students will need to distinguish the native plant seedlings from weeds. Mount samples of target weeds so that students can compare them with what they pull up. Encourage students to be observant; they are capable of noting minute differences among plants just as plant taxonomists do.

Students will need shovels, spading forks, hoes, and other tools. You may be able to borrow tools from parents, the school maintenance department, or a local garden club. You should also consider whether or not you will need to water the garden. If you do, the garden should be close to a water faucet so that students can water with a hose or watering cans when necessary.

One last note: Native animals are adapted to eat native plants. Deer, birds, and insects may visit the native plant garden to eat leaves or seeds or to gather nectar. Be on the lookout!

INVESTIGATING THE TOPIC

Have students investigate the planting site. They should find out how much sun it gets each day, when it is shady, and if the soil contains a lot of sand or clay. These factors will determine which plants are best suited for your particular site.

Invite someone who is knowledgeable about native plant gardening to meet with your class (you should be able to find someone through the local California Native Plant Society chapter or through a nursery that carries native plants). If there is a suitable site, your guest can take the class on a walk to observe native plants growing in your area. If a walk is not possible, your guest may be able to bring a few potted native plants or present a brief slide show. Students can prepare for the visit by developing a list of questions to ask; as a courtesy, mail a copy of the questions to your guest before his or her presentation.

With the help of your guest, local nurseries, and the resources listed at the end of this project, plan a native plant garden with your students. Have students draw plans for the garden showing what will be planted where. Students can research ways that native plants have been used for food, medicine, and baskets.

TAKING ACTION

As a class, decide what tasks need to be done. Make sure each student has a role to play. Tasks may include weeding, digging, planting, and watering. If you have a camera, take photos of the site before, during, and after students plant the garden. Have students record the progress of the project in writing and drawings.

REFLECTING ON THE PROJECT

As the plants mature and flower in the spring, discuss the project with students. You may want students to do library research to find out more about plants and their adaptations. Have students compare what they learn from books with what they observe in their native plant garden. Students can compare the insects living in or visiting the native garden with insects found at a nearby site (perhaps a lawn or hedge). Ask, "How would you compare our garden area before we planted it with the way it is now? Which plants have grown the most? Why do you think that might be? Have you seen any of these plants in the wild? How do they compare with the ones in our garden? How do you think these plants are adapted to living in this area? In what ways might flower or leaf color be an adaptation? Why do different plants grow in different places? How did the kind and number of insects in our garden compare with those found at the other site? Why are some plants dead?" (Insufficient care, overwatering, and disease are several reasons plants die. Annuals die naturally. Some perennials appear dead when actually they are dormant.)

RESOURCES

Ahart, Emma. "A School Nature Center," *Fremontia*, Vol. 14, No. 4 (January 1987), pp. 14–15. One school's native plant garden, which was planted to represent seven of California's major plant communities, is described (*Fremontia* is the California Native Plant Society's journal).

Balls, Edward K. *Early Uses of California Plants.* Berkeley, Calif.: University of California Press, 1970. This book, which includes line drawings and color plates, tells how native plants are grown for food and used to make baskets, medicine, and fish poison.

Danielsen, Charlice W. "Sources of Native Plants: Nurseries, Seeds and Sales," *Fremontia*, Vol. 10, No. 3 (October 1982), pp. 25–28. This list of native plant nurseries and other sources of native plants is available by writing to the California Native Plant Society, 909 12th Street, Sacramento, Calif. 95814.

Fruge, Susan; revised by Tim Gaskin. "A Reader's Guide to Gardening With Natives," *Fremontia*, Vol. 13, No. 1 (April 1985), pp. 25–28. Fruge has compiled an extensive reading list of books aimed at the home gardener, as well as books about the plants of a particular area that are available from the California Native Plant Society, 909 12th Street, Sacramento, Calif. 95814.

Schmidt, Marjorie G. *Growing California Native Plants.* Berkeley, Calif.: University of California Press, 1980. This book provides detailed information about growing conditions needed for a wide selection of native plants.

Sunset New Western Garden Book. By the editors of Sunset Books and *Sunset Magazine.* Menlo Park, Calif.: Lane Publishing Co., 1979. Much useful information about native plants can be found in this large reference source.

ESTABLISHING AN ENERGY TASK FORCE

BACKGROUND INFORMATION

In the unit "Energy," fifth- and sixth-grade students are introduced to common energy sources and concepts. Establishing an energy task force at school can engage students in a real-life conservation effort. The energy task force can help students translate their knowledge and awareness of energy into meaningful actions.

A school-wide energy task force is made up of a group of students and an adult advisor (usually a teacher or principal). The task force's goal is to encourage energy conservation throughout the school. One especially successful program, at DeVargas Elementary School in San Jose, averaged savings of $1,000 a month for eight months during the 1981–1982 school year—a total savings of $8,000 on the school's energy bill.

In addition to saving money, conserving energy helps reduce the strain on the environment. The more energy we conserve, the fewer additional power plants we need. Power plants cause many environmental problems; hydroelectric plants, for instance, drown rivers and surrounding countryside; power plants that burn coal, oil, or gas produce air pollution; and nuclear power plants create radioactive wastes (which present serious disposal problems) and the threat of a nuclear accident.

Energy conservation methods at school are similar to those at home, but on a grander scale. They include turning off lights when no one is in the room, keeping doors and windows closed when heating or air conditioning is in use, and setting thermostats at a moderate temperature. Energy task force students can quickly check each room on campus during recess, lunch, and after school to make sure that lights and other energy-using equipment have not been left on unnecessarily. If energy is being wasted, the task force member can leave a reminder notice for the forgetful parties. Monthly energy-saver awards can be given to classes and staff members who routinely and conscientiously act to conserve energy.

Enthusiastic support of the entire school is vital for significant energy savings. Enlist the backing of the principal and the other teachers. Encourage student awareness of the program. Get the word out about why it is important to save energy and how students can help. You may wish to hold an energy assembly, display energy conservation posters, contribute energy messages to the school bulletin, or plan an energy week when each class will learn something about energy. Energy task force members also can make colorful notices to post next to each light switch in the school to remind everyone to turn off the lights.

INVESTIGATING THE TOPIC

Have students investigate the school's current energy use. Obtain copies of recent utility bills from the principal. Take students on an energy tour of the school and have them record ways that energy is used and how they see energy being wasted. Have students develop a list of ways that students, teachers, and staff can conserve energy. You may want to invite a guest from a local utility or conservation group to visit your class or a school assembly and discuss why and how to conserve energy.

TAKING ACTION

Have students decide how they want to publicize the energy task force's conservation program. Students can design posters and logos, participate in an assembly to introduce the program, write announcements for a school bulletin or newsletter, or make presentations in other classrooms.

Choose responsible, interested students for the energy task force (you may want to choose some task force members from other classes to encourage widespread participation). Recruit enough students so that they can check their assigned rooms in five to ten minutes. Task force members or other students can design and color reminder notices that can be posted next to each light switch. A separate notice can be made to let people know that they have forgotten to turn out the lights.

Help task force members devise a schedule for monitoring school energy waste. You may want to have a different group of students monitor each day of the week so that a large number of students are involved. Design a checklist for task force members to use on their rounds; include a method for students to record for each room or area whether or not energy is being wasted. The De-

Vargas Elementary School's Energy Patrol pamphlet includes the checklist students there used.

Hold a school-wide assembly to introduce the energy task force program. Display student energy conservation posters. Post energy-saving reminders. Bestow monthly awards to classes and staff members who have consistently saved energy. With task force members, monitor the school monthly utility bill; compare energy usage to what was used during the same month in the previous year (remember that energy usage is influenced by the weather; warmer or cooler weather than last year will affect how much energy is used for heating and cooling). Report savings to the whole school so that everyone can share in a successful effort.

REFLECTING ON THE PROJECT

With students, consider the outcome of the school's efforts to save energy. Ask, "What things seemed to help most to conserve energy? What things seemed to be the least successful? What do you think we should do differently next year? Which of the energy-saving techniques we have used at school might work at home, too? Why is it important to conserve energy?"

RESOURCES

DeVargas Elementary School's Energy Patrol, Cupertino Union School District. This packet of information tells how DeVargas established and maintained an energy patrol. A list of procedures, agreement form, patrol checklist, and light switch reminders are included. The packet is available from the California Energy Extension Service/California Energy Network, 1400 Tenth Street, Sacramento, Calif. 95814, (916) 323-4388.

Project NEED (National Energy Education Day). Each ye - this project puts together a packet of activities and information for classroom teacl ers. Some of the suggestions may help increa e awareness of energy issues and conservation in your school. The California Energy Extension Service/California Energy Network also provides this packet.

Help for the Beginning Teacher

This chapter provides opportunities for teachers to reflect upon their teaching in order to grow and improve professionally. Too often teachers are taught to behave like technicians who merely carry out instructions or operations designed by others, whereas teaching should be a creative endeavor blending a variety of techniques with a sense of self-expression that allows teachers to continually refine their craft.

The format of this chapter is one of self-study, in which information is presented, then followed by suggested exercises. Units in this guide exemplify specific educational issues and the teacher is asked to examine a unit or activity with a specific educational issue in mind.

Although aimed at the beginning teacher, this chapter addresses issues that are important to *all* teachers. Oftentimes beginning teachers are more open to reflecting upon their teaching than experienced teachers. Every teacher should take time to think about his or her profession, however, in order to become more confident and competent. These exercises help do that.

Evolving as a Teacher

Many ways of teaching as well as some of the content of this guide fall outside the boundaries of what is considered traditional classroom instruction. Environmental education has never been part of the core curriculum, nor has an integrated curriculum or a non-textbook approach been common in most classrooms. This is changing some as the current reform movement recognizes the value of non-traditional methods and content, but it may be relatively new to you, to your students and their parents, to the principal, and to your colleagues.

As you try out an activity or a unit with your class, keep in mind that it is okay to teach differently than those around you. There are many legitimate ways to teach, just as there are many legitimate ways to learn. The art of teaching is mastered over a lifetime as each teacher experiments and reflects upon the results. Unfortunately, some teachers have developed a method of teaching that leaves little room for experimentation or reflection. As you explore different ways to teach, these teachers may be threatened or discouraged. Persevere anyway. Allow yourself to try new ideas and make mistakes. Change, be it personal or professional, takes time and requires some mistakes to be made.

Approach change in your teaching slowly. Focus on one aspect at a time; for example, if you have taught science sporadically and approached it by having students read and discuss a topic from the science textbook, do not try to teach a unit in this guide, simultaneously introduce cooperative learning to your students, and try to assess students' learning styles. Instead, choose an activity you will be comfortable doing that makes sense conceptually for students to learn at this time. Modify and simplify the lesson to fit your situation, then try it out. Afterwards, reflect upon the lesson, either with your students or by yourself, by identifying the positive and negative aspects. Based on your assessment, choose or design a follow-up lesson. Continue building your repertoire of non-textbook learning activities until you are comfortable teaching and your students are comfortable learning this way. Only then should you consider another focal point, such as cooperative learning or learning styles.

If you are fortunate enough to know another teacher at your school who is interested in classroom innovation also, make an effort to provide mutual support. You may be able to do some planning together, team-teach certain subjects, and reflect together upon your teaching. A mutually supportive relationship can alleviate feelings of isolation and boost the morale of teachers who do not have full support from school officials or colleagues.

Teaching can be a creative, flexible, growth-producing, and challenging profession if you are able to develop the mental attitude and support system to make it so for you. This is more easily said than done; however, trust your intuition as well as your knowledge as you think about and experiment with the lifelong process of becoming a "good teacher."

Self-Study Exercise

Imagine that someone "shadowed" you for an entire day. The person watched you plan, teach, and interact with students and staff. If that person then described what he or she observed to someone else, what would you hope he or she would say?

Unit Teaching

This guide takes a unit approach to providing students with a fundamental understanding of environmental concepts. A unit, as defined here, is a series of classroom experiences designed around a specific theme or topic. These experiences address one or more concepts in a sequential fashion so that students are exposed to increasingly complex ideas.

There are many advantages to teaching concepts through a unit approach. A unit provides a framework or cohesive plan that enables students to learn first simple, then more complex concepts. A unit is broad enough and flexible enough to allow for learning at a variety of levels. A unit approach increases teacher effectiveness because a teacher is best able to facilitate learning in a focused, goal-oriented direction if he or she has a sequential plan. A unit approach also aids in classroom discipline; students recognize when a teacher has a plan and tend to stay focused if they have a clear sense of what will be learned.

In addition, unit teaching increases a teacher's ability to use student-generated ideas. When the teacher has a clear sense where a lesson is headed, he or she is better able to recognize and incorporate related student ideas. Unit teaching also allows the teacher to teach subjects in an integrated fashion, addressing unit themes from many perspectives. This gives students a clear sense of the relationship among subjects and is more like the real world than compartmentalized teaching of various subjects. It saves precious instructional time too, allowing the teacher to address more than one subject within a single lesson.

Another advantage is that unit instruction is easy to evaluate. Because it is based on specific concepts and a clearly delineated plan, instructional objectives and methods for assessing student understanding are easy to identify.

A final benefit is that a unit is usable year after year. Once it is designed and the materials are gathered, the teacher can modify and refine the unit to make it even better. This is where the fun of teaching comes in!

Self-Study Exercise

Any unit should be modified to meet the particular needs of a class. Choose a unit from the guide that interests you and note whether the sequence of activities makes sense for you and your students. Think about how you might modify the unit to take into account differences between your students and students for whom the unit is intended. Within one activity, how might you address these differences? Is your role defined throughout the unit? Make a statement regarding the role you wish to play while teaching this unit. Examine the activities and predict what will confuse or distract students.

Suggest modifications to the unit based on students' interests. Think of ways to integrate other subjects into the unit. Develop a method to evaluate student success at learning a particular concept. Finally, plan ahead. How will you organize and store this unit so it can be used next year?

Components of Planning a Unit

Many factors need to be considered when planning a unit. The following steps help guide a teacher through the process of unit planning.

1. *Choose a topic or theme.* Review the various state frameworks, state curriculum guides, district continuums, and quality review criteria to choose appropriate subject matter themes and concepts for your grade level.

2. *Identify your goals*. Goals are broad, general expressions of the purposes, aims, or results you desire when teaching students about a particular topic and the concomitant concepts. Determine beforehand your goals in presenting the unit.

3. *Narrow the theme*. Examine the concepts and select those that seem most essential and appropriate for your students. Based on these concepts, try to define what theme or topic you will teach.

4. *Identify your instructional objectives*. These objectives should state explicitly the concepts, skills, and attitudes that students will be taught. The objectives can be useful afterwards for evaluating what students learned.

5. *Check your idea*. Before you plan your daily lessons, take a few minutes to reassess your direction. Ask yourself: Do the topic and concepts have instructional significance? Are they relevant to my students' lives? Are they feasible given the constraints of my time, talents, skills, and available materials?

6. *Gather background information*. Read books on the subject, take a related class, and talk with experts who know a great deal about the topic. It is a good idea to keep a running vocabulary list and bibliography and to begin a working content outline for the unit as you gather background information.

7. *Search, select, and create activities*. Keeping your concepts firmly in mind, begin looking at curriculum guides, texts, computer programs, films, and other materials related to your topic. Start developing classroom activities that explicitly address the concepts in a sequential manner. As your ideas fall into place, look for ways to make transitions from one activity to another so that learning builds upon itself. Good teachers operate in much the same way as good cooks; they have a clear idea of what they want to create and they draw from a variety of the best ingredients in order to make their idea a reality.

8. *Think about logistics*. What materials and equipment are needed? What advance planning, preparation, and instructional time are required? How will students be grouped and how will the classroom be arranged? Will any individual students have special needs? Are resource people or parent volunteers necessary?

9. *Identify what needs to be evaluated*. Determine the concepts, skills, and attitudes you hope to impart. How will you assess whether students have acquired them?

10. *Write a final schedule of the unit*. Scripting the sequence of classroom experiences is a good way to develop a strong introduction and conclusion and smooth transitions between activities. Also think through discussion questions and home learning assignments.

Self-Study Exercise

Choose an activity in any unit in this guide. Examine it with the preceding components of planning a unit in mind. Think how the activity fits with the theme of the unit. Review the objective, the background information, and the evaluation section. Notice how logistics are addressed and how the home learning suggestion fits with the activity and the unit as a whole.

Learning Styles

Traditional theories about learning treat intelligence as a single quality that individuals possess in varying degrees. Within the last 20 years, however, researchers in the fields of psychology, neurophysiology, and education have found evidence that there are different kinds of intelligence and that individuals do not possess the same amount of each kind.

There are many theoretical models that attempt to identify different kinds of intelligence. The models presented in this guide are those of Howard Gardner, as described in his book *Frames of Mind*, and the 4MAT model, developed by Bernice McCarthy and Bob Samples. These models identify a set of similar (although not identical) intelligences. The 4MAT model will be summarized here as it has been translated to an operational level of classroom instruction in science. The 4MAT model identifies five categories of learning modalities or ways that the brain prefers to operate on new information. These categories are symbolic or abstract, visual, auditory, kinesthetic, and synergetic.

Symbolic or abstract modalities are when the brain uses abstract codes like letters, numbers, or

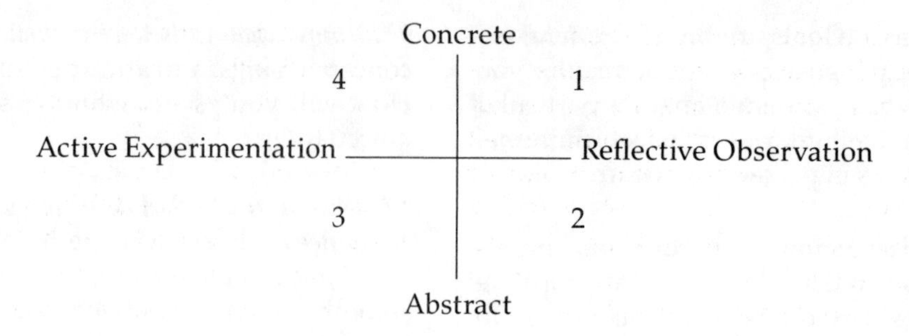

The 4MAT learning style system.

symbols (these modalities can be further distinguished into two subsets—linguistic and mathematical). Visual modalities are in operation when the brain uses visually dominated expression such as art, mapping, or guided imagery. Patterned sound, such as speech, song, and music, is the product of auditory modalities. Kinesthetic modalities are when the brain relies on movement, including dance, as a way of understanding. Synergetic modalities combine other modalities and result in an empathic relatedness among self, other people, and natural systems.

These learning modalities describe the different regions of the brain that are activated by different kinds of input from the environment. The way in which we operate on input from the environment is content-dependent, meaning that our brains "choose" to activate a given modality depending on the kind of input it receives.

The modalities of the brain perceive different input and process input differently. Similarly, the individual has preferential ways of acting upon that input. The sum total of the brain's way of processing input plus the individual's preferential way of acting upon that input is known as a learning style.

The 4MAT learning style system identifies four learning styles that fall into quadrants formed by two axes. One axis ranges from concrete to abstract, the other from active to reflective. Each quadrant represents a combination of learning preferences characterized by the position of the quadrant along the two axes.

Quadrant 1 learners prefer to learn through personal experience. They need to be personally involved and have opportunities to express their opinions and beliefs. They learn through a combination of sensing, feeling, and watching.

Quadrant 2 learners want new and accurate information. They prefer to deal with facts, theories, and models and they strive for accuracy.

Quadrant 3 learners like to find out how things work and how ideas apply in the real world. They are skills oriented and value strategic thinking.

Quadrant 4 learners prefer to make connections between ideas; they look for ways to integrate experience and application. These learners are synthesizers; they strive continually to reach a higher level of understanding.

Self-Study Exercise

Based on this synopsis of learning modalities and styles, comment on your own learning style. What are your preferences, areas of strength, and most comfortable method of learning?

Classroom Management Considerations

When planning for an instructional activity, management issues need to be considered carefully to ensure the activity's success. Following are some management considerations that are particularly important for activities in this guide.

Whole-group instruction is best for presenting information that all students need, for facilitating a discussion in which students are exposed to a variety of ideas and perspectives, for gathering data from which generalizations and inferences will be drawn (more data will be collected if more people participate), and for conducting a lesson that requires adult direction when only one adult is available. Whole-group instruction does not mean differences in students' academic levels are ignored. On the contrary, these considerations must be part of the planning of any lesson, whole-group or otherwise. Ask yourself: Is this the optimum format for the instructional goals I wish to accomplish? Where will students be as they participate in this whole-group lesson? At their desks? Seated in a circle on the floor? Where do I need to be so that all students can see and hear me and I can monitor them? Do any students need special places during this lesson? How will I distribute and collect materials as quickly and efficiently as possible? If the lesson involves presenting information, how can I be sure students received and understood the information? How can I ensure that each student has an opportunity to participate and that students listen to and honor each other's ideas? If the lesson involves gathering data, how can this be done quickly, accurately, and in a format that lends itself to easy reference for discussion purposes? If the lesson involves individual work, what is my policy for those who don't finish their work in the alloted time? What is there to do for students who finish ahead of time? How will I check an individual student's progress and provide feedback as students work? What is the most efficient way to gather students' completed work?

Small-group instruction is the best way to focus instruction so that it meets the needs of a few students and to ensure greater student participation. It allows you to vary the content of what you teach, the level of difficulty, the learning styles addressed, and the teaching strategies employed. It is useful also in situations that require close monitoring by an adult, such as when live animals are handled by students or special tools are used.

Students in small-group instruction may participate in the same activity simultaneously or in different activities. In either case, each group should be considered equal in importance as you plan, organize, and teach them.

When you have decided what learning activity each group will do and who best fits into each group (students may be grouped randomly, by ability or knowledge of a particular skill or concept, or according to social or emotional needs), ask yourself: Do I need other adults to facilitate or monitor groups? What materials are needed for each activity? What is the optimum way of making these materials available? What should I consider to ensure that groups work without disturbing each other? How can I best arrange the room to allow for optimum learning for each group? Will each group finish its lesson at approximately the same time? How can I ensure that all students have something worthwhile to do if they finish their work early? What will be my role during small-group instruction? If I will be teaching one of the groups, how can I minimize interruptions by students from other groups? How can I monitor other groups while instructing one group?

Centers, stations, and *menus* allow one student or a small group of students to participate in a variety of activities simultaneously. They may be temporary or permanent and can be used to teach, reinforce, or enrich a concept or skill. The activities and materials at a particular center or station or within a menu should be geared to the abilities of students but range from simple to difficult and from concrete to abstract. In this way they allow for more flexible instruction than whole-group instruction. They also make it possible for the teacher to move from station to station, interacting with individuals or small groups, thus monitoring students' work.

Once you have determined that a center, station, or menu approach is optimal to achieve your instructional goals and have designed the centers, stations, or menu, ask yourself: Where should each work area be situated in order to allow students to work without distraction, to move among work areas without disturbing others, to have access to directions and materials, and to have plenty of room in which to work? What is the clearest way to label and provide directions at each station? What is the maximum number of students that can work at a given station and how will I indicate this? What is the optimum setup that enables me to work with individuals or small groups yet still monitor the whole class? What record-keeping methods will I use to monitor students' progress and assess their learning? How much time will students have to complete an entire set of stations or an entire menu? What provisions will I make for students who are absent? How will materials be obtained, cared for, replenished, and stored at each work area? Where will ongoing or finished products be stored?

You should introduce all centers, stations, and menus to the whole class. Establish rules and procedures for participating at each work area before work begins. If the work is to be completed over several days, reiterate the rules and procedures before students visit the work areas each day.

It is also important that you discuss with students what was learned at a particular work area, as well as any needed changes required to improve the functioning of the station. This can be done at the end of each work session as well as at the conclusion of the set of stations, centers, or the menu.

Out-of-class activities are ways to use environments other than the classroom for learning. They require special considerations on the part of the teacher. When students leave the classroom they should understand what is expected of them in terms of behavior and participation in the learning activity (some students assume that previously established rules remain behind in the classroom). Ask yourself, Do I need other adults along to help monitor this activity? What materials does each student need to take along? What materials are needed for the group? How will these materials get to and from the classroom? What part of the learning activity (if any) should be done before leaving the classroom? What procedures will I establish to line up students to and from the classroom? What student behavior standards will I require while enroute? What safety issues should be considered enroute and in the out-of-class area? What boundaries will be established for the activity? How will students know and remember the boundaries? Upon arrival at the out-of-class site, what rules should students know? How will I monitor students as they participate in the activity? How will I signal students to get their attention? How can I ensure that the site is left clean and undisturbed? When we return to the classroom, what must be done to wrap up the lesson, put away materials, and move on to the next activity?

Shared materials usually require a few rules to ensure that they are used and stored properly. Ask yourself, What responsibilities do I want students to have in taking care of these materials? How can I make sure that all students have an opportunity to handle the materials and avoid discipline problems that arise when students have to wait too long for their turn? Does this particular set of materials pose any safety considerations? What rules are necessary to ensure that materials are used for the purpose I have in mind?* How can I facilitate cleaning up and putting away materials in an orderly manner? You may want to have several cardboard boxes, dishpans, or tote trays on hand to collect materials quickly. Also, you may want to assign one or more helpers the responsibility of distributing shared materials and returning them to their proper place.

Pets and *plants* can add a lot to the atmosphere of a classroom and provide valuable opportunities for learning. You may want to introduce them gradually rather than on the first day of school, after students have settled into classroom routines. Keep pets and plants where they will not distract students or take up needed workspace. Make sure lighting and heating are conducive to animals' and plants' good health.

Noise level should be considered, especially when students work in small groups or at stations. Keep in mind that noise is not always bad; sometimes noise is the result of an exciting and thought-provoking activity. Ask yourself: Is noise getting in the way of learning? If the answer is no, the issue may be a problem for the teacher rather than students. Most teachers want others (principals, parents, and other teachers) to believe that the teacher has control in his or her classroom. It may take a combination of personal reflection and public relations to dispell the notion that noise indicates a lack of control.

Noise can be disruptive, though. When it is, students need to know to quiet down. Don't wait until the noise has reached unacceptable levels; spell out and model the kinds and levels of noise that are acceptable. Establish one or more non-verbal signals that let students know they are being too noisy. A flick of the lights, a clapping pattern, or a pleasant-sounding bell are good signals (it is self-defeating to try to yell louder than the noise). A highly visible color chart is useful as well. Post red if no noise is allowed, yellow if soft voices only are allowed, and green if normal speaking voices are allowed. Train students and yourself to speak softly or to use "inside voices" to keep down the noise level. If noise continues to be a problem, gather more information by listing all distracting and interfering noises during a day. Decide which noises must be eliminated or decreased and which are acceptable. Go over the list with the class and continually monitor the noise until it has reached an acceptable level.

* You will notice that the activities in this guide usually include an exploratory phase with new materials. This phase is important for learning and as a way to avoid discipline problems. Students need opportunities to explore materials at their own pace and with as little direction as possible. They will then be ready to use the materials in a more structured manner.

Self-Study Exercise

Choose one of the classroom management subtopics like whole-class or small-class instruction, using centers and stations, out-of-class activities, shared materials, pets and plants, or noise level. Make a list of written procedures for addressing this subtopic in your classroom (you might focus on the "ask yourself" questions).

California State Resource Agencies

The California State Resources Agency is responsible for formulating programs and policies governing the acquisition, development, and use of California's natural resources. Organizations within the agency can provide information about our natural resources; some also provide special materials for teachers and students.

The following California State Resources Agency organizations requested to be included in this guide. For a complete list of organizations, contact the Resources Agency at 1416 9th Street, Sacramento, Calif. 95814.

California Coastal Commission
631 Howard Street, Fourth Floor
San Francisco, Calif. 94105-3973
(415) 543-8555

The California Coastal Commission enforces the 1976 Coastal Act, which balances conservation and development along the California coast. The act addresses issues such as public access to the coast, the California marine environment, coastal land resources, and coastal development, including industrial development. The desired balance is accomplished through the Commission's permit process and through the implementation of Local Coastal Plans in which each of California's 67 coastal cities and counties prepare land use plans and zoning ordinances designed to comply with the Coastal Act.

In addition to approving Local Coastal Plans and reviewing coastal development permits, the Commission reviews federal activities (such as plans to explore and extract oil and gas from the Outer Continental Shelf) to make sure they comply with California's federally approved Coastal Zone Management Program. The Coastal Commission also reviews long-range development plans and informs the State Energy Commission of all coastal areas where power plants cannot be built.

California Conservation Corps
1530 Capitol Avenue
Sacramento, Calif. 95814
(916) 445-0307

Conservation Awareness Program
P.O. Box 1380
San Luis Obispo, Calif. 93406
(805) 543-0437

The California Conservation Corps (CCC) is a work ethic program in which young adults work on projects that conserve and enhance California's natural resources. To instill in participants an appreciation and understanding of the natural environment, the CCC has developed a Conservation Awareness Program (CAP) that includes both work-related activities conducted at project sites and after-hours classroom instruction.

California Energy Commission
c/o Public Information Office
1516 Ninth Street, MS 29
Sacramento, Calif. 95814
(916) 324-3298

Among the Energy Commission's major responsibilities are promoting development of alternative energy resources, encouraging energy conservation, assessing California's future energy supply and demand, and establishing sites for power plants of over 50 megawatts. Potential energy sources that the Energy Commission helps to develop include geothermal electric and geothermal direct heat, biomass energy systems, cogeneration, wind power, photovoltaics, clean synthetic fuels, and small hydroelectric generation.

In order to encourage conservation, the Energy Commission establishes energy efficiency standards for new buildings and appliances, provides free home energy audits, and makes grants and loans available to governments, schools, and hospitals. The Energy Commission's efforts to encourage conservation are concentrated in those sectors with the highest levels of energy use and the largest potential for cost-effective conservation.

California Energy Extension Services
1400 Tenth Street
Sacramento, Calif. 95814
(916) 323-4388

The mandate of the California Energy Extension Service (CEES) is to encourage small-scale energy consumers to adopt techniques that save energy, to use energy more effectively, and to take advantage of renewable energy resources. The CEES works toward these goals by funding activities at the local level that offer direct, personalized services.

The CEES urges schools to adopt comprehensive energy education and energy management programs and has organized the California Energy Network to work with teachers and encourage student leadership in this area. The following materials are available from CEES:

Animated Bibliography. This sampler lists computer software in energy education and includes ordering information.

Energy Activities for Primary Classroom. Energy activities pertaining to renewable energy resources are described in this book by the primary grade teacher who developed them.

Energy Sticker Contest. This pamphlet provides how-to instructions for conducting a sticker or poster contest.

Energy Tech Knowledgy. The energy lesson plans and software guide in this book are divided by grade level and address basic skills in language arts, math, social studies, and science.

How to Motivate Staff and Students to Save Energy. Techniques and methods for involving students in school-wide energy management programs are provided in this guide.

How to Organize and Communicate Your Energy Data. This pamphlet provides an introduction to strategies for organizing school energy data and includes math worksheets.

National Energy Education Day Packet. National Energy Education Day (NEED) resources such as activities, skits, issues of the magazine *Energy Exchange*, and an energy education poll are in this kit.

"Power Lines Game." Developed by the Irvine Unified School District, this computer software game for teams of fourth- through sixth-grade students incorporates activities relating to renewable energy resources, electricity, natural gas, and water.

State Lands Commission
1807 Thirteenth Street
Sacramento, Calif. 95814
(916) 322-4105

The State Lands Commission manages the four million acres of land that are held in trust for the citizens of California. In addition, the Commission manages marshland surrounding bays, lakes, and inland waterways, as well as the 600,000 acres of school lands which were granted to California by the federal government to support public education.

The State Lands Commission's goal is to balance prudent development of land with protecting the resources for future use. The State Lands Commission leases land to raise tax revenue for the state and lessen local tax burdens. It also issues permits for marinas, oil and gas extraction, exploration and development of geothermal resources, industrial wharves, tanker anchorages, timber harvest, dredging, grazing, and mining, thus providing current and future environmental needs.

Department of Conservation
1416 Ninth Street, Room 1320
Sacramento, Calif. 95814
(916) 322-7683

The Department of Conservation is responsible for planning and managing the use of land, minerals, and energy resources now and for the future. The department collects information about the surface and undersurface areas of California's landscape, including the location of mineral and energy resources, earthquake faults, landslides, and coastal erosion. It also encourages the development of the state's oil, gas, and geothermal resources in ways that are consistent with other environmental concerns. In addition, the department monitors agricultural lands, including land threatened by urban development.

The Department of Conservation advises local, state, and federal agencies on environmental impact assessments, mineral resources development, outer continental shelf development, and the reclamation of mined lands. This helps these agencies plan for the use of resources under their jurisdiction. The following materials are available from the department:

Introduction to the Energy Resources of California. This primer on non-renewable energy resources includes a geological description of petroleum deposits and of the oil production process from drilling to refining.

Oil and Gas in California. This pamphlet, suitable for fourth- through sixth-grade students as well as teachers, illustrates in pictures and words how oil and gas in California are formed, refined, and distributed.

Department of Fish and Game
1416 Ninth Street, Twelfth Floor
Sacramento, Calif. 95814
(916) 323-1239

The Department of Fish and Game ensures that fish and wildlife are preserved so that California residents can enjoy them now and in the future. Wildlife refers to all species that are not domesticated and includes freshwater and marine aquatic animals. The department manages all wildlife resources within California, including coastal marine areas.

Most forms of wildlife require a specific type of habitat to survive. A major responsibility of the department is to identify these habitats and to work to preserve areas in which wildlife species can survive in sufficient numbers. The department provides the following materials:

Marine Mammals of California. This booklet illustrates and describes 34 of the marine mammals seen or identified near California; whaling, whale conservation, and the Marine Mammal Protection Act also are explained.

Project Wild. These two interdisciplinary, wildlife-related environmental education activity guides for kindergarten through sixth grade and sixth through twelfth grades include 80 activities each and are distributed without charge in workshops sponsored by the department.

"Species Booklets." This series of booklets for fourth- through twelfth-grade students describes in pictures and words the habitats and natural history of many California species.

Wildlife—The Environmental Barometer. The importance of a healthy environment for wildlife and the harmful changes caused by humans which may affect all species, including our own, are detailed in this pamphlet for fourth- through twelfth-grade students.

Wildlife Leaflets. Each of these one-page leaflets for fourth- through twelfth-grade students deals with a single species of wildlife; almost all familiar vertebrates are described.

Department of Forestry
P.O. Box 944246
Sacramento, Calif. 94244
Resource Management: (916) 322-0109
Fire Protection and Fire Control: (916) 445-7228

Included in the Department of Forestry are the Resource Management section and the Department of Fire Protection and Fire Control. The Resource Management section enforces timber harvesting regulations on non-federal land, provides financial and technical assistance for reforestation and forest improvement programs, and offers advice on pest control and urban and rural tree diseases. It also conducts research on using wood fuel and improving milling and harvesting techniques. In addition, it supports three state nurseries which protect and improve the tree seed gene pool.

The Fire Protection and Fire Control department plans and coordinates fire-fighting in areas where the state is responsible. It also administers the "Smokey the Bear" informational program.

The Department of Forestry distributes the following materials:

"Doo-bee" Coloring Book. This coloring book, geared for kindergarten through third-grade students, describes the role of trees in urban areas.

"Smokey the Bear" Materials. Many pamphlets and films are available in which Smokey the Bear describes the need for fire prevention.

The Tree. The role of trees in city environments, the cycle of tree growth, and nature's creation of a micro-climate for an urban tree are presented through the eyes of a child resting under a city tree in this film for fifth- and sixth-grade students.

Department of Parks and Recreation
P.O. Box 942896
Sacramento, Calif. 94296
Publications Section: (916) 322-7000
Office of Interpretive Services: (916) 445-9672

The California Department of Parks and Recreation manages nearly 300 parks, beaches, wilderness areas, natural preserves, historic sites, and recreational areas throughout the state. Its purpose is to provide places where people can discover, understand, and appreciate the interrelationships and interdependencies between themselves and their environment.

The department sponsors environmental living programs at several sites where classes can stay overnight and relive the life of a historic period. Some parks have shorter, daytime programs of a similar nature. Many camping parks offer Junior Ranger programs to educate children in environmental awareness. In addition, visitor centers and museums throughout the parks system offer exhibits, publications, and hands-on activities. The following materials are available from the department:

California Historical Landmarks. The 951 registered historical landmarks of California are presented on a county-by-county basis and are cross-indexed in this guide.

Guide to California State Parks. This large map shows the location of California's state parks and the accompanying index indicates what facilities are available in each park.

"Keep California Golden." Quails and California poppies, the state bird and the state flower, are the subjects of this poster.

Department of Water Resources
Office of Water Conservation
1416 Ninth Street, Room 440
P.O. Box 942836
Sacramento, Calif. 94236

The Department of Water Resources coordinates the management and development of California's water resources. The department's major programs store and deliver water to agricultural and urban areas, protect the public's safety by maintaining flood warning and flood control operations, and prevent waste and unreasonable use of water through conservation techniques. The department also works to use existing resources more efficiently through such methods as waste water reclamation. The following materials are available from the department:

Captain Hydro. In this workbook, which features activities and coloring pages for fifth- through eighth-grade students and is available in Spanish, the water conservation hero Captain Hydro shows the many ways water is wasted daily and steps all of us can take to help save water.

Hands-On Water Activities. This booklet for kindergarten through sixth-grade students, as well as teachers, has simple demonstration experiments and open-ended questions which illustrate properties and facets of water (it is referenced in the *Science Framework Addendum*).

Water Is Your Best Friend. This packet includes a teachers' guide and coloring books for kindergarten through third-grade students; the guide features activities that demonstrate how water is collected, shared, and saved (supplemental flannel board stories are also available).

Water Play. The teachers' guide has activities that promote awareness of water's life-sustaining role and of the need to conserve this limited resource; the accompanying cartoon-style workbook is geared for kindergarten through third-grade students.

Resident Outdoor Schools

Each year 150,000 elementary students in California, usually sixth graders, attend one of 26 resident outdoor schools conducted by school districts or county offices of education. Many students report in later years that the one-week outdoor school program was the most significant experience of their elementary school years. These programs offer two important benefits to students. First, students have an opportunity to gain knowledge of environmental phenomena through an extended experience in a relatively natural environment. Second, students are able to interact socially with other students of varying backgrounds, thereby gaining valuable social skills.

Resident outdoor schools also provide a valuable experience for teachers who attend with their class. Teachers benefit from working with and gaining skills from the professional outdoor school staff. In addition, teachers have an opportunity to gain a better understanding of their students as they observe them in a variety of learning and social situations over an extended period of time.

There are nearly 30 resident outdoor programs currently operated by California public agencies, as well as several privately operated programs. An annotated directory of public and private resident outdoor schools is available from the Orange County Office of Education, P.O. Box 9050, Costa Mesa, Calif. 92626.

Model Outdoor School Curriculum

In terms of academic achievement, resident outdoor school programs relate all of the commonly taught school subjects to a knowledge of the environment. The programs conform with established statewide guidelines and standards and achieve maximum benefit when they are closely tied to regular school programs. In order to strengthen the ties, the San Diego County Office of Education, with the co-sponsorship of California Outdoor School Administrators (COSA), is developing a model resident outdoor school curriculum and program guide. The publication, which will become available at the beginning of the school year in 1988, outlines a program solidly based on the regular school curriculum. It describes a variety of learning experiences and resources that have proved valuable in the past and shows the relationship of the resident outdoor program to the State California Assessment Program (CAP), the Model Curriculum Standards, Science Framework Addendum, and other widely recognized standards. Workshops for resident outdoor school personnel and regular classroom teachers on the use of the new guide are planned. For more information contact:

Science Curriculum Coordinator
San Diego County Office of Education
6401 Linda Vista Road
San Diego, Calif. 92111
(619) 292-3500

California Outdoor School Administrators (COSA)

In 1980 outdoor school program administrators, with the assistance and financial support of the Department of Education, formed COSA for the purpose of working cooperatively to accredit and upgrade programs on a statewide basis. COSA, in cooperation with the Los Angeles County Office of Education, has developed an accreditation process that includes a detailed program and site self-study, followed by an on-site evaluation by a visiting team consisting of program administrators from other agencies. The State Department of Education certifies the process and awards a certificate of achievement to programs that qualify. The publication *Guide to the Self-Evaluation of Resident Outdoor Science Schools* outlines the accreditation process and contains all of the required forms and instructions. Copies may be obtained by contacting:

California State Department of Education
Publication Sales Office
P.O. Box 271
Sacramento, Calif. 95802
(916) 445-1260

Index

Activities by Unit

Activities by Topic

Alphabetical Index of Activities

Index of Copycat Pages